●●●POWER ENGINEERING

Fourth Class
Part A1

Edition 2.5
2014

PanGlobal
TRAINING SYSTEMS

Published by PanGlobal Training Systems Ltd.
Publishers of Power Engineering Learning Materials

The material in this series is aligned with Fourth Class Syllabus, dated October, 2012.
For more info visit http://www.sopeec.org/Syllabus/SyllabusFourthClass.pdf

Address all inquiries to:
PanGlobal Training Systems
1301 – 16 Ave. NW, Calgary, AB, Canada. T2M 0L4

This curriculum is endorsed by the Canadian Institute of Power Engineers (IPE).

Cover image courtesy of EnCana Corporation. The image is a SAGD facility at EnCana's Christina Lake Operation, located in Northeast Alberta.

LEGAL NOTICE

Printed by Data Group
Fourth Class - Part A1
Edition 2.5 June 2014
ISBN13: 978-1-897461-27-3

For information on this and other products visit our website located at **www.powerengineering.org**
Any technical or editorial errors may be also be reported on our website by using our electronic Corrections Submissions Form or faxing suggested corrections to 1-403-284-8863

1301 16th Ave. NW
Calgary, Alberta
T2M 0L4

Fourth Class
Part A1
Edition 2.5

Table of Contents

Table of Contents (continued...)

APPLIED MATHEMATICS

CHAPTER 1

Introduction to Power Engineering

LEARNING OUTCOME

When you complete this chapter you should be able to:

Describe the overall industrial background and certification system for Power Engineering.

LEARNING OBJECTIVES

Here is what you should be able to do when you complete each objective:

1. Define the terms, Power Plant and Power Engineer.

2. Describe the power engineering certification system.

3. List the national standards that are used in Power Engineering-related industries.

OBJECTIVE 1

Define the terms, Power Plant and Power Engineer.

POWER PLANT

A steam boiler is basically a closed container, partially filled with water which is evaporated into steam under pressure by the application of heat. This heat is usually obtained from the burning of a fuel such as: gas, oil or coal in a furnace. Although in some cases, electrical elements may be used to provide the heat.

A boiler may be defined as: a pressure vessel in which a gas or vapour can be generated under pressure, or in which a liquid can be put under pressure, by the direct application of a heat source.

A power plant is many things. For the purposes of this course it may be considered as any process for the generation and utilization of steam. It includes steam generators or boilers, steam turbines, electric generators, motors, refrigeration and air conditioning equipment, control systems, water treatment and fuel handling facilities, emergency and stand-by equipment, and environmental protection equipment.

A power plant provides such output as electric power for light and steam heat or cooling to condition air. This output may be used to provide climate control in buildings, or to condition air or products in industrial processes.

Many governmental agencies having jurisdiction over construction, inspection and operation of such plants define the term "power plant" as meaning:

- any one or more boilers in which steam or other vapour is generated at more than 103 kPa (15 psi), or
- any one or more boilers containing liquid and having a working pressure exceeding 1100 kPa (160 psi), and a temperature exceeding 121°C (250°F), or either one of these, or
- any system or arrangement of boilers referred to in the above subclauses and the engines, turbines, pressure vessels, pressure piping system, machinery and ancillary equipment of any kind used in connection therewith.

The preceding definition applies equally to a small portable boiler or to a steam generator that may be many stories high, as shown in Figure 1.

Figure 1	Large and Small Power Plants

POWER ENGINEER

A power engineer is a skilled worker who operates and maintains the equipment in a power plant. On-the-job activity covers the entire process of heat generation and heat utilization. It is usually not necessary to know all design features of all equipment, but, to make it function safely and economically, one must understand basic design requirements and the limitations involved.

In a large plant, the power engineer may function as a supervisor who directs others in safe and efficient operation on a shift. Including other power engineers operating the

- steam generators or boilers,
- water treatment sections and
- turbines, engines, pumps and other equipment that utilizes heat or energy.

Some of this equipment is illustrated in Figure 2. Work orders may be issued covering the repair of equipment by maintenance staff. The Power Engineer may recommend purchase of depletable supplies, such as salt, and may be totally responsible for one or all shifts.

Referring to Figure 2, a power engineer may be required to operate a small turbine, a large feedwater pump or an industrial diesel engine.

In a smaller plant, the power engineer may operate and maintain equipment, order supplies and generally assume full responsibility for the entire plant. There may be no other staff.

Typical Equipment Operated by Power Engineers

| Figure 2(a) | Small Turbine |

| Figure 2(b) | Large Feedwater Pump |

| Figure 2(c) | Industrial Diesel Engine |

Historical Development of Power Engineering

The power industry has long employed automatic devices for handling and controlling fuels and equipment. Each new power plant exhibits more of the characteristics of automation:

- increased mechanization,
- frequent use of automatic equipment and
- continuous monitoring of processes and costs.

It is difficult to establish exact dates when certification of power engineers first began. Long before the invention of the steam engine, the manual firing of furnaces was under legal scrutiny. A proclamation by Edward I of England in 1306 prohibited the use of sea coals in furnaces and established a commission to enforce the rules for firing furnaces. In Germany, as early as 1350, to curb pollution metal plants were closely monitored and sometimes denied the use of coal.

The steam engine, invented early in the nineteenth century, provided the first source of steady, reliable mechanical power. It was originally used to remove water from mines and thus increase productivity. For many years, the practice was to assemble the engines on site. The mechanics who assembled an engine were loaned to the buyer to commission the engine and often to operate the entire power plant.

Owners hired unskilled workers who started out doing manual labor, often on the coal pile. Through a system of "progression", as these workers acquired experience they were promoted to jobs that required higher skill. As new plants were built and the labour force became more mobile, employers "certified" the progression of a worker moving to a new plant.

To increase efficiency, higher boiler pressures were adopted. This led to serious accidents, due to unqualified operating personnel. Insurance underwriters and governments became involved and took responsibility for the certification of both operators and equipment.

In modern times, there has been a dramatic increase in plant efficiency. Close control of the steam generation process and enforcement of anti-pollution regulations has enlarged the responsibility of the power engineer. More knowledge is required and there is greater opportunity to use both knowledge and skills. For the power engineer who wishes to achieve job satisfaction in this expanding technology, the learning process never ends.

Nature of the Work

Across Canada and many parts of the United States, the power engineering profession is regulated. The government of the jurisdiction (state, province, territory or city) in which an engineer works may have passed an Act that contains a rule similar to the following:

- the holder of a Certificate of Competency, the classification of which authorizes him/her to act as an engineer, may sketch, construct, install, operate, repair, and give advice on all things pertaining to any power plant in which that person is employed, but is not entitled to perform any welding unless holding a Certificate of Competency permitting him/her to do so.

The beginning engineer is most likely to be involved in operation and repair until enough knowledge and experience has been gained to perform the other functions outlined in the Act.

In very small plants, much of the work may be manual:

- opening and closing valves
- operating pumps
- checking the boiler flame
- starting electric motors
- determining the time and operation of water softeners.

All these tasks may be performed by the engineer working alone.

In larger plants, automatic control systems open and close valves and regulate massive equipment formerly controlled by hand. Referring to Figure 3, central control panels and closed circuit television often enable one engineer to operate systems that would require many operators if operated manually.

The engineer's function is that of an interpreter. Mounted on the control panel or computer monitors are the instruments which display information necessary to safely control boilers, generators, industrial processes and air conditioning equipment. On the basis of that information, changes are made automatically. The engineer analyzes malfunctions and trends promptly, and with simple manipulation of knobs and switches or computer controls, commands the plant to proceed with the desired "steady state" operations.

Figure 3	Central Control Panels

Working Conditions

Power engineers expect to have year-round employment without seasonal lay-offs. In plants that never shut down, power engineers usually work eight or twelve hours per day, in rotating shifts on week days, weekends and holidays. Shifts are arranged so that at some point several days "off" are grouped together in a type of vacation leave.

A common practice in many plants is to operate three shifts starting at 8 am, 4 pm, and 12 midnight, with four groups handling these three shifts. The pattern of shift rotation permitting three working groups and one "off" group is essentially a weekly pattern of seven days, rather than the usual five days.

The popular 12-hour shift pattern is a little more complicated. Typical hours of a 12 hour shift schedule consist of 7:00 am to 7:00 pm and 7:00 pm to 7:00 am. One such schedule, shown in Table 1, involves eight crews plus one relief crew which is indicated by (R).

On January 11, for example, Shift 7 in the steam plant works the same daytime hours as Shift 3 in the process plant. On January 12, Shift 7 in the steam plant works the same daytime hours as Shift 4 in the process plant. The same pattern is followed for two consecutive night shifts. On January 15, Shift 7 begins five consecutive days off.

To help promote accident-free performance, most working areas are clean and well-lighted. Central control rooms are frequently air-conditioned.

However, the power engineer must realize that some plant areas may be compromised because of dust, fumes, smoke, high temperatures and high noise levels. Occasionally, the engineer may be required to work in damp or cold areas, in a crouched or prone position to inspect, adjust or repair equipment.

Because work must be performed close to boilers, rotating equipment, electrical equipment, piping and plant processes, the power engineer must guard against burns or other injuries that may occur due to faulty equipment.

Table 1	Typical 12-Hour Shift Problems

12-HOUR SHIFT SCHEDULE

	1	2	3	4	5	6	7	8	9	10	11	12	13	14	15	16	17	18	19	20	21	22	23	24	25	26	27	PLANT
Day	3	4	4	R	1	1	2	2	3	3	4	4	R	1	1	2	2	3	3	4	4	R	1	1	2	2	3	Process
	7	7	8	8	R	5	5	6	6	7	7	8	8	R	5	5	6	6	7	7	8	8	R	5	5	6	6	Steam
Night	2	3	3	4	4	R	1	1	2	2	3	3	4	4	R	1	1	2	2	3	3	4	4	R	1	1	2	Process
	6	6	7	7	8	8	R	5	5	6	6	7	7	8	8	R	5	5	6	6	7	7	8	8	R	5	5	Steam
OFF	1	1	1	1				1	1	1	1	1						1	1	1	1	1					1	
		2	2	2	2	2				2	2	2	2	2						2	2	2	2	2				
			3	3	3	3	3				3	3	3	3	3						3	3	3	3	3			
	4					4	4	4	4	4					4	4	4	4	4					4	4	4	4	
	5	5	5	5	5					5	5	5	5	5					5	5	5	5	5					
			6	6	6	6	6					6	6	6	6	6					6	6	6	6	6			
					7	7	7	7	7					7	7	7	7	7					7	7	7	7	7	
	8	8					8	8	8	8	8					8	8	8	8	8					8	8	8	
	R	R	R					R	R	R	R	R					R	R	R	R	R					R	R	
JAN	11	12	13	14	15	16	17	18	19	20	21	22	23	24	25	26	27	28	29	30	31	1	2	3	4	5	6	
FEB	7	8	9	10	11	12	13	14	15	16	17	18	19	20	21	22	23	24	25	26	27	28	1	2	3	4	5	
MAR	6	7	8	9	10	11	12	13	14	15	16	17	18	19	20	21	22	23	24	25	26	27	28	29	30	31	1	
APR	2	3	4	5	6	7	8	9	10	11	12	13	14	15	16	17	18	19	20	21	22	23	24	25	26	27	28	
MAY	29	30	1	2	3	4	5	6	7	8	9	10	11	12	13	14	15	16	17	18	19	20	21	22	23	24	25	
JUN	26	27	28	29	30	31	1	2	3	4	5	6	7	8	9	10	11	12	13	14	15	16	17	18	19	20	21	
JUL	22	23	24	25	26	27	28	29	30	1	2	3	4	5	6	7	8	9	10	11	12	13	14	15	16	17	18	
AUG	19	20	21	22	23	24	25	26	27	28	29	30	31	1	2	3	4	5	6	7	8	9	10	11	12	13	14	
SEP	15	16	17	18	19	20	21	22	23	24	25	26	27	28	29	30	31	1	2	3	4	5	6	7	8	9	10	
OCT	11	12	13	14	15	16	17	18	19	20	21	22	23	24	25	26	27	28	29	30	1	2	3	4	5	6	7	
OCT	8	9	10	11	12	13	14	15	16	17	18	19	20	21	22	23	24	25	26	27	28	29	30	31	1	2	3	
NOV	4	5	6	7	8	9	10	11	12	13	14	15	16	17	18	19	20	21	22	23	24	25	26	27	28	29	30	
DEC	1	2	3	4	5	6	7	8	9	10	11	12	13	14	15	16	17	18	19	20	21	22	23	24	25	26	27	
JAN	28	29	30	31	1	2	3	4	5	6	7	8	9	10	11	12	13	14	15	16	17	18	19	20	21	22	23	

Methods and Procedures

All operation, testing and repair requires rigid adherence to specific methods and practices covered under local plant practice and manufacturer's instructions. Safety demands that these practices be followed at all times. The power engineer can expect to share in setting up and obeying all such practices and to serve as an example to fellow employees or to those under his or her guidance. A sample of the general rules employed in a typical plant follows. More specific rules would be formulated for the startup and shutdown of boilers and care of other specific machines.

Summary of Care and Operation of the Boiler

There are a number of general rules for the care and operation of our boiler. Some of these may seem simple, but there are many cases on record where boiler failures have been attributed to neglect in following the most elementary rules of operation.

Rule 1:   Know the boiler thoroughly by examining the function and reason for each part.

Rule 2:   Check the boiler flame for stability, color and turbulence as frequently as other duties will permit.

Rule 3:   Maintain the drum water at the normal safe operating level.

Rule 4:   In case of a low drum water level, bank the fires immediately and allow boiler to cool slowly.

Rule 5:   When a boiler is out of service for cleaning, the drum water column connections should be thoroughly cleaned and all scale and mud removed.

Rule 6:   Blowdown the boiler at proper intervals. Short blowdowns at frequent intervals are preferred to long ones with more time in between.

Rule 7:   If equipped, use the soot blowers frequently enough to keep boiler heating surfaces clean. The accumulation of soot means loss of efficiency and decreased capacity due to increase in exit gas temperatures.

Rule 8:   Test safety valves at intervals by increasing the pressure to the point at which they are supposed to blow. If the boiler is equipped with a superheater, be sure that the superheater safety valves blow first.

Rule 9:   The boiler will be thoroughly cleaned and washed out annually. Be sure that no large pieces of loose scale are left in the boiler, as serious tube trouble is liable to result.

Rule 10: The baffles should be examined periodically to see that they are tight and in place.

Rule 11: The steam drum pressure gauge will be tested for accuracy at least every time the boiler is down for cleaning.

Rule 12: Each boiler is fitted with an automatic stop-and-check valve on the steam outlet. These should be checked at regular intervals for scale accumulation.

Rule 13: Oil should be kept out of all boilers and feedwater. When oil is mixed with the soft mud found in a boiler, it will bake to a very hard scale which causes tubes to burn out. When oil is mixed with water, it causes serious foaming.

OBJECTIVE 2

Describe the power engineering certification system.

POWER ENGINEERING CERTIFICATES

Legal Requirements

In the various governmental jurisdictions it is clearly set out in Acts or Regulations that, with few exceptions, a power plant must be operated

a) under the general supervision of the holder of a Certificate of Competency, the classification of which qualifies the holder to act as chief steam engineer of the power plant, and

b) under the continuous supervision of the holder of a Certificate of Competency, the classification of which qualifies the holder to act as shift engineer under the general supervision of a person referred to in clause (1).

A Certificate of Competency is a document issued by a legal authority stating that a power engineer meets certain qualifications and has passed certain required examinations set up by that authority.

In Alberta, for one example, the "Safety Codes Act" establishes the following certificates; other provinces and territories have established a somewhat similar structure.

- First Class Engineer's Certificate of Competency
- Second Class Engineer's Certificate of Competency
- Third Class Engineer's Certificate of Competency
- Fourth Class Engineer's Certificate of Competency
- Fifth Class Engineer's Certificate of Competency
- Special Oil Well Operator's Certificate of Competency
- Special Boiler Operator's Certificate of Competency
- Pressure Welder's Certificate of Competency
- Temporary Certificates, Duplicate Certificates and Out-Of-Province Equivalency Certificates

Typical regulations governing the limitations of certificates may include the following:

Example 1:

A Fourth Class Engineer's Certificate of Competency qualifies the holder to:

a) Take charge of the general care and operation of a power plant having a capacity of not more than 1000 kW as chief steam engineer, and to supervise the engineers in that plant.

b) Take charge of the general care and operation of a power plant consisting of one or more coil-type drumless boilers having an aggregate capacity not exceeding 5000 kW, when used for the sole purpose of underground thermal flooding in oil fields, as chief steam engineer.

c) Take charge of a shift in a power plant having a capacity of not more than 5000 kW, as shift engineer.

d) Take charge of a shift in a power plant consisting of one or more coil type drumless boilers having an aggregate capacity of not more than 10 000 kW, when used for the sole purpose of underground thermal flooding in oil fields, as shift engineer.

e) Take charge of a section of a power plant having a capacity of not more than 10 000 kW, as assistant engineer, under the supervision of the shift engineer in that plant.

f) Take charge of the general care and operation of a power plant having a capacity of not more than 5000 kW and operating at a pressure not more than 140 kPa.

Example 2:

A First Class Engineer's Certificate of Competency qualifies the holder to:

a) Take charge of the general care and operation of any power plant as chief steam engineer, and to supervise the engineers in that plant.

b) Take charge of a shift in any power plant as shift engineer.

The student will find the limitations assigned to other classes of certificates in the local Act and Regulations.

Progression to a Higher Certificate

Both experience and educational requirements must be met to obtain higher Certificates of Competency. One must already hold a lower certificate than that of the class sought, and in addition, must serve a certain number of months in an operating capacity.

An engineer must progress in succession through the various classes. For example, it is not possible to move directly from the Fourth Class Certificate to the Second Class Certificate; the candidate must at some time hold a Third Class Certificate.

The progression route is outlined in the Regulations of each jurisdiction over power engineers. With such a clear-cut route, it is anticipated that each student will plan his or her career so as to reach and enjoy a high level of certification. A First Class Engineer's Certificate of Competency is shown in Figure 4.

Figure 4	Alberta First Class Certificate of Competency

An Example of the Coveted First Class Certificate of Competency

Educational Program Completion

Depending on the jurisdiction and certificate applied for, credits in lieu of plant experience may be granted on successful completion of a learning program in power engineering satisfactory to the chief inspector. Typical successful completion may mean that the student must complete all assignments and pass a final examination. If, for example, a candidate successfully completes such a course for the Fourth Class Certificate, an accredited certificate as shown in Figure 5 will be awarded, entitling that student to an experience credit of six months. Credits are given for completion of appropriate courses towards all certificates.

Note: The certificate issued upon successful completion of a course of study is not a Power Engineer's Certificate of Competency.

Figure 5   Certificate Issued upon Completion of Program

ABC
Institute of Technology
Calgary, Alberta

certifies that

Name of Student

has successfully completed
the certificate program

Fourth Class Power Engineering

_____
Chairman of the Board of Governors

_____
President

_____
Department Manager

_____
Registrar

_____
Date

OBJECTIVE 3

List the national standards that are used in Power Engineering-related industries.

NATIONAL STANDARDS

Why Standards are Necessary

Much of the development of modern industrial plants derives from the production and adoption of standards for industry and power engineers. A standard is a grade or level of accomplishment that is considered desirable because it:

- promotes safety for the public, plant owners and operators. Striving for safety helps to lower insurance costs as well.

- facilitates lower operation and maintenance costs. One can appreciate the confusion that would exist if there were no uniform standards for pipe threads and fittings.

- forms the basis of government inspection of plants and certification examinations of power engineers.

How Standards are Prepared

Standards are issued by national and international organizations. Within these organizations, committees are established to develop safety codes and standards. These committees are composed of experts from industrial, governmental, professional, and insurance organizations.

Since the committees are composed of highly qualified people, the codes are adopted as standards and receive nation-wide recognition through legislation.

The Standards Council of Canada

The Standards Council of Canada functions as the national coordinating body, through which organizations concerned with voluntary standardization may operate and cooperate to recognize, establish and improve standardization in Canada. The following are examples of accredited, standards-writing member organizations:

1. The Canadian Standard Association (CSA): a non-profit, voluntary membership association that has produced two codes which affect the power engineer:

   a) CSA B51 Boiler, Pressure Vessel and Pressure Piping Code

   b) CSA B52 Mechanical Refrigeration Code

2. The Canadian Gas Association which has produced CSA B149.1 Installation Code for Natural Gas Burning Appliances and Equipment.

3. Underwriters Laboratories of Canada which issues standards and tests products. Products meeting the standard bear a ULC label.

The American Society of Mechanical Engineers (ASME)

The ASME is an organization that has developed extensive standards for such equipment as pressure vessels, piping and valves. The ASME codes often form a basis for provincial boiler and pressure vessels regulations. The following is a list of the twelve Sections of the ASME Boiler and Pressure Vessel Codes.

Section I:	Power Boilers
Section II:	Materials - Part "A" Ferrous Material Specifications
Section II:	Materials - Part "B" Nonferrous Material Specifications
Section II:	Materials - Part "C" - Specifications for Welding Rods, Electrodes and Filler Metals
Section II:	Materials - Part "D" - Properties (Metric)
Section II:	Materials - Part "D" - Properties (Customary)
Section III:	Rules Construction Nuclear Power Plant Components - Division 1
Section III:	Rules Construction Nuclear Power Plant Components - Division 2
Section IV:	Rules for Construction of Heating Boilers
Section V:	Nondestructive Examination
Section VI:	Recommended Rules for Care and Operation of Heating Boilers
Section VII:	Recommended Guidelines for the Care of Power Boilers
Section VIII:	Rules for Construction of Pressure Vessels - Division 1
Section VIII:	Rules for Construction of Pressure Vessels - Division 2 - Alternative Rules
Section VIII:	Rules for Construction of Pressure Vessels - Division 3 - Alternative Rules
Section IX:	Welding and Brazing Qualifications
Section X:	Fiber-Reinforced Plastic Pressure Vessels
Section XI:	Rules for Internal Inspection of Nuclear Power Plant Components
Section XII:	Rules for the Construction and Continued Service of Transport Tanks

See **IMPORTANT NOTE** below, re ANSI/ASME codes

American National Standards Institute (ANSI)

ANSI, similar to the Standards Council of Canada, recognizes standards developed by specific groups, such as The National Fire Protection Association, American Gas Association and ASME.

Examples of standards developed by ANSI and of interest to the Power Engineer include:

B. 31.1 Power Piping

B. 31.3 Process Piping Code

B. 31.5 Refrigeration Piping

B. 16.5 Steel Pipe Flanges and Flanged Fittings

K. 61.1 Safety Requirements for Storage and Handling of Anhydrous Ammonia

IMPORTANT NOTE: Though originally issued and identified as ANSI standards, the codes mentioned above, B31.1, B31.3, B31.5, and B16.5 are now owned, issued, and maintained by ASME.

Local Regulations

At the municipal level, enforcement usually involves building codes, fire codes, or health department regulations. For example, such regulations may rule that a cylinder of hydrogen must not be stored in a boiler room. Local regulations may also specify the location of fire-fighting equipment, or of escape routes from a plant. As with all the organizations discussed above, safety is their prime consideration.

This page has intentionally been left blank.

CHAPTER 1 - QUESTIONS

1. Power engineers are

    a) automatically safety code officers in a power plant.

    b) qualified to perform any welding jobs in a power plant.

    c) skilled workers who operate and maintain the equipment in a power plant.

    d) qualified to perform any electrical jobs in a power plant.

    e) qualified to make design changes in a power plant.

2. When oil mixes with water in the boiler, the resultant effect is

    a) serious foaming.

    b) increased heat transfer.

    c) accumulation of soot.

    d) decrease in water level.

    e) shifting and loosening of baffles.

3. In a power plant, the power engineer may function as a supervisor who directs others in the _____ operation on a shift.

4. Which of the following duties is a holder of a Fourth Class Engineer's Certificate of Competency in Alberta not qualified to perform?

    a) As shift engineer, take charge of a power plant having a capacity of more than 10 000 kW.

    b) As chief steam engineer take charge of the general care and operation of a power plant having a capacity of not more than 1000 kW and supervise the engineers in that plant.

    c) As shift engineer, take charge of a shift in a power plant consisting of one or more coil type drumless boilers having an aggregate capacity of not more than 10 000 kW, when used only for underground thermal flooding in oil fields.

    d) As shift engineer, take charge of a shift in a power plant having a capacity of not more than 5000 kW.

5. In Alberta, a Fourth Class Power Engineer's certificate of competency qualifies the holder to take charge of the general care and operation of a power plant having a capacity of not more than _____ kW as chief steam engineer and to supervise the engineers in that plant.

6. Invented in the 19th century, the first source of mechanical power that was steady and reliable was the _____.

CHAPTER 1 - ANSWERS

1. (c)

2. (a)

3. safe

4. (a)

5. 1000 kW

6. steam engine

SI Units

LEARNING OUTCOME

When you complete this chapter you should be able to:

Perform simple calculations involving SI units.

LEARNING OBJECTIVES

Here is what you should be able to do when you complete each objective:

1. *List basic SI units; identify and list symbols for unit prefixes.*

2. *Perform unit analyses in simple problems.*

3. *List derived SI units and their symbols.*

4. *Perform conversions between SI and Imperial units.*

INTRODUCTION

Various systems of measurement have been used in different parts of the world for centuries. However, because each system was designed with its own base units, conversions from one system to another presented many problems. It became obvious that a standard system would have to be developed. This system would have to be precise to allow for accurate measurement, yet simple enough to allow for conversions from one unit to another within the system.

Such a system - the Metric System - was developed in France in the seventeenth century and was gradually adopted by other countries. In 1960, the latest version of the Metric System was developed and named Le Systeme International d'unites (the International System of Units), more commonly called SI. The last major addition to SI occurred in 1971 with the addition of the "mole" as the base unit for the amount of a substance.

The SI system is based on the units kilogram, metre and second. In Canada, it replaced the older Imperial system of units, based on the foot, pound and second.

Currently, the United States still uses the Imperial system of units but it is now called the United States Customary System of Units (USCS).

OBJECTIVE 1

List basic SI units; identify and list symbols for unit prefixes.

BASIC UNITS

There are seven base units in SI, as shown in Table 1.

Table 1	SI Base Units	
Quantity	Name of Base Unit	Symbol
Length	metre	m
Mass	kilogram	kg
Time	second	s
Electric Current	ampere	A
Thermodynamic temperature	kelvin	K
Amount of substance	mole	mol
Luminous intensity	candela	cd

Note: The base unit, kilogram, is the only one with a prefix. It was selected as a base unit since the gram was considered to be too small to be functional.

Several SI base units may be familiar to you while others may not. In any case, the student must know this chart thoroughly before proceeding with this chapter.

Multiples and Submultiples of Base Units

One area with which SI is simple to work, compared to other systems, is that of converting small units to large and vice versa.

For example, convert a distance (miles) to a value with smaller units (inches). First, the distance in miles would be converted to yards, or feet, using 1 mile = 1760 yards, or 1 mile = 5280 feet. Then, using 1 foot = 12 inches or possibly 1 yard = 3 feet, the correct value and units would be obtained. However, the conversion factors have to be exact and an error could occur simply because the conversion may require several steps to complete.

In SI, conversion factors are not required. Changing from a larger unit to a smaller one, or vice versa, simply requires that you multiply or divide the unit by 10 or a multiple of 10 (i.e., 100, 1000, etc.) This calculation can be done merely by moving a decimal point, in most cases.

A specific set of prefixes is used to denote the resulting units after a decimal point has been moved. Table 2 indicates the various prefixes and the asterisks indicate those most commonly used.

To illustrate the use of prefixes, consider the unit of length, the metre, in SI with some prefixes, as shown in Table 3.

Table 2		Metric Prefixes		
Prefix	**Symbol**	**Factor by Which Unit is Multiplied**		
exa	E	1 000 000 000 000 000 000	10^{18}	
peta	P	1 000 000 000 000 000	10^{15}	
tera	T	1 000 000 000 000	10^{12}	
giga	G	1 000 000 000	10^{9}	
* mega	M	1 000 000	10^{6}	
* kilo	k	1 000	10^{3}	
hecto	h	100	10^{2}	
deca	da	10	10^{1}	
		1	10^{0}	
deci	d	0.1	10^{-1}	
* centi	c	0.01	10^{-2}	
* milli	m	0.001	10^{-3}	
* micro	μ	0.000 001	10^{-6}	
nano	n	0.000 000 001	10^{-9}	
pico	p	0.000 000 000 001	10^{-12}	
femto	f	0.000 000 000 000 001	10^{-15}	
atto	a	0.000 000 000 000 000 001	10^{-18}	

Table 3		Metric Prefixes	
Name	**Symbol**	**Meaning**	**Multiply Metres By**
megametre	Mm	one million metres	1 000 000
kilometre	km	one thousande metres	1 000
hectometre	hm	one hundred metres	100
decametre	dam	ten metres	10
decimetre	dm	one tenth of a metre	0.1
centimetre	cm	one hundreth of a metre	0.01
millimetre	mm	one thousandths of a metre	0.001
micrometre	um	one millionth of a metre	0.000 001

Although any multiple or submultiple of a unit may be used, it is recommended that prefixes representing 10 raised to the power of a multiple of 3 (i.e. 10^{-3}, 10^{3}, 10^{-6}, 10^{6}, 10^{9}, etc.) are selected. For example, kilometre (km = 10^{3} × m) is preferred to hectometre (10^{2} × m).

The following are examples of conversions from one prefix to another:

Example 1:

Convert 0.723 km to metres.

Solution:

1 km = 1000 m (or there are one thousand metres per kilometre) written as 1000 m/km.

$$0.723 \text{ km} = 0.723 \text{ km} \times \frac{1000 \text{ m}}{\text{km}}$$

$$= \textbf{723 m (Ans.)}$$

Example 2:

Convert 0.045 m to millimetres.

Solution:

$$\text{Since } 1 \text{ m} = 1000 \text{ mm}$$

$$0.045 \text{ m} = 0.045 \times 1000 \frac{\text{mm}}{\text{m}}$$

$$= \textbf{45 mm (Ans.)}$$

Exmple 3:

Convert 109 mm to centimetres.

Solution:

$$\text{Since } 1 \text{ cm} = 10 \text{ mm}$$

$$109 \text{ mm} = 109 \text{ mm} \times \frac{1 \text{ cm}}{10 \text{ mm}}$$

$$= \textbf{10.9 cm (Ans.)}$$

OBJECTIVE 2

Perform unit analysis in simple problems.

BASIC UNITS

In the preceding examples, the units are included in the solutions. Units should be included in all calculations if possible. If the student conducts a "unit analysis" for a solution and when the units for the final solution are proven to be correct, then the numeric result is usually correct.

For example, a unit analysis for Example 3 would be:

$$mm \times \frac{cm}{mm} = cm$$

The millimetres cancel out, leaving only cm in the final answer.

$$\cancel{mm} \times \frac{cm}{\cancel{mm}} = cm$$

If the problem had been solved this way:

$$109 \text{ mm} \times \frac{10 \text{ mm}}{1 \text{ cm}} = 1090 \text{ cm}$$

A unit analysis would reveal your error:

$$mm \times \frac{mm}{cm} = \frac{mm^2}{cm} \text{ which is not a unit of length}$$

For simple problems, such as Example 3, do a unit analysis while solving the problem:

$$109 \text{ mm} \times \frac{1 \text{ cm}}{10 \text{ mm}} = 10.9 \text{ cm}$$

For more advanced calculations, it might be easier to perform a separate unit analysis. The important thing to remember is: **Always do a unit analysis**.

Example 4:

Find the area of a rectangle that is 1.5 m long, and 93 cm wide. Use the formula, A = L x W.

In cases like this, when units are multiplied together, they need to be in the same units. In this example, the final unit was not specified, so there are various ways of solving the problem.

Solution A:

Change both dimensions to centimetres.

A = L x W

= (1.5 m x 100 cm/1 m) x 93 cm

= 150 cm x 93 cm

= **13 950 cm²** (Ans.)

Solution B:

Change both dimensions to metres.

$$A = L \times W$$
$$= 1.5 \text{ m} \times (93 \text{ cm} \times 1 \text{ m}/100 \text{ cm})$$
$$= 1.5 \text{ m} \times (0.93 \text{ m})$$
$$= \mathbf{1.395 \ m^2 \ (Ans.)}$$

Alternate Solution B:

From Solution A:

Since,

$$A = 13\ 950 \text{ cm}^2$$
$$1 \text{ m}^2 = 1 \text{ m} \times 1 \text{ m}$$
$$= 100 \text{ cm} \times 100 \text{ cm}$$
$$= 10\ 000 \text{ cm}^2$$

Then,

$$1.395 \text{ m}^2 = 1.395 \text{ m}^2 \times (10\ 000 \text{ cm}^2/1 \text{ m}^2)$$
$$= \mathbf{13\ 950 \ cm^2 \ (Ans.)}$$

Example 5:

Convert 278 827 cg to kg.

Solution:

$$278\ 827 \text{ cg} \times (1 \text{ g}/100 \text{ cg}) \times (1 \text{ kg}/1000 \text{ g})$$
$$= \mathbf{2.788\ 27 \ kg \ (Ans.)}$$

Example 6:

Convert 1 000 000 mm to km.

Solution:

$$1\ 000\ 000 \text{ mm} \times (1 \text{ m}/1000 \text{ mm}) \times (1 \text{ km}/1000 \text{ m})$$
$$= \mathbf{1 \ km \ (Ans.)}$$

Notice in these examples that the conversion was done in two steps. Sometimes it is easier to convert a value to unity (1 kg, 1 m, etc.) and then to convert to the final unit.

Writing SI Symbols

The following basic rules for writing SI symbols and numbers with SI units should be understood before attempting problems using SI units and symbols.

- Always use the correct symbol. For example, use kg for kilogram, rather than something like klg which does not exist.

- SI unit symbols must always be written in roman type. For example, use kg, not *kg*.

- Symbols are lower case letters, unless they are derived from a proper name. For example, use s (second), not S. (One exception to this rule will be mentioned later.)

- Symbols are always singular. For example, 75 kg, not 75 kgs.

- Do not use a period after a symbol, unless the symbol is at the end of a sentence. For example, use ". . . 27 m long.", not ". . . 27 m. long."

- Do not leave a space between a prefix and a unit symbol. For example, use kg, not k g.

- Use only the symbol with numerals. Use the full name of the unit when the number is written out. For example, use 5 m, not 5 metres. Use five metres, not five m.

- Leave a space between a number and a symbol. For example, use 18 kg, not 18kg. An exception to this would be when a letter does not immediately follow a number, such as in 18°C.

- When writing numbers, use decimals rather than fractions. For example, use 1.5 kg, not 1 1/2 kg.

- If a number is less than one, use a zero before the decimal point. For example, use 0.8 m, not .8 m.

- Numbers must be separated into blocks of three digits each, instead of using commas. For example, use 78 232 456.738 92 mm, not 78,232,456.73892 mm. However, if a number has only four digits on either side of the decimal place, a space is optional. For example, use 3.1416 cm or 3.141 6 cm.

- A half-high dot is used to signify multiplication in SI. For clarity in learning in this text, when multiplying, use the multiplication sign (×) instead of a dot. For example, use 178 × 97.3 m, not 178 • 97.3 m

OBJECTIVE 3

List derived SI units and their symbols.

MEASURING PHYSICAL QUANTITIES

The following is an introduction to several other units that are used in the SI system. The topics are discussed in greater detail in other chapters.

Length

Although the SI unit of length is the metre (m), multiples or submultiples are often used in everyday situations. Engineering drawings frequently use millimeters (mm), the textile industry often uses centimetres (cm) and highway distances may be given in kilometres (km). For navigational purposes, the nautical mile, a distance of 1852 m, has been in use for a long time and is presently included in SI.

Area

In SI, the product of any two quantities produces the unit of the resultant quantity. For example, unit length (1 m) multiplied by unit width (1 m) equals unit area (1 m^2). Although the square metre (m^2) is the unit of area, the square centimetre (cm^2) and the square millimetre (mm^2) are often used.

When measuring land area, such as a farm, the hectare (ha) is often used.

$$1 \text{ ha} = 1 \text{ hm}^2$$
$$= 1 \text{ hm x } 1 \text{ hm}$$
$$= 100 \text{ m x } 100 \text{ m}$$
$$= 10\ 000 \text{ m}^2$$

For measuring extremely large geographical areas, the square kilometre (km^2) is used.

Volume

The cubic metre (m^3) is the unit of volume in SI.

$$1 \text{ m}^3 = 1 \text{ m x } 1 \text{ m x } 1 \text{ m}$$

The cubic centimetre (cm^3) is often used for laboratory work.

$$1 \text{ cm}^3 = 1 \text{ cm x } 1 \text{ cm x } 1 \text{ cm}$$

The cubic decimetre (dm^3) is also used for measuring solids, liquids or gases.

$$1 \text{ dm}^3 = 1 \text{ dm x } 1 \text{ dm x } 1 \text{ dm}$$
$$= 0.1 \text{ m x } 0.1 \text{ m x } 0.1 \text{ m}$$
$$= 0.001 \text{ m}^3$$

The cubic decimetre is given the name "litre" (L). (If the student refers back to the rules on writing of SI symbols, the litre (L) is the one exception referred to in bullet 3).

Since

$$1 \ dm^3 = 1 \ L$$

And

$$1 \ L = 0.001 \ m^3$$

Then

$$1000 \ L = 1 \ m^3$$

The millilitre (mL) is often used as a unit of volume in medicine, cooking and laboratories.

Speed and Velocity

Speed is defined as the distance a body travels in a unit of time. Speed and velocity are not identical, although their units are. The unit for distance is the metre (m); the unit for time is the second (s).

In SI, the quotient of any two quantities produces the unit of the resultant quantity. In the case of speed, a distance of one metre (1 m) divided by a time of one second (1 s) results in a unit of speed of one metre per second (1 m/s).

Kilometres per hour (km/h) are often used to describe automobile and airplane speeds.

Ships and aircraft often use the knot (kn) as a measure of speed. One knot is a speed of one nautical mile per hour.

$$1 \ kn = one \ nautical \ mile \ per \ hour$$

$$1 \ kn = one \ thousand \ eight \ hundred \ and \ fifty-two \ metres \ per \ hour \ (1852 \ m/h)$$

Since,

$$1 \ hr = 3600 \ s \ (60 \ s/min \times 60 \ min/hr)$$

Then,

$$1 \ kn = 1852 \ m/h \times (1 \ h/3600 \ s)$$

$$= 0.514 \ m/s$$

The manner in which the unit for speed (m/s) was written is important. When two symbols are combined to form a unit, the following rules must always be applied:

- Use a slash (oblique stroke) with symbols rather than the word "per". For example, use km/h, not km per h.

- Use the word "per" when writing full names of symbols rather than a slash. For example, use kilometres per hour, not kilometres/hour.

Velocity is often used as a measurement instead of speed where a directional component is required. For example, a transport truck carrying hog fuel for the utility boiler of a wood veneer plant, travelling at a speed of 100 km/h has a velocity of 100 km/h in an easterly direction.

Acceleration

Acceleration is defined as the rate of change of velocity. The unit of velocity is measured in m/s. The word "rate" indicates a unit of time, the second (s). Acceleration deals with change in velocity (m/s) per unit of time, the second (s), or acceleration is metres per second, per second. The unit becomes m/s/s.

Then,

$$\text{metres per second, per second} = \frac{m/s}{s}$$

$$= \frac{m/s}{s} \times \frac{1/s}{1/s} \text{ \{multiply top \& bottom by, } \frac{1}{s} \text{ which does not change the value\}}$$

$$= m/s \times \frac{1}{s}$$

$$= m/s^2$$

Therefore, the unit for acceleration is m/s^2 .

Mass

The mass of a body refers to the quantity of matter that it contains. (The term "weight" is not the same as mass; the difference between the terms is explained in another chapter.) In everyday use, the term "weight" is frequently misused to mean "mass" when working in SI.

The unit of mass is the kilogram (kg). Large masses may be expressed in megagrams (Mg), equal to one thousand kilograms. This is also called a metric ton or tonne (t).

$$1000 \text{ g} = 1 \text{ kg}$$

$$1000 \text{ kg} = 1 \text{ Mg}$$

$$1000 \text{ kg} = 1 \text{ t}$$

Density

Density refers to the mass of a unit volume of a substance. Since mass is in kilograms (kg) and volume is in cubic metres (m^3), density is measured in the units, kilograms per cubic metre, kg/m^3.

Temperature

The degree Celsius (°C) is the unit encountered in everyday use. For scientific work, the unit of temperature is the kelvin (K) which is an absolute value. The terms "Celsius degree", "degree Kelvin", "K" and "deg" are all incorrect and must not be used when expressing a temperature.

Force

A force is the pull or push exerted on a body. It may make a body begin to move, move faster, move slower, or come to rest. When a force is applied to a mass and causes the mass to accelerate, the force may be calculated using the following formula:

$$\text{Force = Mass x Acceleration}$$

$$= kg \times m/s^2$$

$$= kgm/s^2$$

The unit kgm/s^2 is called a newton (N).

Work

Work is done when a force moves a body through a distance. The following formula gives the amount of work done.

Work = Force x Distance

= N x m

= Nm (newton metre)

The newton metre (Nm) is called a Joule (J).

Energy

The term 'energy' means the ability to do work. In other words, energy can be converted to work and when work is done energy is expended. Since the unit of work is the joule (J), then energy is also expressed in joules, or a multiple of joules.

There are two main forms of mechanical energy. Potential energy is energy due to the position of a body. Kinetic energy is energy due to the motion of a body.

Power

Power is defined as the rate of doing work. As was mentioned earlier, the word "rate" indicates a unit of time, the second (s). Power then, is a measure of work, in joules (J), done over a given time period in seconds (s).

Power = Work/Time

= J/s

When one joule of work is done per second, we say the power developed is one watt (W).

J/s = W

The kilowatt (kW) and megawatt (MW) are usually used to indicate larger values of power, where

1 kW = 1 000 W   and 1 MW = 1 000 000 W..

Pressure

Pressure is defined as the force exerted over a unit area of a surface.

Pressure = force/area

= N/m^2

A force of 1 N acting on an area of 1 m^2 is called a pascal (Pa). i.e. 1 N/m^2 = 1 Pa.

Most equipment such as boilers, pumps and compressors develop pressures which are expressed in kilopascals (kPa) or megapascals (MPa) since the pascal (Pa) is a relatively low pressure.

A unit of pressure sometimes associated with SI is the bar.

1 bar = 100 kPa

However, the bar is not a recognized unit in SI.

A millibar (mbar) is equal to a pressure of one hundred pascals (100 Pa). It may be used only when performing international meteorological work.

In the United States Customary System (USCS), the standard pressure unit is the psi, which equals 6.895 kPa.

Note: Some of the units introduced in the last few topics have been given a symbol beginning with a capital letter. These symbols are derived from a proper name; some examples are newton (N), joule (J), watt (W), and pascal (Pa). Refer to Page 2-8, "Writing SI Symbols", bullet 3.

Table 4 shows a number of commonly used units.

Table 4	Derived Units		
Quantity	**Unit**	**Symbol**	**Derivation**
Area	square metre	m^2	m x m
Volume	cubic metre	m^3	m x m x m
Speed	metre per second	m/s	distance per unit time
Acceleration	metre per second squared	m/s^2	change in speed per unit time
Density	kilogram per cubic metre	kg/m^3	mass per unit volume
Specific volume	cubic metres per kilogram	m^3/kg	the volume of one kg
Frequency	hertz	Hz	1/s; reciprocal of time
Force	newton	N	$kg\ m/s^2$; mass times acceleration
Pressure	pascal	Pa	N/m^2; force per area
Energy (work)	joule	J	N m; force times displacement
Power	watt	W	J/s; energy per time
Concentration	mole per litre	mol/L	mole per unit volume
Molar Mass	gram per mole	g/mol (kg/kmol)	mass per unit mole
Molar volume	cubic metre per mole	m^3/mol	volume per unit mole
Mass flow rate	kilogram per second	kg/s	kilogram per unit time

OBJECTIVE 4

Perform conversions between SI and Imperial units.

UNIT CONVERSIONS

There may be occasions when units from one system may have to be converted to units of another system. The conversion chart shown below can be used to convert from SI units to Imperial units and vice versa.

Table 5	Unit Conversions		
Length/ Distance	1 in = 2.54 cm	**Force**	1 lb = 4.448 N
	1 cm = 0.3937 in		1 N = 0.225 lb
	1 ft = 0.3048 m	**Pressure**	1 lb/in^2 (psi) = 6.895 kPa
	1 m = 3.28 ft		1 kPa = 0.145 lb/in^2 (psi)
	1 mile = 1609 m		1 bar = 100 kPa
Area	1 in^2 = 6.45 cm^2		1 bar = 14.51 psi
	1 cm^2 = 0.155 in^2		1 psi = 0.069 bar
	1 ft^2 = 0.093 m^2	**Energy**	1 ft lb = 1.356 J
	1 m^2 = 10.75 ft^2		1 J = 0.737 ft lb
	1 sq mile = 2.59 km^2		1 Btu = 1.055 kJ
	1 km^2 = 0.386 sq mile		1 kJ = 0.948 Btu
Volume	1 in^3 = 16.39 cm^3		1 kcal = 3.968 Btu
	1 cm^3 = 0.061 in^3		1 Btu = 0.252 kcal
	1 ft^3 = 0.0283 m^3		1 kcal = 4.186 kJ
	1 m^3 = 35.336 ft^3		1 kJ = 0.239 kcal
Capacity	1 qt = 1.136 L		1 hp-hr = 2.685 MJ
	1 L = 0.88 qt		1 MJ = 0.372 hp-hr
	1 gal = 4.546 L		1 watt-hr = 3.6 kJ
	1 L = 0.22 gal		1 kJ = 0.278 watt-hr
Mass	1 lb = 0.454 kg	**Power**	1 hp = 0.746 kW
	1 kg = 2.2 lb		1 kW = 1.34 hp

Example 7:

Convert 22 miles to kilometres.

Solution:

$$1 \text{ mile} = 1609 \text{ m}$$
$$= 1.609 \text{ km}$$

From the chart:

$$22 \text{ miles} = 22 \text{ miles x } 1.609 \text{ km/miles}$$
$$= \textbf{35.398 km (Ans.)}$$

Example 8:

Convert 13 790 kPa to pounds per square inch.

Solution:

$$1 \text{ psi} = 6.895 \text{ kPa}$$

From the chart:

$$13\ 790 \text{ kPa} = 13\ 790 \text{ kPa x } 1 \text{ psi/6.895 kPa}$$
$$= \textbf{2000 psi (Ans.)}$$

As the student becomes more familiar with SI, some of the commonly used conversions will become familiar; for example, 1 inch = 2.54 cm, or 25.4 mm. Another common conversion is 1 psi = 6.895 kPa.

Once the student has memorized some of the common conversions, some of the others can be derived. For example, suppose a cube has sides of 3.75 feet and the student wishes to calculate the number of cubic metres in the cube. The problem could be solved in the following manner, without referring to a conversion chart, knowing from memory that 1 inch = 2.54 cm:

$$\text{Each side length} = 3.75 \text{ feet x } 12 \text{ inches/foot}$$
$$= 45 \text{ in}$$

$$\text{Each side length in SI} = 2.54 \text{ cm/inch x } 45 \text{ inches}$$
$$= 114.3 \text{ cm}$$
$$114.3 \text{ cm x } 1 \text{ m/100 cm} = 1.143 \text{ m}$$

$$\text{Volume of Cube} = (2.54 \text{ cm/in x } 45 \text{ in})^3$$
$$= (1.143 \text{ m})^3$$
$$= \textbf{1.49 m}^3 \textbf{ (Ans.)}$$

Notice that the unit, m, is also cubed.

As the student becomes more proficient with conversions, the same problem can be solved more quickly:

$$\text{Side Length} = (3.75 \text{ ft x } 12 \text{ in/ft}) \text{ x } 2.54 \text{ cm/in x } 1 \text{ m/100 cm}$$
$$= 1.143 \text{ m}$$
$$\text{Volume } = (1.143 \text{ m})^3$$
$$= \textbf{1.49 m}^3 \textbf{ (Ans.)}$$

This page has intentionally been left blank.

CHAPTER 2 - QUESTIONS

1. The base SI unit used to display the measurement of thermodynamic temperature is

    a) Fahrenheit.

    b) Kelvin.

    c) Celsius.

    d) Rankine.

2. The prefix used to represent one hundred times a unit is

    a) mega.

    b) micro.

    c) deci.

    d) hecto.

3. Convert the following to metres:

    a) 289 cm

    b) 1828 mm

    c) 1.45 km

    d) 17 dm

    e) 17 dam

4. Convert the following to centimetres:

    a) 131 m

    b) 2.7 km

    c) 14 dm

    d) 25.4 mm

    e) 118.3 dam

5. Convert the following to kilograms:

    a) 450 g

    b) 7.3 Mg

    c) 3921.2 mg

    d) 145 hg

    e) 10 000 dg

CHAPTER 2 - ANSWERS

1. (b)

2. (d)

3. a) 2.89 m
   b) 1.828 m
   c) 1 450 m
   d) 1.7 m
   e) 170 m

4. a) 13 100 cm
   b) 270 000 cm
   c) 140 cm
   d) 2.54 cm
   e) 118 300 cm

5. a) 0.45 kg
   b) 7 300 kg
   c) 0.003 921 2 kg
   d) 14.5 kg
   e) 1 kg

Basic Arithmetic Operations

LEARNING OUTCOME

When you complete this chapter you should be able to:

Perform basic arithmetic operations without the use of a calculator.

LEARNING OBJECTIVES

Here is what you should be able to do when you complete each objective:

1. Add and subtract integers.

2. Multiply and divide whole and decimal numbers.

3. Perform arithmetic operations involving combinations of addition, subtraction, multiplication, division and powers in the proper sequence.

INTRODUCTION

While much of this material may be elementary to some students, a review may refresh the memory and sharpen the skills of other students who finished their schooling many years ago. If your mathematical skills are sharp, then skip to the questions at the end of this chapter. If you have trouble with some questions, find the corresponding part of the chapter and study it carefully.

Because many people now rely on calculators for doing even the most basic arithmetic operations, they may have forgotten many of the skills they learned in school. However, in order to manipulate algebraic expressions and solve equations, the student must understand how to do the basic arithmetic operations without using a calculator. Therefore, in studying this chapter, students are urged to set their calculators aside and complete the calculations by hand unless specific instructions to the contrary are given.

OBJECTIVE 1

Add and subtract integers.

BASIC NUMBERS

When working with numbers, the main objectives are speed and accuracy. Most people now rely on the electronic calculator to accomplish both objectives. However, unless a person understands how to manually perform basic mathematical operations, the accuracy of answers given by the calculator cannot be assessed.

Some basic terms require definition at the outset:

- natural numbers are the numbers used for counting. They are 1, 2, 3, 4, 5, 6... The symbol "..." means "and so on". That is, the numbers continue on indefinitely according to the pattern of adding 1 to each number to obtain the next number.

- whole numbers are the natural numbers and zero. They are 0, 1, 2, 3....

- prime numbers are whole numbers other than 0 and 1 that are exactly divisible only by themselves and 1. Examples of prime numbers are 2, 3, 5, 7, and 11.

- signed numbers are numbers fronted by either a positive or a negative sign. Numbers preceded by a positive sign are called positive numbers, while, numbers preceded by a negative sign are called negative numbers. Zero is neither positive nor negative.

- integers are the positive and negative whole numbers and zero. They are -4, -3, -2, -1, 0, +1, +2, +3, +4. . . .

A number of signs and symbols are used throughout this chapter including:

Sign	Meaning
+	Addition or positive number
-	Subtraction or negative number
×	Multiplication
÷	Division
<	Less than, as -3 < -1
>	Greater than, as +4 > -5
=	Equal to, as 7 × 6 = 42
(), {}, []	Brackets (brackets side-by-side can also serve to indicate multiplication, as (3)(4) = 12.

THE NUMBER SYSTEM

All Numbers Have Names

Numbers are symbols. They answer the question, "How many?" They may be applied to any kind of object without discrimination. One may say, "I count six", or "There are one hundred". The engineer usually applies them to one object, speaking of a turbine rating of 100 MW (megawatts), or calculating the heat units in a certain quantity of water as equal to 1000 J (one thousand joules).

In elementary manipulation of numbers, the term, "digit", may be used to designate fingers and a number less than ten. Digits are grouped into word names of numbers. Hyphens are used to find word names for numbers such as: 29, 52, 75.

29 is written twenty-nine.

75 is written seventy-five.

The Decimal System

A number system has a rigid structure. Power engineers use the decimal structure or system, a number system scaled in units of ten, for much of their work. It is known as decimal notation because it is based on the Latin word for ten: decem. Ordinary whole numbers are decimal numbers (decimals, for short). For example, the number 4542 is made up of 4000 + 500 + 40 + 2, or four places of digits.

The value of any place is ten times that to its right.

4542 = 4 x 1000 + 5 x 100 + 4 x 10 + 2 x 1

4542 = 4 x 10 x 10 x 10 + 5 x 10 x 10 + 4 x 10 + 2 x 1

It is good engineering practice to use a type of shorthand called exponential notation for $10 \times 10 \times 10$ and similar expressions.

For $10 \times 10 \times 10$ write 10^3 (read "ten cubed "or "ten to the third power")

For 10×10 write 10^2 (read "ten squared" or "ten to the second power")

10^1 is equal to 10 and the 1 is rarely shown.

10^0 is equal to 1 (Any number to the power 0 equals 1, which is sometimes called "unity").

Thus

3^5 means $3 \times 3 \times 3 \times 3 \times 3$; 30^4 means $30 \times 30 \times 30 \times 30$

If Y stands for any number, Y^4 means $Y \times Y \times Y \times Y$.

If Y stands for 2, then Y^8 is equal to 256.

The Line Concept of Numbers

Numbers may be represented as points on a line:

Zero is a number with no value. All numbers to the left may be thought of as negative numbers: -1, -2, -3, etc. All numbers to the right of the zero are then positive numbers, usually written without the positive sign (+), but the positive sign is always understood to exist.

The Place Value of Numbers

A chart is a convenient method of recognizing place values of numbers, whether positive or negative, and their names.

The example shown below, in Table 1 is written: 21 505 920 065 and is read: twenty-one billion, five hundred five million, nine hundred twenty thousand, sixty-five.

Table 1			Place Values								
Billions			**Millions**			**Thousands**			**Ones**		
- Hundreds	- Tens	- Ones	- Hundreds	- Tens	- Ones	- Hundreds	- Tens	- Ones	- Hundreds	- Tens	- Ones
2	1		5	0	5	9	2	0	0	6	5
billions			millions			thousands			ones		

716 543 212 is read: seven hundred sixteen million, five hundred forty-three thousand, two hundred twelve.

Addition of Whole Numbers

Addition is basically a system of counting. The sum 3 + 4 is determined by counting first a set of 3 objects, then another set of 4 objects, joining the two sets, and counting all the objects. In the statement 3 + 4 = 7, 3 is called an addend, 4 is an addend, and 7 is their sum. To add large numbers, place the ones under the ones in one column, and tens, hundreds, and so on are forced to fall in their proper columns.

Example 1:

      a) Add 17 + 5 + 123

Solution:

a)
```
   17
    5
  123
  ___
  145  (Ans.)
```

1) The ones are added first: 7 + 5 + 3 = 15, write 5, carry 1 to the tens
2) The tens are added: 1 + 0 + 2 = 3 and 1 from the ones column; write 4
3) The hundreds column: 1 + 0 = 1, write 1

b)
```
   84
   92
  127
  ___
  303  (Ans.)
```

c)
```
    123
  1 526
 17 825
 _____
 19 474  (Ans.)
```

It is desirable to separate larger numbers into groups of three, with a space between groups. A space is not necessary with four digit numbers except when they are in a column and must be aligned with larger numbers.

Subtraction of Whole Numbers

Subtraction undoes addition. We subtract to get the difference between two numbers or the difference between two sets of numbers. The minus sign (-) is placed between two numbers to indicate that the second number must be subtracted from the first.

Larger numbers are arranged as in addition. Ones are subtracted first, then tens, then thousands and so on.

6778	is the same as	6000 + 700 + 70 + 8
-2314	is the same as	- 2000 - 300 - 10 - 4
4464	is the same as	4000 + 400 + 60 + 4

Also,

37	is the same as	20 + 17
-18	is the same as	- 10 - 8
19	is the same as	10 + 9

Example 2:

(a)   Subtract 18 from 37

Solution:

a)
```
     37
  -  18
  _____
     19  (Ans.)
```
1) Borrow from the tens column, read 17 - 8, write 9
2) Subtract 1 from the 3 to make up for the 1 borrowed from the tens column.
   Read 2 - 1, write 1

b)
```
   1 654
   - 965
  _____
     689  (Ans.)
```

c)
```
   87 051
   - 32 499
  _____
   54 552  (Ans.)
```

OBJECTIVE 2

Multiply and divide whole and decimal numbers.

MULTIPLICATION OF WHOLE NUMBERS

In multiplication, two numbers, called factors, are counted to get a third number, called a product. The number which is multiplied is called the multiplicand. The number by which it is multiplied is called the multiplier. The resulting number is called the product. Thus 3×5 is found by counting 3 sets of 5 objects each, joining them and counting them all:

$$3 \times 5 = 5 + 5 + 5 = 15$$

When a number must be added to itself several times, the process may be shortened considerably by multiplication. Multiplication tables, such as Table 2, are used and must be memorized.

Table 2	Multiplication Tables									
X	1	2	3	4	5	6	7	8	9	10
1	1	2	3	4	5	6	7	8	9	10
2	2	4	6	8	10	12	14	16	18	20
3	3	6	9	12	15	18	21	24	27	30
4	4	8	12	16	20	24	28	32	36	40
5	5	10	15	20	25	30	35	40	45	50
6	6	12	18	24	30	36	42	48	54	60
7	7	14	21	28	35	42	49	56	63	70
8	8	16	24	32	40	48	56	64	72	80
9	9	18	27	36	45	54	63	72	81	90
10	10	20	30	40	50	60	70	80	90	100

Again numbers must be carried to be placed under the correct tens, hundreds, etc., columns as in addition.

$827 \times 9 = 7443$ is arrived at as follows:

$9 \times 7 = 63$ write 3 and carry 6 to the tens column

$9 \times 2 = 18$ plus the 6 carried over, making 24; write 4, carry 2

$9 \times 8 = 72$ plus the 2 carried over, making 74; write 74

Example 3:

a)
```
    34   multiplicand
  x  6   multiplier
  ─────
   204   product
```

b)
```
     37
   x 29
   ─────
    333
  + 740
  ─────
   1073   (Ans.)
```

c)
```
      1 364
    x 5 004
    ───────
      5 456
  + 6 820 000
  ───────────
    6 825 456   (Ans.)
```

The product of any number multiplied by zero is zero.

DIVISION OF WHOLE NUMBERS

Division is sharing. The sign for division is ÷ and it is read "divided by." The expression 15 ÷ 5 means that 15 objects are shared or divided into 5 sets. Division is the process of calculating how many times one number is contained in another. It is the converse of multiplication. The number that is divided is the dividend, the number it is divided by is the divisor and the answer is the quotient.

Thus, dividing 34 916 by 7:

$$
\begin{array}{r}
4988 \\
7\overline{)34\,916} \\
\underline{28} \\
69 \\
\underline{63} \\
61 \\
\underline{56} \\
56 \\
\underline{56} \\
0
\end{array}
$$

7 will not divide into 3, but will go into 34. We try the largest number of times it will go, put this in the quotient, write the result under 34 and subtract. Carry the 9 down as shown and continue the solution.

It often happens that division cannot be carried out exactly. When the divisor does not go an exact number of times into the dividend, the excess is called the remainder.

DECIMAL NUMBERS

Reading and Writing Decimal Numbers

A decimal fraction is a fraction which has 10 or a power of 10 as a denominator.

Thus $\frac{26}{10}$ or $\frac{76}{100}$ or $\frac{532}{10\,000}$ are decimal fractions.

In writing a decimal fraction, it is convenient to omit the denominator and indicate what it is by placing a point or period (called a decimal point) in the numerator so that there will be as many figures to the right of this point as there are zeros in the denominator.

The above fractions now become 2.6, 0.76 and 0.0532, read as "two decimal six, zero decimal seven-six and zero decimal zero-five-three-two". The zero is sometimes omitted.

The term "common" is used to describe all fractions other than those which are decimal fractions. For example 1/2, 3/4, etc., are common fractions, their equivalents 0.5 and 0.75 are decimal fractions. To change 1/2 to 0.5 the rule is:

- add zeros to the numerator and divide by the denominator. Place the decimal point so as to make as many digits to the right of the decimal point as there were zeros added.

For example, to change 3/4 to a decimal, add two zeros to the numerator and divide by the denominator.

$$
\begin{array}{r}
75 \\
4\overline{)300} \\
\underline{28} \\
20 \\
\underline{20} \\
0
\end{array}
$$

Write the result as 0.75. (There are two digits to the right of the decimal).

Notice that when the decimal number has no digits to the left of the decimal point, a zero is placed to the left of that decimal point.

Ordering of Decimal Numbers

Table 3 shows the order and names of the places to both the left and the right of the decimal point, with the number 765 432.135 79 illustrating the simplicity of the decimal number system.

Table 3						Place Values					
- Hundred Thousands	- Ten Thousands	- Thousands	- Hundreds	- Tens	- Ones	- Decimal	- Tenths	- Hundredths	- Thousandths	- Ten Thousandths	- Hundred Thousandths
7	6	5	4	3	2	.	1	3	5	7	9

The decimal point is located between the ones and tenths places, where whole numbers end and fractions begin. Thus:

$$765\ 432.135\ 79 = 765\ 432 + \frac{1}{10} + \frac{3}{100} + \frac{5}{1000} + \frac{7}{10000} + \frac{9}{100000}$$

$$765\ 432.135\ 79 = 765\ 432 + \frac{13\ 579}{100\ 000}$$

Addition and Subtraction of Decimal Numbers

Adding or subtracting with decimals is similar to adding or subtracting with whole numbers. The important difference is the decimal point. The simplest way to add or subtract is to first line up the decimal points. It may be easier to write extra zeros to the right of the decimal point so that the numerals have the same number of decimal places. Carrying figures from column to column in the presence of a decimal point does not affect the procedure.

Example 4:

Find the sum of 60.95 + 4.0604 + 314.1 + 330

Solution:

```
    60.9500
     4.0604
   314.1000
   330.0000
   709.1104     (Ans.)
```

Example 5:

Subtract 3.1416 from 8.1

Solution:

```
     8.1000
     3.1416
     4.9584     (Ans.)
```

Multiplication of Decimal Numbers

Location of the Decimal Point

To multiply using decimals, multiply as though both factors were whole numbers and then place the decimal point in the result. The sum of the decimal places in the factors is the number of decimal places in the product.

For example:

$$0.035 \times 3 = 0.105$$

$$0.7 \times 7 = 4.9$$

$$0.0984 \times 0.06 = 0.005904$$

$$0.073 \times 0.1 = 0.0073$$

Multiplying by 10 and Power of 10

To multiply by 10, merely move the decimal point one place to the right. To multiply by 100 ($100 = 10^2$), move the decimal point two places to the right. To multiply by 10 000 ($10\,000 = 10^4$), move the decimal point four places to the right.

Division of Decimal Numbers

The best method of division by the beginner is to move the decimal point in both the divisor and dividend so that the divisor becomes a whole number.

Thus: $\dfrac{21.7}{0.0014} = \dfrac{217\,000}{14} = 15\,500$

In this case, the decimal point was moved four places to the right. The decimal place must always be moved the same number of places in both the numerator and denominator.

Example 6:

Find the value of $0.0867 \div 0.21$

Solution:

$$
\begin{array}{r}
.4128 \text{ (or round off to 0.413) (Ans.)} \\
0.21\overline{)0.0867} = 21\,\overline{)8.6700} \\
\underline{84} \\
27 \\
\underline{21} \\
60 \\
\underline{42} \\
180 \\
\underline{168} \\
12
\end{array}
$$

Notice that the quotient is written over the dividend so that the quotient decimal point comes over the dividend decimal point. As many zeroes as are required can be added to the dividend without affecting its value.

Write large numbers in groups of three starting with the decimal point. Four digit numbers not placed in a column of larger numbers need not be so spaced. Thus 1 234 567.890 98 is acceptable. If necessary, 0.7854 may be written as 0.785 4 if it is in a column of large numbers.

OBJECTIVE 3

Perform arithmetic operations involving combinations of addition, subtraction, multiplication, division and powers in the proper sequence.

OPERATIONS WITH SIGNED NUMBERS

It was stated earlier in the module that the "+" and "-" signs have two meanings: "+" may indicate the operation of addition or it may indicate a positive number; "-" may indicate the subtraction operation or it may indicate a negative number.

Signed numbers can be added, subtracted, multiplied or divided. A few examples will be looked at first, then the rules pertaining to signed numbers will be summarized.

Example 7:

a) $(+3) + (+4) = +7$

b) $(-4) + (-8) = -12$

c) $(+6) + (-2) = +4$

d) $(+4) + (-7) + (-5) + (+10) + (-32) + (+9)$

   $= (+4) + (+10) + (+9) + (-7) + (-32) + (-5)$

   $= (+23) + (-44)$

   $= -21$

e) $(+2) - (+4) + (-3) - (-6) - (-9)$

   $= (+2) + (-4) + (-3) + (+6) + (+9)$

   $= (+17) + (-7)$

   $= +10$

f) $(-5)(-2) = +10$

g) $(-18)(5) = -90$

h) $(+3)(-3)(-4)(-2)$

   $= (-9)(-4)(-2)$

   $= (-9)(+8)$

   $= -72$

i) $(-2)^4$

   $= (-2)(-2)(-2)(-2)$

   $= (4)(4)$

   $= 16$

j) $(-1)^{113} = -1$

k) $(-80) \div (-20) = 4$

l) $(27) \div (-3) = -9$

m) $(-4)^0 = 1$ {any number to the zero power equals 1}

Summarizing the rules relating to operations with signed numbers:

- When adding numbers which have the same sign, add the numbers and place the common sign in front of the sum.

- When adding numbers which have opposite signs, subtract the smaller number from the larger number and assign to the difference the sign of the larger number.

- When adding more than two numbers, two different techniques can be used. The numbers can be added "two at a time" from left to right; or, the positive numbers can be added, then the negative numbers can be added; and finally rule 2 above can be used.

- When subtracting signed numbers, first change the sign of the number to be subtracted. Then change the subtraction sign to an addition sign. Finally, use the rules of addition to evaluate the expression. (A shorter version of this rule is "change the sign of the number to be subtracted and then add").

- When multiplying signed numbers, if the numbers have the same sign, their product is positive. If the numbers have opposite signs, their product is negative.

- When multiplying several signed numbers, if there is an even number of negative numbers, then the product is positive. If there is an odd number of negative numbers, then the product is negative.

- If a negative number is raised to an even power, then the result is positive. If a negative number is raised to an odd power, then the result is negative.

- When dividing signed numbers, if the numbers have the same sign, their quotient is positive. If the numbers have opposite signs, their quotient is negative. It should be noted here that zero divided by any number is zero and any number divided by zero is undefined.

That is:
$$\frac{0}{-17} = 0$$
And
$$\frac{13}{0} = \text{undefined}$$

Order of Operations

In the previous section, examples showed situations involving only one basic operation: addition, subtraction, multiplication or division. When evaluating an expression that involves all operations, the order of the operations is most important.

The most common approach to remembering the order of operations is referred to as the **BEDMAS** method:

1. **Brackets** - carry out all operations within brackets (treat each as a mini-equation using these rules). If there are brackets within brackets, work from the innermost set of brackets to the outermost set.

2. **Exponents** - all exponents (powers) should be calculated

3. **Division** - carry out all division operations, working from left to right

4. **Multiplication** - carry out all multiplication operations, working from left to right

5. **Addition** - carry out all addition operations

6. **Subtraction** - carry out all subtraction operations

Division and multiplication can be performed at the same time without affecting the result. The same is true of addition and subtraction. They are presented in this order to maintain an easy to remember acronym.

CHAPTER 3 - QUESTIONS

1. Prime numbers are

    a) numbers which have either a positive or negative sign in front.
    b) numbers used for counting.
    c) whole numbers other than 0 and 1 that are exactly divisible only by themselves and 1.
    d) positive and negative whole numbers and zero.

2. Two numbers, or factors, are multiplied to get a third number called a

    a) multiplier.
    b) product.
    c) multiplicand.
    d) multiplication.

3. The sum of 6.95 + 40.62 + 219.5 + 284.5 is

    a) 384.25
    b) 456.78
    c) 523.54
    d) 551.57

4. The simplest way to add or subtract decimal numbers is to

    a) round up the decimals to their nearest whole number.
    b) line up the decimal points.
    c) round down the decimals to their nearest whole number.
    d) omit the denominator and indicate what it is by placing a decimal point in the numerator so that there shall be as many figures to the left of this point as there are zeroes in the denominator.

5. The result of $2[36 \div (18 - 9) + 25 - 3^2]$ is

    a) 40
    b) 32
    c) 54
    d) 49

CHAPTER 3 - ANSWERS

1. (c)

2. (b)

3. (d)

4. (b)

5. (a)

CHAPTER 4

Fractions, Decimals & Percentages

LEARNING OUTCOME

When you complete this chapter you should be able to:

Perform basic arithmetic operations involving fractions, decimals and percentages.

LEARNING OBJECTIVES

Here is what you should be able to do when you complete each objective:

1. Identify proper and improper fractions and mixed numbers.

2. Add, subtract and multiply fractions and reduce them to lowest terms.

3. Convert fractions to decimal numbers and decimal numbers to fractions.

4. Evaluate percentage problems.

INTRODUCTION

Fractions are represented by an integer above a line with another integer below the line. This is known as a common fraction. The top number is called numerator; the bottom number, the denominator.

Why are the words numerator and denominator used? Numerator originates from the Latin word numera-tus, meaning to count, and denominator is from the Latin word nominatus, meaning name. So a numerator indicates how many and the denominator indicates the name or size of units,

$$\frac{\text{numerator}}{\text{denominator}} = \frac{14}{37}$$

which in this case means that one complete unit would contain 37 equal pieces, but we are only considering 14 of them.

OBJECTIVE 1

Identify proper and improper fractions and mixed numbers.

FRACTIONS

Fractions are numbers that can be interpreted in several ways. A fraction can be thought of as a ratio of two integers (e.g., 2/3) as an indicated division (e.g., 3/4 means 3 ÷ 4), or as one or more parts of a unit (e.g., 5/11 means a unit divided into 11 equal parts, of which 5 of the equal parts are considered.

Fractions can take a number of forms. Proper fractions are less than one in which the numerator or integer on top is less than the denominator, or integer, on the bottom. Improper fractions are greater than one, with the numerator larger than the denominator. Mixed numbers are integers followed by a proper fraction. Some typical examples of these three forms of fractions are:

- Proper fraction: $\frac{2}{3}, \frac{3}{8}, \frac{17}{23}$

- Improper fraction: $\frac{5}{3}, \frac{9}{8}, \frac{13}{7}$

- Mixed number: $2\frac{1}{4}, 9\frac{7}{8}, 15\frac{3}{4}$

In the fraction $\frac{5}{8}$, 5 is the numerator and 8 is the denominator.

In the improper fraction $\frac{5}{3}$, 5 is the numerator and 3 is the denominator.

Converting Improper Fractions to Mixed Numbers

Divide the top by the bottom; the answer is a whole number and the remainder, if any, is placed over the same denominator, thus:

$$\frac{5}{2} = 2\frac{1}{2}$$

$$\frac{19}{4} = 4\frac{3}{4}$$

$$\frac{45}{4} = 11\frac{1}{4}$$

Converting Mixed Numbers to Improper Fractions

Multiply the whole number by the denominator of the fraction, add on the numerator and place the result over the same denominator, thus:

$$2\frac{2}{3} = \frac{(2 \times 3) + 2}{3} = \frac{8}{3}$$

or

$$11\frac{5}{8} = \frac{(11 \times 8) + 5}{8} = \frac{93}{8}$$

Reduction of Fractions

Any factors of the numerator which are shared by the denominator are called common factors. Common factors can be eliminated from both the numerator and the denominator without changing the value of the fraction.

A fraction has been reduced to its lowest terms when the numerator and denominator are prime to each other; that is, when they have no common factors.

Example 1:

Reduce $\frac{75}{105}$ to the lowest terms.

Solution:

$$\frac{75}{105} = \frac{5 \times 15}{5 \times 21} = \frac{3 \times 5}{3 \times 7} = \frac{5}{7} \text{ (Ans.)}$$

This shows that both the numerator and the denominator of a fraction can be divided by the same number without changing the value of the fraction.

Equivalent Fractions

If both numerator and denominator of a fraction are multiplied by the same number, the value of the fraction remains unchanged. For example:

$$\frac{6}{7} = \frac{6 \times 4}{7 \times 4} \text{ (multiplying top and bottom by 4)} = \frac{24}{28}$$

If both numerator and denominator of a fraction are divided by the same number, the value of the fraction remains unchanged.

Thus

$$\frac{4}{12} = \frac{2}{6} \text{ (dividing top and bottom by 2)}$$

$$\frac{2}{6} = \frac{1}{3} \text{ (dividing top and bottom by 2 again)}$$

$$\text{or: } \frac{4}{12} = \frac{1}{3} \text{ (dividing top and bottom by 4)}$$

Example 2:

Reduce $\frac{9}{12}$ to fourths.

Solution:

$$12 \div 4 = 3$$

then:

$$\frac{9 \div 3}{12 \div 3} = \frac{3}{4} \text{ (Ans.)}$$

OBJECTIVE 2

Add, subtract and multiply fractions and reduce them to lowest terms.

ADDITION OF FRACTIONS

Like Fractions

When fractions have the same denominator, addition or subtraction is simple. The numerators are added or subtracted and the denominator remains the same; thus:

$$\frac{2}{5} + \frac{3}{5} = \frac{5}{5} = 1$$

$$\frac{1}{5} + \frac{1}{5} + \frac{3}{5} = \frac{5}{5} = 1$$

$$\frac{7}{9} - \frac{1}{9} = \frac{6}{9} = \frac{2}{3}$$

Unlike Fractions

Before adding or subtracting common fractions, they must be brought to the same denominator, thus:

$\frac{1}{8}, \frac{1}{4}$ and $\frac{1}{16}$ cannot be added directly

They must be brought to the same denominator and then their numerators added, thus:

$$\frac{1}{8} = \frac{2}{16}, \quad \frac{1}{4} = \frac{4}{16}, \quad \frac{1}{16} = \frac{1}{16}$$

Adding the numerators: 2 + 4 + 1 equals 7. The sum is therefore $\frac{7}{16}$.

Example 3:

Add $\quad \frac{4}{9} + \frac{7}{12} + \frac{13}{24}$

Solution A:

This example is solved using the concept of Lowest Common Multiple (LCM). The LCM is the smallest common multiple of two or more numbers.

Adding fractions with different denominators requires the LCM of the denominators to be found.

Thus, to find the LCM of 9, 12, 24:

multiples of   9 = 9, 18, 27, 36, 45, 54, 63, **72**, 81

                12 = 12, 24, 36, 48, 60, **72**, 84

                24 = 24, 48, **72**, 96

The LCM is the lowest multiple of the largest denominator that is also a multiple of the other denominators, which in this case is 72.

$$\frac{4}{9} = \frac{4 \times 8}{9 \times 8} = \frac{32}{72}$$

$$\frac{7}{12} = \frac{7 \times 6}{12 \times 6} = \frac{42}{72}$$

$$\frac{13}{24} = \frac{13 \times 3}{24 \times 3} = \frac{39}{72}$$

Therefore:

$$\frac{4}{9} + \frac{7}{12} + \frac{13}{24} = \frac{32}{72} + \frac{42}{72} + \frac{39}{72} = \frac{113}{72} = 1\frac{41}{72} \text{ (Ans.)}$$

Solution B:

The LCM of 9, 12 and 24 can also be found by factoring each number into its lowest factors.

$9 = 3 \times 3$

$12 = 2 \times 2 \times 3$

$24 = 2 \times 2 \times 2 \times 3$

The lowest common multiple (LCM) will be $2 \times 2 \times 2 \times 3 \times 3 = 72$ which becomes the lowest common denominator for the fractions, 4/9, 7/12, and 13/24.

Therefore:

$$\frac{4}{9} = \frac{32}{72} \qquad \frac{7}{12} = \frac{42}{72} \qquad \frac{13}{24} = \frac{39}{72}$$

$$\frac{32 + 42 + 39}{72} = \frac{113}{72} = 1\frac{41}{72} \text{ (Ans.)}$$

Subtraction of Fractions

The same principles apply to subtraction as to addition; the quantities are brought to the same, common denominator and then one of the numerators is subtracted from the other.

Example 4:

$$\frac{7}{8} - \frac{11}{64} = \frac{56}{64} - \frac{11}{64} = \frac{45}{64} \text{ (Ans.)}$$

Multiplication of Fractions

In multiplication of two or more fractions, all numerators must be multiplied together and placed above the product of all denominators. For example:

$$1\frac{1}{2} \times 2\frac{2}{3} \times \frac{7}{16} = \frac{3}{2} \times \frac{8}{3} \times \frac{7}{16} = \frac{168}{96} = \frac{7}{4} = 1\frac{3}{4} \text{ (Ans.)}$$

However, factors which appear one in the numerator and one in the denominator may be cancelled out to simplify the calculation. In the last example:

$$\frac{3}{2} \times \frac{8}{3} \times \frac{7}{16}$$

The threes cancel out and 8 divides into 16 twice. The expression then becomes:

$$\frac{\overset{1}{3}}{2} \times \frac{\overset{1}{8}}{3} \times \frac{7}{\underset{2}{16}} = \frac{7}{4} = 1\frac{3}{4} \text{ (Ans.)}$$

Division of Fractions

When dividing by a fraction, invert it and multiply.

Example 5:

$$\frac{\frac{3}{7}}{\frac{2}{5}} = \frac{3}{7} \times \frac{5}{2} = \frac{15}{14} = 1\frac{1}{14} \text{ (Ans.)}$$

Example 6:

$$\frac{\frac{2}{5}}{\frac{9}{11}} = \frac{2}{5} \times \frac{11}{9} = \frac{22}{45} \text{ (Ans.)}$$

Example 7:

$$\frac{2\frac{1}{7}}{1\frac{1}{4}} = \frac{\frac{15}{7}}{\frac{5}{4}} = \frac{15}{7} \times \frac{4}{5} = \frac{12}{7} = 1\frac{5}{7} \text{ (Ans.)}$$

Example 8:

$$2\frac{1}{2} \times 3\frac{2}{3} \div 1\frac{4}{7} = \frac{5}{2} \times \frac{11}{3} \div \frac{11}{7} = \frac{5}{2} \times \frac{\cancel{11}^{1}}{3} \times \frac{7}{\cancel{11}_{1}} = \frac{35}{6} = 5\frac{5}{6} \text{ (Ans.)}$$

Example 9:

$$2\frac{1}{2} \div \frac{5}{16} = \frac{\cancel{5}^{1}}{\cancel{2}_{1}} \times \frac{\cancel{16}^{8}}{\cancel{5}_{1}} = 8 \text{ (Ans.)}$$

Principles

The following principles may be stated for fractions:

- multiplying or dividing both numerator and denominator by the same number does not change the value of the fraction.

- multiplying the numerator or dividing the denominator by a number multiplies the fraction by that number.

- dividing the numerator or multiplying the denominator by a number divides the fraction by that number.

OBJECTIVE 3

Convert fractions to decimal numbers and decimal numbers to fractions.

CONVERTING DECIMAL NUMBERS

A decimal number is a fraction that has 10 or a power of 10 as the denominator.

Thus $\frac{26}{10}$ or $\frac{76}{100}$ or $\frac{532}{10\,000}$ are decimal fractions.

When writing a decimal fraction, it is convenient to omit the denominator and indicate what it is by placing a point or period (.), called a decimal point, in the numerator so that there shall be as many figures to the right of this point as there are zeros in the denominator.

The above fractions now become 2.6, 0.76 and 0.0532, read as "two decimal six, decimal seven-six, and decimal zero-five-three-two.

The term "common" is used to describe all fractions in which the numerator and denominator are whole numbers.

It will be necessary from time to time to convert from one form of fraction to another. The techniques used are summarized, with an example given for each.

1. To change from a common fraction to a decimal fraction, simply divide the numerator by the denominator. On a calculator, this technique becomes quite straightforward.

    $$\frac{4}{100} = 4 \div 100 = 0.04; \quad \frac{3}{5} = 3 \div 5 = 0.6$$

2. To change a decimal fraction to a common fraction, write the nonzero portion of the decimal fraction as the numerator. Then write, as the denominator, a one (1) with a zero for every digit, or place, after the decimal. Finally, simplify the numerator and denominator by reduction.

    $$0.125 = \frac{125}{1000} = \frac{5}{40} \text{ (dividing numerator and denominator by 25)}$$

    $$= \frac{1}{8} \text{ (dividing numerator and denominator by 5)}$$

OBJECTIVE 4

Evaluate percentage problems.

PERCENTAGES

When quantities must be compared, fractions are not always helpful; nor are decimals necessarily ideal for rapid calculations. In many cases, it is better to arrange matters so that all fractions considered have a denominator of 100.

The words "per cent" mean "by the hundred" and the symbol used to represent percent is %. Thus, 10% means 10 per hundred and can be written as a common fraction, 10/100, or as a decimal fraction, 0.10, representing one tenth of a whole number.

For example, 10% of 40 litres of oil would be:

$$\frac{10}{100} \times 40 = \frac{10 \times 40}{100} = \frac{400}{100} = 4 \text{ litres}$$

Since a fraction is part of unity and a percentage is part of one hundred, a fraction can be converted into a percentage by multiplying by 100. Conversely, a percentage can be changed to a fraction by dividing by 100. Thus, the common fraction, 3/4, becomes (3 × 100)/4 = 75% or the decimal fraction, 0.75, becomes 0.75 × 100 = 75% and vice versa, the percentage, 75, becomes 75/100 or 0.75.

To express percentage increase or decrease, the rules are:

$$\% \text{ increase} = \frac{\text{increase}}{\text{original amount}} \times 100$$

$$\% \text{ decrease} = \frac{\text{decrease}}{\text{original amount}} \times 100$$

Example 10:

A spring 12 cm long is stretched to 15 cm. Calculate the percent increase in length.

Solution:

increase = final length - original length

$= 15 \text{ cm} - 12 \text{ cm}$

$= 3 \text{ cm}$

$\% \text{ increase} = \dfrac{\text{increase}}{\text{original length}} \times 100$

$= \dfrac{3}{12} \times 100$

$= \mathbf{25\% \ (Ans.)}$

Percentage Problems

As an operator, you may have to deal with percentages in solving questions such as the following:

1. "This year's gas consumption is what percentage of last year's?"

2. "By what percentage did this year's gas consumption increase over last year's?"

3. "Last year's gas consumption was lower than this year's by what percentage?"

The answers to the above questions are all different. For example, if this year's gas consumption is 24×10^6 m^3 and last year's was 18×10^6 m^3, then the answers to the above questions would be:

1. $$\frac{24 \times 10^6 m^3}{18 \times 10^6 m^3} \times 100$$

$$= 24 \times \frac{1\,000\,000}{18 \times 1\,000\,000} \times 100$$

$$= \frac{2\,400\,000\,000}{18\,000\,000}$$

$$= \frac{2400}{18}$$

$$= 133\frac{1}{3}\% \text{ (Ans.)}$$

2. $$\frac{6 \times 10^6 m^3}{18 \times 10^6 m^3} \times 100 = 33\frac{1}{3}\% \text{ (Ans.)}$$

3. $$\frac{6 \times 10^6 m^3}{24 \times 10^6 m^3} \times 100 = 25\% \text{ (Ans.)}$$

There are three basic types of percent problems:

- To find a certain percentage of a number (n).

- To find a number (n) when a percent of it is known.

- To find what percent (p) one number is of another number.

Example 11:

12% of 500 is what number (n)?

Solution:

$$n = \frac{12}{100} \times 500 = 12 \times 5 = 60 \text{ (Ans.)}$$

Example 12:

5% of what number is 10 ?

Solution:

$$\frac{5}{100}(n) = 10$$

$$n = \frac{10 \times 100}{5} = 200 \text{ (Ans.)}$$

Example 13:

21 is what percentage of 300 ?

Solution:

$$\frac{p}{100} \times 300 = 21$$

$$p = \frac{21}{300} \times 100 = \frac{21}{3} = 7 \text{ (Ans.)}$$

This page has intentionally been left blank.

CHAPTER 4 - QUESTIONS

1. Fractions are a ratio of

   a) numbers which have either a positive or negative sign in front.
   b) numerators.
   c) denominators.
   d) integers.

2. Reduce the following fractions to lowest terms.

   a) 18/48
   b) 21/39
   c) 15/30
   d) 25/64
   e) 12/4

3. Convert the following improper fractions to mixed numbers. Reduce the fraction portion to lowest terms.

   a) 9/4
   b) 13/3
   c) 18/8
   d) 19/4
   e) 11/5

4. Which of the following is not a true statement pertaining to fractions?

   a) Multiplying or dividing both numerator and denominator by the same number does not change the value of the fraction.
   b) Multiplying the numerator or dividing the denominator by a number multiplies the fraction by that number.
   c) Multiplying or dividing both numerator and denominator by the same number changes the value of the fraction.
   d) Dividing the numerator or multiplying the denominator by a number divides the fraction by that number.

5. Add the following groups of fractions. Express your answer as a mixed number if required.

   a) 1/4, 3/16, 9/32
   b) 11/13, 5/39, 2/3
   c) 3/6, 1/8, 1/3
   d) 9/5, 6/15, 26/75
   e) 7/8, 11/120, 3/12

6. Do the following subtractions. Convert your answer to mixed numbers in lowest terms if required.
   a) 15/4 - 1/3
   b) 11/12 - 1/6
   c) 13/15 - 3/5
   d) 21/25 - 1/2
   e) 13/3 - 5/6

7. Multiply the following fractions. Reduce your answer to lowest terms.
   a) 3/4 × 5/6 × 2/3
   b) 1/4 × 1/2 × 3/8
   c) 9/16 × 2/3
   d) 3/5 × 1/3 × 3/4
   e) 4/5 × 1/5 × 9/5

8. Divide the following fractions. Reduce your answer to lowest terms.
   a) 4/9 ÷ 5/6
   b) 12/13 ÷ 3/4
   c) 1/2 ÷ 6/7
   d) 11/12 ÷ 1/4
   e) 5/9 ÷ 2/3

9. Convert the following fractions to decimals.
   a) 3/5
   b) 1/4
   c) 17/100
   d) 1/10
   e) 9/16

10. Convert the following fractions or decimals to percent. Show only two decimal places.
   a) 13/16
   b) 29/45
   c) 68/70
   d) 0.192
   e) 0.356

CHAPTER 4 - ANSWERS

1. (d)

2. $\frac{3}{8}$, $\frac{7}{13}$, $\frac{1}{2}$, $\frac{25}{64}$, 3

3. $2\frac{1}{4}$, $4\frac{1}{3}$, $2\frac{1}{4}$, $4\frac{3}{4}$, $2\frac{1}{5}$

4. (c)

5. $\frac{23}{32}$, $1\frac{25}{39}$, $\frac{23}{24}$, $2\frac{41}{75}$, $1\frac{13}{60}$

6. $3\frac{5}{12}$, $\frac{3}{4}$, $\frac{4}{15}$, $\frac{17}{50}$, $3\frac{1}{2}$

7. $\frac{5}{12}$, $\frac{3}{64}$, $\frac{3}{8}$, $\frac{3}{20}$, $\frac{36}{125}$

8. $\frac{8}{15}$, $1\frac{3}{13}$, $\frac{7}{12}$, $3\frac{2}{3}$, $\frac{5}{6}$

9. 0.6, 0.25, 0.17, 0.1, 0.5625

10. 81.25%, 64.44%, 97.14%, 19.2%, 35.6%

CHAPTER 5

Ratio & Proportion

LEARNING OUTCOME

When you complete this chapter you should be able to:

Describe the concepts of ratio and proportion.

LEARNING OBJECTIVES

Here is what you should be able to do when you complete each objective:

1. Find ratios of one quantity to another quantity.

2. Solve word problems involving ratios and proportions.

OBJECTIVE 1

Find ratios of one quantity to another quantity.

RATIO

A ratio is the number of times that one number is contained in another number. It is a way to express the relative sizes of two or more quantities with the same units. For example, if the stroke of a pump is 300 mm and the diameter of the pump cylinder is 150 mm, the ratio of stroke to diameter is 300 to 150, or, reducing it to its lowest terms, 2 to 1. The ratio could be left in its original form, but reducing it to its lowest terms conveys a much better idea of the comparative size of the two dimensions.

In order to get a ratio between two quantities, they must be in the same units. Tonnes and kilometres cannot be compared, nor can grams and metres, as they are entirely different kinds of measurements. Tonnes and kilograms cannot be compared, unless both masses are converted to either tonnes or kilograms; likewise with metres and centimetres unless both measurements are converted to either metres or centimetres.

Example 1:

What is the ratio between a mass of 3 tonnes and a mass of 200 kg?

Solution:

First, the values must be converted to the same units. Either number can be converted to the other's units.

$$3 \text{ tonnes} \times 1000 \text{ kg/tonne} = 3000 \text{ kg}$$

Now the ratio between the two numbers with the same units can be found.

$$\text{The ratio} = \frac{3000 \text{ kg}}{200 \text{ kg}}$$

$$= \frac{15}{1}$$

Which can be stated as **15 to 1 (Ans.)**

Example 2:

What is the ratio between measurements of 3 m and 80 mm?

Solution:

Convert 3 m to millimetres:

$$\text{The ratio} = \frac{3000 \text{ mm}}{80 \text{ mm}}$$

$$= \frac{75}{2}$$

Which can be stated as **75 to 2 (Ans.)**

The rule then for finding the ratio between two quantities is:

- **Reduce both quantities to the same units and divide the first quantity by the second quantity.**

OBJECTIVE 2

Solve word problems involving ratios and proportions.

PROPORTION

When two ratios have the same value (are equal), the four quantities composing the ratios are said to be in proportion. Thus, the ratio 3 to 1 has the same value as the ratio 9 to 3 and this could be stated as:

3 is to 1 as 9 is to 3

But, it is customary to replace the words by dots which have the same meaning. Therefore, the last statement can be rewritten as:

3 : 1 :: 9 : 3

A proportion can also be stated in the fractional form:

$$\frac{3}{1} = \frac{9}{3}$$

Or with an equal sign:

3 : 1 = 9 : 3

Application of Proportion

The two outer terms (3 and 3) are called the extremes, while the two inner terms (1 and 9) are called the means.

Extreme   Extreme

3:1   ::   9:3

Mean   Mean

The product of the means is always equal to the product of the extremes. For example, in the above proportion:

3 x 3 = 1 x 9

From this, we get the rules:

- **The product of the two means divided by either extreme gives the other extreme.**
- **The product of the two extremes divided by either mean gives the other mean.**

These rules of proportion may be applied where two quantities are in a given ratio to each other, but only one of the quantities is known and the student wishes to find the other. The proportion is displayed in the form shown above, but the missing quantity is denoted by an 'x' or other suitable symbol.

Example 3:

If 10 tonnes of coal cost $85.00, what will $3\frac{1}{2}$ tonnes cost if the cost per tonne is the same?

Solution:

The ratio of the prices must be the same as the ratio of the weights.

Let x = the price of $3\frac{1}{2}$ tonnes.

$$x : 85 :: 3\frac{1}{2} : 10$$

$$x = \frac{3\frac{1}{2} \text{ tonnes} \times \$85.00}{10 \text{ tonnes}}$$

$$= \$29.75 \text{ (Ans.)}$$

Example 4:

Brass is a mixture of copper and zinc. How much copper must be mixed with 80 kg of zinc if the ratio of zinc to copper is 3 to 7?

Solution:

Zinc : Copper : 3 : 7

80 : Copper : 3 : 7

$$\text{Copper} = \frac{80 \text{ kg} \times 7}{3}$$

$$= \textbf{186.7 kg (Ans.)}$$

Example 5:

A certain chemical mixture should be in the ratio of 3 parts A, 5 parts B and 2 parts C. A 15 kg batch is to be mixed. What quantities of A, B and C should be used in the batch?

Solution:

It can be seen that 3 parts A, 5 parts B and 2 parts C add up to a total of 10 parts in this mixture.

$A = \dfrac{3}{10}$ of the mixture

$B = \dfrac{5}{10}$ or $\dfrac{1}{2}$ of the mixture

$C = \dfrac{2}{10}$ or $\dfrac{1}{5}$ of the mixture

To find the amount of A needed in the batch:

A : 15 :: 3 : 10

A = 15 kg x 3/10

= **4.5 kg (Ans.)**

To find the amount of B needed for the batch:

B : 15 :: 5 : 10

B = 15 kg x 1/2

= **7.5 kg (Ans.)**

To find the amount of C needed for the batch:

C : 15 :: 1 : 5

$C = 15 \text{ kg} \times \dfrac{1}{5}$

= **3 kg (Ans.)**

A quick check is needed to make sure the amounts calculated for A, B and C equal the specified total of 15 kg.

4.5 kg A + 7.5 kg B + 3 kg C = 15 kg

Inverse Proportion

So far, the solved problems are examples of direct proportion. Thus, in the example involving the cost of $3\frac{1}{2}$ tonnes of coal, the price increased directly as the mass increased. An increase in weight means an increase in price; whereas, a decrease in weight means a decrease in price.

However, there are some instances where the opposite holds true; that is, an increase in one factor means a corresponding decrease in the other. Such cases are called inverse proportions.

The most common examples of inverse proportion are problems involving the size and speed of gear wheels that are meshed together, or the size and speed of pulleys that are connected together by belts. The speeds of such gear wheels and pulleys are inversely proportional to their diameters. The ratio between the speeds will be the same as the ratio between the diameters or number of teeth, but the smaller pulley or gear will run at a faster speed than the larger pulley or gear.

Example 6:

A gear wheel 300 mm in diameter and revolving at a speed of 100 r/min drives a gear wheel 120 mm in diameter. What is the speed of the second gear?

Solution: (note the ratio is inversed)

Speed of 2nd gear wheel : Speed of 1st wheel :: Diameter of 1st gear wheel : Diameter of 2nd gear wheel

2nd Speed : 100 :: 300 : 120

$$\text{2nd Speed} = \frac{100 \text{ r/min} \times 300 \text{ mm}}{120 \text{ mm}}$$

= **250 r/min (Ans.)**

Example 7:

A supply fan is driven by an electric motor by means of V-belts. The pulley on the motor shaft has an 80 mm diameter and rotates at 1750 r/min. The diameter of the pulley on the fan shaft is 280 mm. What is the speed of the fan?

Solution:

Fan speed : Motor speed :: Diameter motor pulley. Diameter fan pulley.

Fan speed : 1750 :: 80 : 280

$$\text{Fan speed} = \frac{1750 \text{ r/min} \times 80 \text{ mm}}{280 \text{ mm}}$$

= **500 r/min (Ans.)**

Example 8:

A driving gear has 55 teeth and turns at 600 r/min. If the driven gear has 80 teeth, how fast does it turn?

Solution:

Let the speed of the 80 tooth (driven) gear = x

Driven speed : Driver speed :: Driver teeth : Driven teeth

x : 600 :: 55 : 80

$$x = \frac{600 \text{ r/min} \times 55 \text{ teeth}}{80 \text{ teeth}}$$

= **412.5 r/min (Ans.)**

CHAPTER 5 - QUESTIONS

1. A manufacturer employs 500 females and 1500 males.

   a) What is the ratio of females to males?

   b) What is the ratio of males to females?

   c) What is the ratio of females to the total number of employees?

   d) What is the ratio of males to total number of employees?

2. A gas plant receives product from three different wells, A, B and C in the proportion of 3 parts, 7 parts and 2 parts respectively. If the total amount of gas processed is 2 400 000 m³, how much gas comes from each well?

3. A 150 mm diameter pulley drives another larger pulley measuring 4000 mm in diameter. If the small one rotates at a speed of 240 r/min, what is the speed of the larger one?

4. Gear A has a 120 mm diameter. What is the diameter of gear B if gears A and B have radii in the ratio of 5:3?

CHAPTER 5 - ANSWERS

4th Class • Part A1

1. a) 1 Female : 3 Males
   b) 3 Males : 1 Female
   c) 1 Female : 4 Employees
   d) 3 Males : 4 Employees

2. A = 600 000 m^3
   B = 1 400 000 m^3
   C = 400 000 m^3

3. 9 r/min

4. 72 mm

Equations & Transposition

LEARNING OUTCOME

When you complete this chapter you should be able to:

Transpose equations in order to find values for different variables in a formula.

LEARNING OBJECTIVES

Here is what you should be able to do when you complete each objective:

1. Transpose and solve equations involving addition, subtraction, multiplication, division and powers, and solve word problems using transposition.

INTRODUCTION

Equations and transposing of their terms is much easier if values are included. This allows us the opportunity to verify that our transposition is correct. For example, if 10 = 5 x 2, then 5 = 10 ÷ 2 and 2 = 10 ÷ 5. The equations all consist of three terms and the values are common in all equations. If the equations contain only alpha values and no numerics, then proving the transposition becomes more difficult since there are no mathematical values given. Thus the use of "mental numerics."

OBJECTIVE 1

Transpose and solve equations involving addition, subtraction, multiplication, division and powers, and solve word problems using transposition.

EQUATIONS

An equation is a statement about certain things that balance each other. It is the mathematical way to state an equivalency. Any arithmetical expression that contains an "equals" sign is an equation. For example:

$$W = \frac{1}{2}D + 0.75 \text{ mm}$$

and

$$C = \pi \times D$$

are equations.

In each of these examples, the expression on the right of the equal sign is identical in value to the expression on the left; therefore, the statement of this equality forms an equation. The two sides of an equation must always be equal or balanced, just as the masses in the two pans of a druggist's scales must be equal if the scales are to balance.

Formulas are generally written with a single letter or symbol on the left representing the quantity whose value is to be found. This symbol is the subject of the equation. The letters and symbols representing the known quantities are arranged on the right hand side of the equation as a formula for this unknown quantity.

The formula for the area of a circle, $A = 0.7854 \, D^2$ is written this way because it is normally used to find the value of the area when the diameter is known. If the area is known and the diameter is unknown, the formula must be changed to show how to obtain the value of the diameter from the value given for the area. In other words, the formula must be changed into the form:

$$D = \sqrt{\frac{A}{0.7854}}$$

The formula for the volume of a cylinder is usually written: $V = \pi r^2 h$. However, if the volume was given and the student was required to find the height, it would be more convenient to have h standing alone on the left side of the equation and the other values on the right side. The formula would then become:

$$h = \frac{V}{\pi r^2}$$

However, whenever changes or transformations are made in a formula, the equality between the two sides of the equation must not be destroyed. No matter what form the formula is changed to, the expression on the left side must equal the expression on the right.

TRANSPOSITION

The process of moving a letter or number from one side of an equation, changing its sign so as not to disturb the equality, is called transposing or transposition.

If a steel rod 100 mm long has a mark dividing it into two parts 70 mm and 30 mm long, as in Figure 1(a), the length of the pin can be expressed by 100 mm or 70 mm + 30 mm.

Then:

$$100 \text{ mm} = 30 \text{ mm} + 70 \text{ mm}$$

It is evident that one part is equal to the whole length minus the other part.

$$100 \text{ mm} - 70 \text{ mm} = 30 \text{ mm}$$

In this last equation, the equality remains, but one term has been transposed from the right of the original equation to the left. Notice that the 70 mm has been transposed by changing its sign from positive to negative.

Figure 1	Steel Rod

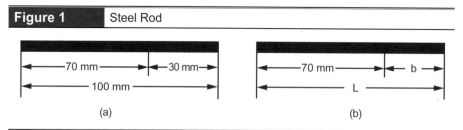

(a)   (b)

If one part of the rod shown in Figure 1(b) is 70 mm long, the other part is b mm long and the whole length is L mm.

Then:

$$L = b + 70 \text{ mm}$$

And

$$L - 70 \text{ mm} = b$$

Or

$$L - b = 70 \text{ mm}$$

Here, the same process of transposing a term by changing its sign to the exact opposite, positive to negative, has been followed.

Likewise, a negative term can be transposed by changing its sign from negative to positive. Hence, any term may be transposed from one side of an equation to the other by changing its sign.

If

$$b = L - 70 \text{ mm}$$

Then

$$b + 70 \text{ mm} = L$$

This process may also be explained in another way, which is often useful. The same quantity can be added to or subtracted from both sides of the equation. To the formula, b = L - 70 mm, add 70 mm to both sides of the equation, or add 70 mm = 70 mm to the original equation.

$$b + 70 \text{ mm} = L - 70 \text{ mm} + 70 \text{ mm}$$

$$b + 70 \text{ mm} = L$$

This manipulation produces the same result as transposing the 70 mm. Therefore, if equal quantities are added to equal quantities, the sums are equal. If equal quantities are subtracted from equal quantities, the remainders are equal.

The formula relating the circumference and the diameter of a circle is $C = \pi \times D$. If the circumference (C) is known and D is to be discovered, then π can be transposed by dividing both sides of the equation by π.

$$\frac{C}{\pi} = \frac{\pi D}{\pi}$$

Now π will cancel itself on the right side of the equation, since $\pi / \pi = 1$, leaving:

$$\frac{C}{\pi} = D$$

Now, to return to the original equation ($C = \pi \times D$), both sides can be multiplied by π, as follows:

$$\frac{C}{\pi} \times \pi = \pi \times D$$

$$C = \pi \times D$$

Then, if equal quantities are multiplied by equal quantities, the products are equal. If equal quantities are divided by equal quantities, the quotients are equal.

The foregoing statements about equations can be summarized as follows:

- The two sides of an equation will remain equal if at all times any operations performed on one side are also performed on the other side.

When both sides of $C = \pi \times D$ are divided by π, then D on the right hand side of the equation is both multiplied and divided by π. These operations are equal but opposite in direction, so they cancel each other. Numbers cancel each other because a number divided by itself equals one and one times any quantity is equal to the original quantity. In the following equation, π divided by π equals one and the one is not normally written in the final equation.

$$\frac{C}{\pi} = \frac{\pi \times D}{\pi}$$

$$\frac{C}{\pi} = 1 \times D$$

$$\frac{C}{\pi} = D$$

The formula for determining the area of a rectangle, $A = L \times W$, is written this way because in most cases, it is used to get the value of the area (A) when the length (L) and width (W) are known. If the area and length are known and the width is required, the equation must be changed to a different form.

$$\frac{A}{L} = \frac{L \times W}{L}$$

Whatever changes or transformations are made in a formula, the equality between the two sides of the equation must remain. It does not matter what form the equation is changed to, the expression on the left side must equal the expression on the right.

There are several valid rules or methods by which an equation can be changed; they all involve performing the same operations to both sides of the equation so that the two sides remain equal.

- Add or subtract the same value to or from each side of the equation.

- Multiply or divide each side of the equation by the same value, as long as it is not zero.

- Take any root of each side of the equation or raise each side of the equation to any power.

It is worthwhile reviewing the order of operations at this point.

1. If there are multiple sets of brackets, simplify what is inside the innermost brackets first, then work outwards.

2. Perform any operations involving exponents.

3. Carry out multiplication or division next, working from LEFT to RIGHT.

4. Finally, addition or subtraction is carried out.

Example 1:
Solve the following equation for d.

$$L = ab(d - t)$$

Solution:
First, divide each side of the equation by ab.

$$\frac{L}{ab} = \frac{ab\,(d - t)}{ab}$$

Now, the equation has become:

$$\frac{L}{ab} = d - t$$

Then, add t to both sides of the equation:

$$\frac{L}{ab} + t = d - t + t$$

The result is then:

$$\frac{L}{ab} + t = d \textbf{ (Ans.)}$$

Example 2:

Solve the following equation for y.

$$\frac{a}{c} = \frac{x + y}{y}$$

Solution:

1. Multiply both sides of the equation by the product cy to get rid of the fractions. Note the brackets around x + y.

$$\frac{cya}{c} = \frac{cy(x + y)}{y}$$
$$ya = c(x + y)$$

2. Expand the right side by multiplying all the terms in the brackets by c.

$$ya = cx + cy$$

3. Subtract cy from each side to get all terms with y on one side.

$$ya - cy = cx + cy - cy$$
$$ya - cy = cx$$

4. Extract the common factor y from each term on the left side. (i.e. factor the left side of the equation).

$$y(a - c) = cx$$

5. Divide both sides by the term (a - c); cancel the common factors from the numerator and denominator of the left side. In this case the only common factor is the whole term (a - c).

$$\frac{y(a - c)}{(a - c)} = \frac{cx}{(a - c)}$$

$$y = \frac{cx}{(a - c)} \text{ (Ans.)}$$

Example 3:

Solve the following equation for r.

$$\frac{r}{c} = \frac{ab}{r}$$

Solution:

1. Multiply both sides by c and r.

$$\frac{crr}{c} = \frac{ab\ cr}{r}$$

$$r^2 = abc$$

2. To solve for r, take the square root of r^2. To maintain the balance, take the square root of the entire right hand side of the equation as well.

$$\sqrt{r^2} = \sqrt{abc}$$

$$r = \sqrt{abc} \text{ (Ans.)}$$

Cross Multiplication

Examination of the last example (Ex.3) shows that in the beginning the 'c' was on the left side and below the line as a denominator. Then, at the end of Step 1, it appeared on the right side, but above the line as a multiplier. This process involved multiplication and cancellation. Another (short cut) method of moving factors within an equation is called **cross multiplication.**

Following the process of multiplication or division and cancellation, the following can be determined:

- Factors changed from one side of an equation to the other have the same value but are opposite in operation. Thus, in isolating a particular term, terms can be moved across the equal sign by changing their operating sign.

Example 4:

Solve the following equation for d:

$$\frac{a}{b} = \frac{c}{d}$$

$$\frac{a}{b} \diagdown \diagup \frac{c}{d}$$

Solution:

The arrows across the equal sign indicate the path that symbols should travel.

$$d = \frac{cb}{a} \text{ (Ans.)}$$

A review of this problem using multiplication, division and cancellation should arrive at the same answer.

Example 5:

Solve the following equation for r.

$$\frac{mn}{qr} = \frac{st}{w}$$

Solution:

Move each term across the equal sign to isolate r above the line.

$$\frac{mnw}{qst} = r \text{ (Ans.)}$$

This is a time saving shortcut but full meaning of the operation must be kept in mind.

SOLVING WORD PROBLEMS

Word problems are engineering problems that are simply stated in words. They usually involve using an equation and rearranging that equation, if necessary, to calculate a particular unkonwn. This involves transposition, adjusting a formula to isolate a variable in an equation, thus making it the subject of the equation. The following are examples (6 and 7) that provide a quick overview of transposition and then some examples (8 and 9) of how it can be used to solve word problems.

Example 6:

The power, P, in a circuit is given by:

$$P = I \times V$$

where I is current and V is voltage.

Transpose the equation to create one in which V is the subject.

Solution:

To transpose the equation for V , the formula V = _____ must be created.

To do this:

1. Isolate V

    a) P = I x V

    b) $\dfrac{P}{I} = \dfrac{I \times V}{I}$

    c) P / I = V

2. Move V to the Left Hand Side (LHS) of the equation

    a) **V = P/I (Ans.)**

Example 7:

The final velocity V of an object with initial velocity U undergoing constant acceleration A over time T is given by the equation.

$$V = U + A \times T$$

Transpose the equation to one which has T as the subject.

Solution:

Steps

1. Isolate T

    a) V = U + A x T

    b) V - U = A x T

    c) $\dfrac{V - U}{A} = \dfrac{A \times T}{A}$

    d) $\dfrac{V - U}{A} = T$

2. Move T to the Left Hand Side (LHS) of the equation

    a) **T** $= \dfrac{V - U}{A}$ **(Ans.)**

Example 8:

A gas cylinder with pressure P_1, temperature T_1 and volume V_1 expands into a new volume V_2 creating having a new pressure P_2 and temperature T_2. The relationship between these quantities is given by the equation.

$$\frac{P_1 \times V_1}{T_1} = \frac{P_2 \times V_2}{T_2}$$

Solution:

Transpose the equation to one which has T_1 as the subject.

1. Isolate T_1

 a) $\dfrac{P_1 \times V_1}{T_1} = \dfrac{P_2 \times V_2}{T_2}$

 b) $\dfrac{P_1 \times V_1 \times T_1}{T_1} = \dfrac{P_2 \times V_2 \times T_1}{T_2}$

 c) $P_1 \times V_1 \times T_2 = \dfrac{P_2 \times V_2 \times T_1 \times T_2}{T_2}$

 d) $\dfrac{P_1 \times V_1 \times T_2}{P_2 \times V_2} = \dfrac{P_2 \times V_2 \times T_1}{P_2 \times V_2}$

 e) $\dfrac{P_1 \times V_1 \times T_2}{P_2 \times V_2} = T_1$

2. Move T to the Left Hand Side (LHS) of the equation

 a) $T_1 = \dfrac{\mathbf{P_1 \times V_1 \times T_2}}{\mathbf{P_2 \times V_2}}$ **(Ans.)**

Alternatively:

1. Invert Both sides

 a) $\dfrac{P_1 \times V_1}{T_1} = \dfrac{P_2 \times V_2}{T_2}$

 b) $\dfrac{T_1}{P_1 \times V_1} = \dfrac{T_2}{P_2 \times V_2}$

 c) $\dfrac{T_1 \times P_1 \times V_1}{P_1 \times V_1} = \dfrac{T_2 \times P_1 \times V_1}{P_2 \times V_2}$

 d) $T_1 = \dfrac{T_2 \times P_1 \times V_1}{P_2 \times V_2}$

Example 9:

A gas cylinder has a volume of 0.16 m^3. It is filled with nitrogen to a pressure of 140 kPa absolute. The cylinder is fully evacuated to another vessel having a volume of 0.50 m^3. The system temperature is constant during the time of the evacuation at 25°C. What is the final absolute pressure? Note: The pressures must be absolute and the temperature must be in degrees K, where K = deg C + 273.

Solution:

Equation to use

$$\frac{P_1 \times V_1}{T_1} = \frac{P_2 \times V_2}{T_2}$$

Where P_1 = 140 kPa, V_1 = 0.16 m^3, P_2 = ?, V_2 = 0.50 m^3 and $T_1 = T_2$ = 25 + 273 = 298 K

1. Isolate P_2

    a) $\dfrac{P_1 \times V_1}{T_1} = \dfrac{P_2 \times V_2}{T_2}$

    b) $\dfrac{P_1 \times V_1 \times T_2}{T_1 \times V_2} = P_2$

2. Move P_2 to the Left Hand Side (LHS) of the equation

    a) $P_2 = \dfrac{P_1 \times V_1 \times T_2}{T_1 \times V_2}$

3. Insert Values and Solve

    a) $P_2 = \dfrac{140 \text{ kPa} \times 0.16 \text{ m}^3 \times 298 \text{ K}}{0.50 \text{ m}^3 \times 298 \text{ K}}$

    = **44.8 kPa (Ans.)**

This page has intentionally been left blank.

CHAPTER 6 - QUESTIONS

1. Solve the following equations for A.

   a) $b = \frac{1}{2}h (A + C)$

   b) $C = \frac{9}{5}A + 32$

   c) $\frac{CDE}{AFG} = \sqrt{B}$

   d) $N = \frac{6A^2}{B^3}$

   e) $I = \frac{AB}{Ar + R}$

2. The surface area (A) of a sphere is $4m^2$ and is calculated using the formula, $A = 4\pi r^2$. What is the radius (r)?

3. The formula $V = u + at$ gives a final velocity, V, if the initial velocity (u), acceleration (a), and time (t) are known. Solve the equation for a.

4. Substitute the given numerical terms and evaluate the following equation to find the minimum required thickness (t) of a boiler drum.

$$t = \frac{PR}{SE - (1 - Y) P} + C$$

   t = Minimum required thickness in mm (unknown)

   P = Maximum allowable working pressure

     = 7000 kPa

   R = Inside radius of cylinder

     = 750 mm

   S = Stress value

     = 120 658.24 kPa

   E = Joint Efficiency

     = 0.5

   Y = Temperature coefficient

     = 0.4

   C = Corrosion allowance

     = 0

5. A short cut method of moving factors of an equation is called

   a) substitution.

   b) transposition.

   c) cross multiplication.

   d) neutralization.

CHAPTER 6 - ANSWERS

1. a) $A = \dfrac{2b}{h} - C$

   b) $A = \dfrac{5}{9}(C - 32)$

   c) $A = \dfrac{CDE}{FG\sqrt{B}}$

   d) $A = \sqrt{\dfrac{B^3 N}{6}}$

   e) $A = \dfrac{-IR}{Ir - B}$ alternate answer: $A = \dfrac{IR}{B - Ir}$

2. 0.56 m

3. $a = \dfrac{V - u}{t}$

4. t = 93.53 mm

5. (c)

Length, Lines & Simple Plane Figures

LEARNING OUTCOME

When you complete this chapter you should be able to:

Describe measurement of length, types of lines and angles, and calculate perimeters and areas of simple plane figures.

LEARNING OBJECTIVES

Here is what you should be able to do when you complete each objective:

1. Describe linear measurement systems and convert measurement units from one system to another.

2. Define parallel and perpendicular lines and types of angles.

3. Describe types of simple plane figures, including triangles and quadrilaterals, and calculate their areas.

4. Describe the components of a circle and find its circumference, area and diameter.

OBJECTIVE 1

Describe linear measurement systems and convert measurement units from one system to another.

LINEAR MEASUREMENT SYSTEMS & CONVERSIONS

Length

Length can be thought of in two different ways:

- an object is a number of units long.
- the ends of an object are displaced from each other by a number of units.

In the second case, movement of a person, vehicle or object can be considered as a displacement from one point to another.

Throughout history, length has been judged by several different standards. Many were associated with human body measurement. The "cubit", length of the forearm from the elbow to the tip of the middle finger, ranged from about 46 - 53 cm depending on whose arm was being used. The "foot" finally became standardized at 12 inches or 30.48 cm to eliminate the variations in the different "foot" sizes used.

Imperial Measure
(also United States Customary System (USCS))

12 inches (in) = 1 foot (ft)

3 feet = 1 yard (yd)

5.5 yards = 1 rod

320 rods = 1 mile (mi)

1760 yards = 1 mile

5280 feet = 1 mile

SI Measure

1000 millimetres (mm) = 1 metre (m)

100 centimetres (cm) = 1 metre

10 decimetres (dm) = 1 metre

10 metres = 1 decametre (dam)

100 metres = 1 hectometre (hm)

1000 metres = 1 kilometre (km)

The metric system is based on the metre as a unit of length. A platinum standard metre was prepared in 1799 and later a platinum and iridium standard metre was used because it was more stable through temperature fluctuations. In 1960, light from Krypton 86, generated under specific conditions, was established as a non-changing standard and the metre was defined as 1 650 763.73 wave lengths. This measurement is accurate at 10^{-8} m or 1/100 of a micron.

Other forms of measurement are now defined in terms of their comparison to SI. For a full explanation of the SI system, see the Chapter on S.I. Units.

Accuracy of length measurement will depend on the precision necessary for the job. A 50 cm shoelace may be 49 or 51 cm and go unnoticed or have little consequence. However, a precision piece for a space vehicle, specified at 500.00 mm, could cause a disaster if it were manufactured at 490 or 510 mm.

Table 1 shows some common units derived from the metre.

Table 1		Metric Units Derived from the Metre
Length in Metres		**Name and Abbreviation**
1000	10^3	kilometre (km)
1	10^0	metre (m)
0.01	10^{-2}	centimetre (cm)
0.001	10^{-3}	millimetre (mm)
0.000 001	10^{-6}	micron (μ pronounced mu)
0.000 000 000 1	10^{-10}	angstrom (A°)

The unit of kilometre is applied to measurements such as distances between cities. The metre is used for distance between objects such as a boiler and a wall or as the height of a stack. The centimetre is used for such measurements as the neck size, sleeve length or height of a person while the millimetre measures precipitation.

The micron is used for fine machine work measurements or measuring the size of bacteria. The angstrom unit is mostly employed for measuring the wavelength of light.

When a distance is measured in metres, it is assumed to be accurate to the nearest metre. For example, a rope may be said to be 12 m long, which means that it is closer to 12 m than to 11 m or 13 m. If the rope is said to be 1200 cm, it is closer to 1200 cm than it is to 1199 or 1201 cm. If the rope is said to be 12 000 mm long, it is closer to 12 000 mm than to 11 999 mm or 12 001 mm.

The units used for measurement should be reasonable, depending on the required precision.

Imperial units may be converted to SI units, or vice versa, by use of the conversion listed in Table 2. These conversions may also be found in the Academic Supplement, Handbook of Formulae and Physical Constants.

Table 2		Measurement Conversions
1 inch	=	25.4 millimetres
1 foot	=	30.48 centimetres
1 yard	=	0.914 metres
1 mile	=	1.61 kilometres
1 millimetre	=	0.0394 inches
1 centimetre	=	0.394 inches
1 metre	=	1.094 yards
1 kilometre	=	0.621 miles

The following examples illustrate the use of the above table.

Example 1:

Convert a single measurement of 5 yd, 2 ft and 6 in to metres.

Solution:

$$5 \text{ yd x 36 in/yd} = 180 \text{ in}$$
$$2 \text{ ft x 12 in/ft} = 24 \text{ in}$$
$$180 \text{ in} + 24 \text{ in} + 6 \text{ in} = 210 \text{ in}$$
$$210 \text{ in x 25.4 mm/in} = 5334 \text{ mm} = \textbf{5.334 metres (Ans.)}$$

Example 2:

Convert a single measurement of 4 mi, 340 yd to kilometres.

Solution:

$$4 \text{ mi x 1760 yd/mi} = 7040 \text{ yd}$$
$$7040 \text{ yd} + 340 \text{ yd} = 7380 \text{ yd}$$
$$7380 \text{ yd x 0.914 m/yd} = 6745 \text{ m}$$

$$\frac{6745 \text{ m}}{1000 \text{ m/km}} = \textbf{6.745km (Ans.)}$$

Example 3:

Convert a single measurement of 3 m, 2 dm, 4 cm to inches.

Solution:

$$3 \text{ m x 100 cm/m} = 300 \text{ cm}$$
$$2 \text{ dm x 10 cm/dm} = 20 \text{ cm}$$
$$300 \text{ cm} + 20 \text{ cm} + 4 \text{ cm} = 324 \text{ cm}$$
$$324 \text{ cm x 0.394 in/cm} = \textbf{127.7 in. (Ans.)}$$

Example 4:

Convert a single measurement of 6 dam, 3 m, 7 cm to feet.

Solution:

$$6 \text{ dam x 1000 cm/dam} = 6000 \text{ cm}$$
$$3 \text{ m x 100 cm/m} = 300 \text{ cm}$$
$$6000 \text{ cm} + 300 \text{ cm} + 7 \text{ cm} = 6307 \text{ cm}$$
$$6307 \text{ cm x 0.394 in/cm} = 2485 \text{ in}$$

$$\frac{2485 \text{ in}}{12 \text{ in/ft}} = \textbf{207.08 feet (Ans.)}$$

Mensuration

Mensuration, the branch of mathematics dealing with measurement or the determination of length, area and volume, has many applications in industrial plants, including:

- calculating of the areas of heat transfer surfaces in heat exchangers or boilers.

- finding the capacity of a tank or pipeline.

- calculating furnace volumes.

To be more effective in controlling process changes and to have a greater understanding of the plant, the plant operator should be familiar with such measurements.

Regardless of the shape of an object, any single dimension (height, length, depth or width) is measured in units of length such as: metres, millimetres and centimetres.

Any measurement of area is in square units (m^2, mm^2, km^2, etc.) while the measurements of volume are in cubic units (m^3, mm^3, cm^3, etc.). For example, the volume of liquid contained in a spherical tank may be measured in cubic units, such as m^3.

Even though measurement in Canada is officially based on the SI system, many industries still have equipment built to Imperial specifications. For example, pressure gauges may be in pounds per square inch or flow in gallons per minute. The nuts and bolts that hold the equipment together may still be measured in fractions of an inch. Much of the new machinery and equipment is now manufactured to SI standards, but most facilities have both SI and USCS measurements in their equipment. For this reason, it is still important to have some understanding of the Imperial system and how to convert measurements back and forth between Imperial and SI.

OBJECTIVE 2

Define parallel and perpendicular lines and types of angles.

PARALLEL & PERPENDICULAR LINES

Measurement of the distance between two points is the same as the measurement of a straight line between the two points. In theory, a line has no width or depth and is made of an infinite number of points laid side by side. A line is often represented by a pencil line to give a visible indication of where it exists. Referring to Figure 1, lines which are exactly the same distance apart at all points are said to be parallel. A horizontal line is perfectly level and a vertical line is exactly "plumb" or straight up and down, forming a right angle with a horizontal surface.

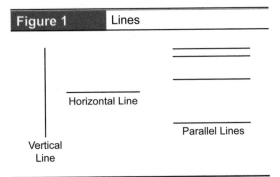

Figure 1 — Lines

Horizontal Line

Vertical Line

Parallel Lines

Lines at right angles (i.e. 90 degrees) to each other are said to be perpendicular to each other. Note that a perpendicular is not necessarily a vertical line. In each of the three sketches in Figure 2, AB is perpendicular to CD.

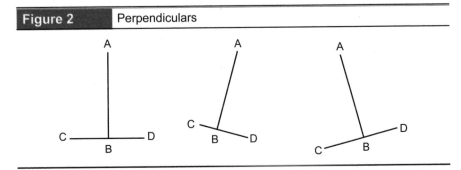

Figure 2 — Perpendiculars

ANGLES

When straight lines meet or cross, they form an angle, the corner included between two straight lines. A sharp corner is called an acute angle (measuring less than 90°); a square corner is called a right angle (measuring exactly 90°); and a blunt corner is called an obtuse angle (measuring between 90° and 180°). These various angles are shown in Figure 3.

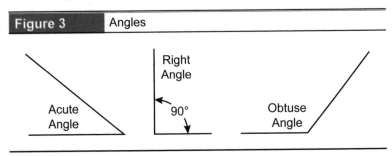

Figure 3 — Angles

Acute Angle

Right Angle

90°

Obtuse Angle

OBJECTIVE 3

Describe types of simple plane figures, including triangles and quadrilaterals, and calculate their areas.

SIMPLE PLANE FIGURES

Plane figures have length and width but no thickness. This objective will focus only on those figures enclosed by straight lines. Faces of objects may be in the shape of plane figures. Area and volume calculations are made using measurements of these figures, but a plane figure makes no attempt to show the depth of an object, only height and width.

Plane figures with three or more sides are collectively called polygons. Figures with a specific number of sides have individual names such as hexagon, a six-sided figure.

Perimeter or Circumference

Perimeter or circumference is the distance measured around the outline of a plane figure. In the case of figures enclosed by straight lines, the perimeter is found by adding together the lengths of the sides. The perimeter of the square, rectangle, equilateral triangle, and equilateral or regular hexagon and octagon are found as shown in Table 3:

Table 3	Calculation of Perimeters	
Figure		**Perimeter**
Square	Let s = length of side	4s
Rectangle	Let a = long side; b = short side	2a + 2b
Equilateral Triangle (equal sides)	Let s = length of side	3s
Regular Hexagon (equal sides)	Let s = length of side	6s
Regular Octagon (equal sides)	Let s = length of side	8s

Measure of Area

The area of any figure is its surface measurement; the unit of measurement is the square metre. A square metre is the area of a square having sides one metre long. The smallest unit is the square millimetre which is the area of a square having sides one millimetre long. Other units are the square centimetre and the hectare, which measures 10 000 square metres.

The following table shows the relationship between these units:

Table 4	Metric Conversions
100 mm²	=	1 cm²
10 000 cm²	=	1 m²
10 000 m²	=	1 ha
100 ha	=	1 km²

Note: $1 \text{ m}^2 = (100 \times 100)\text{cm}^2 = 10\ 000 \text{ cm}^2 = 10^4 \text{ cm}^2$

$1 \text{ m}^3 = (100 \times 100 \times 100)\text{cm}^3 = 1\ 000\ 000 \text{ cm}^3 = 10^6 \text{ cm}^3$

Triangles

Triangles are three-sided figures. If the three sides are of equal length, it is called an equilateral triangle. An isosceles triangle has two sides of equal length and a third side that is longer or shorter. If one of the angles is a right angle, the result is a right triangle. The sum of the angles of a triangle equals 180°. A scalene triangle has no two sides or angles equal and no right angle. An obtuse triangle contains an angle greater than 90°. Figure 4 shows examples of common triangles.

Figure 4	Common Triangles

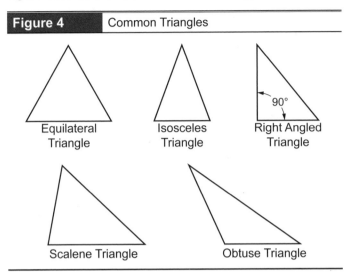

Equilateral Triangle   Isosceles Triangle   Right Angled Triangle

Scalene Triangle   Obtuse Triangle

Areas of Triangles

The following formulae allow for calculation of triangle areas when:

- the perpendicular height of any triangle, plus the length of its base are known.
- the triangle is equilateral and the length of the side is known.
- the perpendicular height of the triangle is unknown, but lengths of the three sides are.

Figure 5	Any Triangle

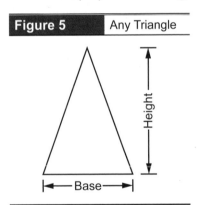

Height

Base

The area of any triangle is calculated using the following formula:

$$\text{Area} = \frac{1}{2} \text{ base x perpendicular height}$$

Figure 6	Equilateral Triangle

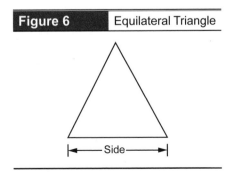

Side

To calculate the area of an equilateral triangle, the following formula is used:

$$Area = 0.433 \times S^2$$

Figure 7 | S Rule

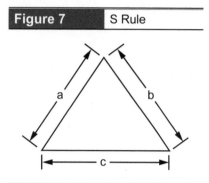

If the perpendicular height of the triangle is unknown, but lengths of the three sides are, then the following formula is used:

$$Area = \sqrt{S(S-a)(S-b)(S-c)}$$

where: $S = \dfrac{1}{2}$ the sum of the three sides

If lengths of the three sides are respectively equal to a, b and c, then:

$$S = \frac{a+b+c}{2}$$

Quadrilaterals

Quadrilaterals, shown in Figure 8, are figures that have four straight sides and include the square, rectangle, rhomboid, rhombus, trapezoid and trapezium. Parallelograms are figures that have four straight sides with the opposite sides parallel to each other. The square, rectangle, rhomboid and rhombus are parallelograms.

When all the angles of a quadrilateral are added together, their sum is 360°.

Figure 8 | Quadrilaterals

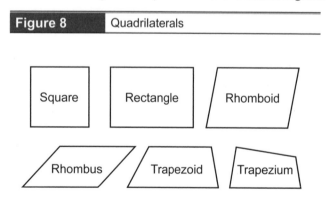

A square is a four-sided figure with all four sides of equal length and all angles right angles.

A rectangle is a parallelogram in which all the angles are right angles but opposite sides are equal and adjacent sides are unequal.

A rhomboid is a four-sided figure with the opposite sides parallel but the angles are not right angles.

A rhombus is a four-sided figure in which the four sides are of equal length but the angles are not right angles.

A trapezoid is a quadrilateral having only two sides parallel.

A trapezium is a quadrilateral having no two sides parallel.

Areas of Quadrilaterals

Calculation of the area of a quadrilateral usually involves the multiplication of two dimensions, length and width. Before multiplying these, they must be brought to the same unit.

Multiplying length in metres by width in metres gives square metres while multiplying length in centimetres by width in centimetres gives square centimetres.

The following are the formulae for finding the areas of these figures:

SInce the length and width of a square are equal, we usually refer to the side length as 's'. The area can then be shown as:

$$\text{Area} = (\text{side})^2 = s^2$$

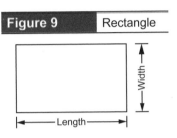

Figure 9   Rectangle

Area = Length × Width

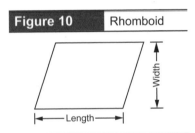

Figure 10   Rhomboid

Area = Length × Width

OBJECTIVE 4

Describe components of a circle and find its circumference, area and diameter.

CIRCLES

A circle (Fig. 11) is a figure with one continuous boundary line, called the circumference. The circumference is always at the same distance from a point called the center of the circle. The distance from the center to the circumference is called the radius (radii is plural). A straight line drawn through the center and touching the circumference on each side is called the diameter; it is equal to twice the radius.

Figure 11	Circle

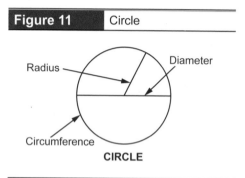

CIRCLE

A sector, shown in Figure 12, is a part of a circle bounded by two radius lines and a part of the circumference called an arc.

$$\text{Length of arc} = \text{Circumference of circle} \times \frac{\text{Angle of Sector}}{360°}$$

Figure 12	Sector

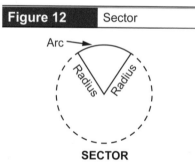

SECTOR

A quadrant, Figure 13, is a sector comprising a quarter of a circle, the angle between the radius lines being a right angle.

Figure 13	Quadrant

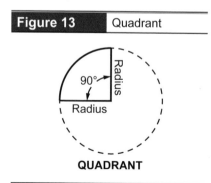

QUADRANT

Circumference of a Circle

To find the circumference of a circle, a special formula is used. If the diameter and circumference of any circle are actually measured, it will be found that the circumference is approximately 3.1416 × the diameter.

Since the value 3.1416 occurs very often in calculations, a special symbol has been adopted to denote it. Instead of having to write down the actual figures every time, the symbol "π" (the Greek letter "pi") is used.

The formula used to find the circumference of a circle when the diameter is known is:

Circumference = π x Diameter

$$C = \pi D$$

If radius is given instead of diameter, the radius must be multiplied by two to give the diameter; the formula becomes:

Circumference = π x 2 x Radius

or $C = 2\pi R$

Area of a Circle

$$\text{Area} = \pi R^2$$
$$= \frac{\pi}{4} \times D^2$$
$$= 0.7854\, D^2$$

Finding the Diameter of a Circle from the Area

Often the area of a circle is given and it is required to find the diameter of the circle. The formula to use is:

$$\text{Diameter of a circle} = \sqrt{\frac{\text{Area of a Circle}}{0.7854}}$$

Example 5:

What is the diameter of a circular opening having an area of 1963.5 cm^2?

Solution:

$$\text{Diameter of a circle} = \sqrt{\frac{\text{Area of a Circle}}{0.7854}}$$
$$= \sqrt{\frac{1963.5 \text{ cm}^2}{0.7854}}$$
$$= \sqrt{2500 \text{ cm}^2}$$
$$= \textbf{50 cm (Ans.)}$$

This page has intentionally been left blank.

CHAPTER 7 - QUESTIONS

1. Lines that are exactly the same distance apart at all points are said to be

    a) perpendicular.
    b) quadrilaterals.
    c) plumb.
    d) parallel.

2. Quadrilaterals are figures that have

    a) four straight sides.
    b) two straight sides.
    c) four straight sides with the opposite sides parallel.
    d) four sides of equal length and all angles right angles.

3. The perimeter of a rectangle is found by

    a) multiplying the lengths of all sides.
    b) dividing the lengths of the opposite sides.
    c) adding together the length of the sides.
    d) adding the length of each long and short side and then squaring the result.

4. How many pieces of pipe 20 cm long could be cut from a 6 ft length?

5. Convert $51\frac{7}{8}$ yd to meters.

6. A rectangle is 5 cm wide by 8 cm high. What would be the height of a rhombus with a 6 cm base, if it has the same area as the rectangle?

7. Which occupies more area and how much more: a circle with a radius of 7 m or a square with 13 m sides?

8. Two triangular lots are to be covered with new sod. Lot A is in the shape of an equilateral triangle, with side length equal to 40 m. Lot B has sides equal to 40 m, 30 m and 60 m. Which lot will require the least amount of sod?

9. A circle with a circumference of 60 cm is cut into quadrants. What is the area of each piece and the lengths of its straight sides?

CHAPTER 7 - ANSWERS

1. (d)

2. (a)

3. (c)

4. 9

5. 47.434 5 m

6. 6.67

7. Square with a larger area of 15.06 m^2

8. Lot B

9. Area of each piece = 71.63 cm^2
   Length of each straight side = 9.55 cm

Areas & Volumes of Solids

LEARNING OUTCOME

When you complete this chapter you should be able to:

Calculate the volumes of rectangular objects, cylinders, and spheres and the surface areas of cylinders and spheres.

LEARNING OBJECTIVES

Here is what you should be able to do when you complete each objective:

1. Convert between commonly used volume units.

2. Calculate the volume of a rectangular prism.

3. Calculate the surface area and volume of a cylinder.

4. Calculate the surface area and volume of a sphere.

OBJECTIVE 1

Convert between commonly used volume units.

VOLUME

Volume is a measure of the three dimensional (height, width and length) capacity of an object. In SI, the basic unit of volume is the cubic metre, abbreviated m^3.

$1 m^3 = 1 m \times 1 m \times 1 m$

In practice, cubic metres are quite large, so to avoid always having to use decimal or fractional quantities of cubic metres, volume units are used which are derived from the SI submultiples of the metre. For example:

$1 cm^3 = 1 cm \times 1 cm \times 1 cm$

(In the past, a cm^3 was also commonly referred to as a cc for cubic centimetre)

$1 mm^3 = 1 mm \times 1 mm \times 1 mm$

Note, in converting from one set of volume units to another, the "cubic" relationship must be maintained. For example, to convert 1 m^3 into cm^3:

$1 m^3 = 1 m \times 1 m \times 1 m$

$= 100 cm \times 100 cm \times 100 cm$

$= 1\ 000\ 000\ cm^3$

It is a common error for students to apply the linear relationship and incorrectly conclude that $1 m^3 = 100 cm^3$ rather than the correct $1\ 000\ 000\ cm^3$.

Example 1:
Convert 0.5 m^3 into cm^3.

Solution:

$1 m^3 = 1\ 000\ 000\ cm^3$

$0.5 m^3 = 0.5 \times 1\ 000\ 000\ cm^3$

$= \mathbf{500\ 000\ cm^3\ (Ans.)}$

Another common unit of volume in the SI system is the litre (denoted by L).

By definition: $1 L = 1000 cm^3$

$1 m^3 = 1000 L = 1 kL$

OBJECTIVE 2

Calculate the volume of a rectangular prism.

VOLUME OF A RECTANGULAR PRISM

The volume of a rectangular prism equals length × width × depth, each dimension being expressed in the same units. That is to say, all dimensions must be in centimetres to give volume in cubic centimetres (cm^3), all in metres to give volume in cubic metres (m^3), and so on.

Example 2:

A rectangular tank, as illustrated below, is 6 m long, 4 m wide and 2 m deep. What is its capacity in m^3?

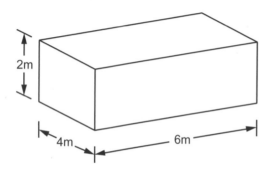

Solution:

$$Volume = length \times width \times depth$$
$$= 6\ m \times 4\ m \times 2\ m$$
$$= \textbf{48 m}^3 \textbf{ (Ans.)}$$

Example 3:

The base of a 27.3 kL storage tank is 4 m by 4.2 m. To what height must the tank be built?

Solution:

Divide the volume in m^3 by the area of the base in m^2 to get the height (depth) in m.

$$27.3\ kL = 27.3\ m^3$$
$$Volume = length \times width \times depth$$
$$Area\ of\ base = length \times width$$

$$Height = \frac{Volume}{Area}$$

$$Height = \frac{27.3\ m^3}{4\ m \times 4.2\ m}$$

$$Height = \textbf{1.625 m (Ans.)}$$

OBJECTIVE 3

Calculate the surface area and volume of a cylinder.

SURFACE AREA OF A CYLINDER

If the shell or lateral surface of a cylinder could be unrolled and spread out, as shown in Figure 1, its surface would form a rectangle with length equal to the circumference (πD) of the cylinder and width equal to the height (h) of the cylinder.

The total surface area of the cylinder is the lateral surface area plus the area of the two ends or bases.

Lateral surface area = πDh

Area of two bases = 2 x (0.7854D^2)

Total surface area = πDh + 2 x (0.7854D^2)

Note: 0.7854 = $\frac{\pi}{4}$

Figure 1	Surface Area

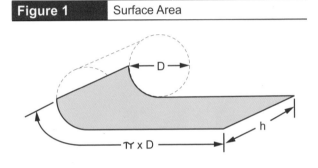

Example 4:

A cylindrical tank is 5 m in diameter and 22 m long. Find its lateral surface area.

Solution:

Lateral surface area = πDh

= 3.1416 x 5 m x 22 m

= **345.58 m^2 (Ans.)**

Example 5:

Calculate the total surface area of a cylindrical fuel tank with flat ends if the tank is 10 m long and 6 m in diameter.

Solution:

Lateral (shell) surface area (A_S):

$$A_S = \pi Dh$$
$$= 3.1416 \times 6 \text{ m} \times 10 \text{ m}$$
$$= 188.5 \text{ m}^2$$

Area of the two ends (A_E):

$$A_E = 2 \times (0.7854D^2)$$
$$= 2 \times [0.7854 \times (6 \text{ m})^2]$$
$$= 2 \times [0.7854 \times 36 \text{ m}^2]$$
$$= 2 \times [28.27 \text{ m}^2]$$
$$= 56.54 \text{ m}^2$$

Total surface area (A_T):

$$A_T = A_S + A_E$$
$$= 188.5 \text{ m}^2 + 56.54 \text{ m}^2$$
$$= \mathbf{245.04 \text{ m}^2 \text{ (Ans.)}}$$

VOLUME OF A CYLINDER

The volume (V) of a cylinder can be calculated by multiplying the area of the base (0.7854 D^2) by the height (h) or length (l):

$$V = 0.7854D^2h$$

Example 6:

Find the volume of a cylindrical tank 10 m in diameter and 30 m long.

Solution:

$V = 0.7854D^2h$

$= 0.7854 \times (10 \text{ m})^2 \times 30 \text{ m}$

$= 0.7854 \times 100 \text{ m}^2 \times 30 \text{ m}$

$= 0.7854 \times 3000 \text{ m}^3$

$= \textbf{2356.2 m}^3$ **(Ans.)**

Example 7:

Calculate the volume of the fuel tank in Example 5.

Solution:

$V = 0.7854D^2h$

$= 0.7854 \times (6 \text{ m})^2 \times 10 \text{ m}$

$= 0.7854 \times 36 \text{ m}^2 \times 10 \text{ m}$

$= 0.7854 \times 360 \text{ m}^3$

$= \textbf{282.74 m}^3$ **(Ans.)**

OBJECTIVE 4

Calculate the surface area and volume of a sphere.

SURFACE AREA OF A SPHERE

A sphere is a solid bounded by a curved surface called the circumference in which every point is the same distance from the centre point.

The radius (r) of a sphere is a straight line drawn from the centre point to the circumference and is equal to one-half the diameter (D).

The surface area of a sphere can be found by multiplying the square of the radius by 4π.

$$\text{Surface area (A)} = 4\pi r^2$$

Example 8:

Find the surface area of a sphere having a diameter of 8 cm.

Solution:

$$r = \frac{D}{2}$$

$$= \frac{8 \text{ cm}}{2}$$

$$= 4 \text{ cm}$$

$$\text{Surface area (A)} = 4\pi r^2$$

$$= 4 \times 3.1416 \times (4 \text{ cm})^2$$

$$= 4 \times 3.1416 \times 16 \text{ cm}^2$$

$$= \textbf{201 cm}^2 \textbf{ (Ans.)}$$

Example 9:

Find the area of insulation required to completely cover a chlorine storage sphere, whch has a diameter of 9 m.

Solution:

$$r = \frac{D}{2}$$

$$= \frac{9}{2} \text{ m}$$

$$= 4.5 \text{ m}$$

$$\text{Surface area (A)} = 4\pi r^2$$

$$= 4 \times 3.1416 \times (4.5 \text{ m})^2$$

$$= 4 \times 3.1416 \times 20.25 \text{ m}^2$$

$$= \textbf{254.5 m}^2 \textbf{ (Ans.)}$$

VOLUME OF A SPHERE

The volume (V) of a sphere can be found by multiplying the cube of the radius by $\left(\frac{4}{3}\right)\pi$.

$$V = \left(\frac{4}{3}\right)\pi r^3$$

Example 10:

A solid cast iron ball has a radius of 1 m. If each cubic metre of cast iron has a mass of 7210 kg, find the total mass of the ball.

Solution:

$$V = \left(\frac{4}{3}\right)\pi r^3$$

$$= \frac{4}{3} \times \pi \times (1 \text{ m})^3$$

$$= \frac{4}{3} \times 3.1416 \times 1 \text{ m}^3$$

$$= 4.189 \text{ m}^3$$

Therefore:

$$\text{mass} = 4.189 \text{ m}^3 \times 7210 \text{ kg/m}^3$$

$$= \textbf{30 203 kg (Ans.)}$$

ADDITIONAL EXAMPLES

Most problems involve a combination of two or more concepts. The following examples utilize information from this chapter as well as other chapters.

An effort is made to show the logical steps used to solve the problem, but do not make the assumption that this is the only approach which can be used.

Example 11:

A boiler drum has hemispherical heads (ie. the two heads together make a sphere). The diameter of the drum is 80 cm; the drum is 5 m in length, including the heads.

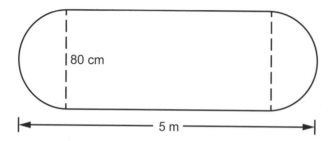

Calculate:

　　a) The area of insulation required to cover the entire drum.

　　b) The total volume of the drum.

Solution:

　　a) The total surface area of the boiler drum is equal to the lateral area (shell area) plus the surface area of the sphere which makes up the ends. The diameter (D) of the drum is 80 cm or 0.8 m.

$$r = \frac{D}{2}$$

$$= \frac{0.8 \text{ m}}{2}$$

$$= 0.4 \text{ m}$$

The length (h) of the shell is equal to the total length of the drum minus the diameter of the two combined heads.

$$h = 5 \text{ m} - 0.8 \text{ m}$$

$$= 4.2 \text{ m}$$

Therefore:

$$A = \pi Dh + 4\pi r^2$$

$$= (3.1416 \times 0.8 \text{ m} \times 4.2 \text{ m}) + (4 \times 3.1416 \times (0.4 \text{ m})^2)$$

$$= (3.1416 \times 3.36 \text{ m}^2) + (4 \times 3.1416 \times 0.16 \text{ m}^2)$$

$$= 10.56 \text{ m}^2 + (3.1416 \times 0.64 \text{ m}^2)$$

$$= 10.56 \text{ m}^2 + 2.01 \text{ m}^2$$

$$= \textbf{12.57 m}^2 \textbf{ (Ans.)}$$

b) The total volume of the drum is equal to the total volume of the cylinder plus the total volume of the sphere. Therefore the total volume is:

$$V = 0.7854 \, D^2 \, L + \left(\frac{4}{3}\right) \pi \, r^3$$

$$= [0.7854 \times (0.8 \text{ m})^2 \times 4.2 \text{ m}] + \left[\frac{4}{3} \times 3.1416 \times \left(\frac{0.8 \text{ m}}{2}\right)^3\right]$$

$$= (0.7854 \times 0.64 \text{ m}^2 \times 4.2 \text{ m}) + \left[\frac{4}{3} \times 3.1416 \times (0.4 \text{ m})^3\right]$$

$$= (0.7854 \times 2.69 \text{ m}^3) + \left(\frac{4}{3} \times 3.1416 \times 0.064 \text{ m}^3\right)$$

$$= 2.113 \text{ m}^3 + (3.1416 \times 0.085 \text{ m}^3)$$

$$= 2.113 \text{ m}^3 + 0.267 \text{ m}^3$$

$$= \mathbf{2.38 \text{ m}^3 \text{ (Ans.)}}$$

Example 12:

Calculate the stroke of a single cylinder, positive displacement pump if the cylinder is 3 cm in diameter and the pump delivers 3392.9 cm³/min. The pump is operating at 60 effective strokes per minute.

Solution:

The first step is to find the volume delivered for each stroke of the pump:

$$\text{Volume} = \frac{3392.9 \text{ cm}^3/\text{min}}{60 \text{ strokes/min}}$$

$$= 56.55 \text{ cm}^3/\text{stroke}$$

The volume of a cylinder is:

$$V = 0.7854 \, d^2 h$$

$$56.55 \text{cm}^3 = 0.7854(3 \text{ cm})^2 h$$

Transposing:

$$h = \frac{56.55 \text{ cm}^3}{0.7854(3 \text{ cm})^2}$$

$$= \frac{56.55 \text{ cm}^3}{0.7854 \times 9 \text{ cm}^2}$$

$$= \frac{56.55 \text{ cm}^3}{7.069 \text{ cm}^2}$$

$$= \mathbf{8 \text{ cm} \text{ (Ans.)}}$$

Example 13:

Calculate the cost of painting a sphere, which is 12 m in diameter. One litre of paint covers 8 m² and costs $4.50.

Solution:

The surface area of a sphere is:

$$A = 4\pi r^2$$

$$= 4 \times 3.1416 \times (6 \text{ m})^2$$

$$= 4 \times 3.1416 \times 36 \text{ m}^2$$

$$= 452.39 \text{ m}^2$$

Since each litre covers 8 m², the total number of litres used is the total area divided by the area covered by one litre.

$$\text{Number of litres} = \frac{\text{Surface area}}{\text{Coverage/litre}}$$

$$= \frac{452.39 \text{ m}^2}{8 \text{ m}^2 L}$$

$$= 56.55 \text{ L}$$

Since only full litres can be purchased, 57 L are required.

Total cost:

$$\text{Total cost} = \text{Number of litres} \times \text{cost/litre}$$

$$= 57 \text{ L} \times \$4.50/\text{L}$$

$$= \textbf{\$256.50 (Ans.)}$$

CHAPTER 8 - QUESTIONS

1. What is the total surface area of a closed cylinder that is 10 cm high and 4 cm in diameter?

    a) 125.66 cm^2

    b) 89.78 cm^2

    c) 25.13 cm^2

    d) 150.8 cm^2

2. Find the lateral area (in m^2) of a steam pipe 15 cm in diameter and 3 m long.

    a) 66.25 m^2

    b) 89.78 m^2

    c) 1.414 m^2

    d) 120.74 m^2

3. Find the volume in cubic centimeters of a cylinder having a radius of 3 cm and a height of 8 cm.

    a) 226.2 cm^3

    b) 153.24 cm^3

    c) 162.57 cm^3

    d) 225.05 cm^3

4. A rectangular piece of sheet iron 625 cm^2 in area is rolled to form a cylinder 9 cm in diameter. Find the height and volume of this cylinder.

    a) 22.1 cm, 1405.94 cm^3

    b) 12.25 cm, 987.45 cm^3

    c) 18.25 cm, 1129.55 cm^3

    d) 21.9 cm, 1323.25 cm^3

CHAPTER 8 - ANSWERS

4th Class • Part A1

1. (d)

2. (c)

3. (a)

4. (a)

ELEMENTARY MECHANICS

CHAPTER 9

Introduction to Basic Mechanics

LEARNING OUTCOME

When you complete this chapter you should be able to:

Define basic terms used in the study of mechanics.

LEARNING OBJECTIVES

Here is what you should be able to do when you complete each objective:

1. Define mass, force, acceleration, velocity and weight.

2. Define & perform simple calculations involving force, pressure, work, power and energy.

INTRODUCTION

Mechanics is a branch of physics that deals with forces and their effect of these forces on bodies at rest and in motion. The science of mechanics is therefore used when studying the forces acting upon:

- a girder supporting a boiler

- the leverage exerted in tightening a bolt with a wrench

- the work done in pumping water to a supply tank

- the work done in raising an elevator in its shaft

Each of these processes involves the action or movement of forces. There are two branches of mechanics: statics and dynamics. Statics deals with forces and their effects on rigid bodies at rest. Dynamics deals with motion and its effects of forces acting upon rigid bodies in motion.

Newton's Laws of Motion

Many of the problems in mechanics deal with forces and motion; therefore, it is important for the student to know and understand the laws of motion. These laws were summarized by Sir Isaac Newton as follows:

1. Every body will continue in its state of rest, or uniform motion in a straight line, unless it is acted upon by an external force.

2. The rate of change of motion is proportional to the force producing the change and takes place in the direction in which the force acts.

3. To every action, there is an equal and opposite reaction. When one object exerts a force on a second object, the second object exerts a reactive force of equal magnitude and opposite direction on the first object.

OBJECTIVE 1

Define mass, force, acceleration, velocity and weight.

MASS

Mass is the quantity of matter a body contains. The unit of mass in the SI system is kilogram (kg).

FORCE

Force may be defined as any action on a body which tends to change its size, shape or its state of rest or motion. In the SI system, the unit of force is newton (N).

ACCELERATION & VELOCITY

To understand what acceleration is, it is useful to understand what velocity is. Velocity is the rate of change in position that occurs during a given time. The unit of velocity in the SI system is the metre per second (m/s).

Example 1:

If a body moves on its x-axis from the 10 m position to the 30 m position in 4 seconds, then it will change position by 20 m in 4 seconds. What is its velocity?

X •———————•————————————•———————— X
   0   10 m   30 m
Origin

Solution:

$$\text{Velocity} = \frac{\text{Change in position}}{\text{Time}}$$
$$= \frac{20 \text{ m}}{4 \text{ s}}$$
$$= 5 \text{ m/s (Ans.)}$$

Now acceleration can be defined more easily.

Acceleration is the rate of change in velocity that occurs during a given time. The unit of acceleration in the SI system is the metre per second squared (m/s^2).

Example 2:

If a body is moving toward the right at a velocity of 10 m/s, and 4 seconds later it is found to be moving to the right at a velocity of 30 m/s, then it has changed velocity by 20 m/s (30 m/s - 10 m/s) during the 4 seconds. What is its rate of acceleration?

v = 10 m/s   v = 30 m/s

time = NOW   time = NOW + 4 seconds

Solution:

$$\text{Acceleration} = \frac{\text{Change in velocity}}{\text{Time}}$$

$$= \frac{20 \text{ m/s}}{4 \text{ s}}$$

$$= \frac{20}{4} \times \frac{\text{m/s}}{\text{s}}$$

$$= 5 \text{ m/s}^2 \text{ (Ans.)}$$

Note: A velocity of 5 m/s means that a body's position will change by 5 m over the duration of 1 second (that is, a rate of change of position of 5 m/s)

An acceleration of 5 m/s² means that a body's velocity will change by 5 m/s over the duration of 1 second (that is, a rate of change of velocity of 5 m/s per second, or 5 m/s²)

Relationship between Mass, Force and Acceleration

For all cases:

Force = mass x acceleration

If the unit of mass in the SI system is the kg and the unit of acceleration is m/s², then:

Force = mass (kg) x acceleration (m/s²)

$$= \text{kgm/s}^2$$

In the SI system the unit of force, kgm/s² is called a newton (N).

That is:

1 N = 1 kg x 1 m/s²

This means:

- If a force of 1 N is applied to a mass of 1 kg, then that mass will accelerate at 1 m/s².

Or

- If a mass of 1 kg is observed to be accelerating at 1 m/s², then there must be a force of 1 N acting upon the mass.

Or

- If an unknown mass is found to be accelerating at 1 m/s² under the influence of a 1 N force, then that mass must be 1 kg.

Example 3:

A mass of 1000 kg is to be accelerated at 15 m/s². What force is required?

Solution:

Force = mass (kg) x acceleration (m/s²)

$$= 1000 \text{ kg x } 15 \text{ m/s}^2$$

$$= 15\,000 \text{ kgm/s}^2$$

$$= 15\,000 \text{ N}$$

$$= \textbf{15 kN (Ans.)}$$

Since the newton is a relatively small unit, the kilonewton (kN) is often used.

1 kN = 1000 N

Acceleration Due to Gravity

If a body is within the earth's field of gravity, there is an attraction to the earth's centre due to this "pull" of gravity. Bodies which are allowed to fall will fall towards the earth at an increasing velocity due to the pull of gravity. The velocity will be found to increase by approximately 9.81 m/s over the duration of each second of time. This principle is referred to as the acceleration due to gravity.

$$\text{Acceleration due to gravity} = \frac{\text{Change in velocity}}{\text{Time}}$$

$$= \frac{9.81 \text{ m/s}}{1\text{s}}$$

$$= 9.81 \text{ m/s}^2$$

This acceleration should be remembered as it is of great importance when dealing with mechanics problems.

Force of Gravity

Since the acceleration due to the earth's gravity may be taken as 9.81 m/s^2, then the force of the earth's gravity acting on a mass of 1 kg will be:

$$\text{Force} = \text{mass (kg) x acceleration (m/s}^2)$$

$$= 1 \text{ kg x } 9.81 \text{ m/s}^2$$

$$= 9.81 \text{ N}$$

The direction of this force will be downward (i.e., toward the earth). Thus, a mass of 1 kg on the earth's surface will be subjected to a downward force (force due to pull of gravity) of 9.81 N.

Example 4:

A body has a mass of 200 kg. What will be the magnitude of the force due to the earth's gravity acting upon this mass?

Solution:

$$\text{Force} = \text{mass (kg) x } 9.81 \text{ (N/kg)}$$

$$= 200 \text{ kg x } 9.81 \text{ N/kg}$$

$$= \textbf{1962 N (Ans.)}$$

WEIGHT

Weight: A Controversial Term

The mass of a body is unchanging, and does not vary according to its location.

The force of gravity on a body varies from location to location, depending on the value of the acceleration due to gravity. The value, 9.81 m/s^2, is only an average value for the acceleration due to the earth's gravity on the surface of the earth. It is much less at a distance of 50 km above the earth's surface.

It is for this reason that the SI system expresses the quantity of material (e.g. meat or concrete) in terms of the kilogram (an unchanging mass unit) rather than the newton. The newton is a unit of measurement of the imprecise concept "weight" (which is an inexact word often used to denote the force of gravity on the material).

In fact, the term "weight" has sometimes been used to mean "mass" and sometimes to mean "force of gravity." In engineering courses, a clear distinction must be made between mass and force of gravity. Therefore, the Canadian Standards Association recommends that the term "weight" be avoided.

OBJECTIVE 2

Define & perform simple calculations involving force, pressure, work, power and energy.

FORCE & PRESSURE

Force

Force has previously been defined as the action on a body which tends to change its size, shape, state of rest or state of motion. In the SI system, the unit of force is called the newton (N).

Pressure

Pressure is defined as force per unit area and acts in a direction normal to or at right angles to a surface:

$$Pressure = \frac{Force}{Area}$$

The unit of pressure in the SI system is defined as the pressure resulting from a force of 1 N acting uniformly over an area of 1 m². This unit is the pascal (Pa).

$$1 \text{ Pa} = 1 \frac{N}{m^2}$$

The pascal is a very small unit; both kilopascals (1000 Pa) and megapascals (1 000 000 Pa) are often used when dealing with high pressures.

$$1 \text{ kPa} = 1000 \frac{N}{m^2}$$
$$1 \text{ MPa} = 1 \text{ 000 000} \frac{N}{m^2}$$

Example 5:

A force of 1000 N is exerted uniformly over an area of 0.25 m². What is the pressure?

Solution:

$$Pressure = \frac{Force}{Area}$$

$$Force = 1000 \text{ N}$$

$$Area = 0.25 \text{ m}^2$$

$$Pressure = \frac{1000 \text{ N}}{0.25 \text{ m}^2}$$

$$= 4000 \frac{N}{m^2}$$

$$= \textbf{4000 Pa or 4 kPa (Ans.)}$$

WORK, POWER & ENERGY

Work

If a force is applied to a body and causes it to move through a distance, then work is done. Work is the product of the force applied (newtons) and the distance moved (metres).

Work done = force (N) × distance (m)

Therefore, the work done when a force of one newton moves through a distance of 1 metre is one newton metre (Nm). This unit of work is called a joule (J).

1 joule (J) = 1 newton metre (Nm)

Example 6:

A force of 100 N acting on a body moves it a distance of 10 m. What is the work done by the force on the body?

Solution:

Work done = Force x Distance

= 100 N x 10 m

= 1000 Nm

= 1000 J

Note: 1000 joules = 1 kilojoule

Work done = **1 kJ (Ans.)**

Power

Power is the rate of doing work, i.e., it is the quantity of work done in a given time.

$$\text{Power} = \frac{\text{Work Done}}{\text{Time}}$$

$$= \frac{\text{Nm}}{\text{s}}$$

$$= \frac{\text{joule}}{\text{s}}$$

The unit joule/s is a watt.

$$\frac{1 \text{ joule}}{\text{s}} = 1 \text{ watt}$$

The watt (W) is a small unit of power, so the units kilowatt or megawatt are used for many applications.

1 kilowatt (kW) = 1000 W

1 megawatt (MW) = 1 000 000 W

Example 7:

If a force of 100 N acts on a body which is moved a distance of 10 m in 5 seconds, what power is developed?

Solution:

$$\text{Power} = \frac{\text{Force x Distance}}{\text{Time}}$$

$$= \frac{100 \text{ N x 10 m}}{5 \text{ s}}$$

$$= 200 \frac{\text{Nm}}{\text{s}}$$

$$= 200 \frac{\text{J}}{\text{s}}$$

$$= \textbf{200 W (Ans.)}$$

Energy

Energy is defined as the capacity of a body or substance to perform work. In other words, a body possesses energy when it is capable of doing work. Energy can be contained in many forms and its presence is observed only by its effects.

Some forms of energy are solar, chemical, nuclear, electrical and mechanical. The study of mechanics is concerned with the two forms of mechanical energy:

- Potential
- Kinetic

Potential Energy

Potential energy is the ability of a body to do work by virtue of its position. For example, water stored behind a dam contains potential energy due to its position and can be made to do work. If the water is released, it will flow to a lower point due to the force of gravity. A stretched spring also has potential energy which increases as it is stretched (within certain limits).

Potential energy due to gravity can be expressed as:

Potential Energy (PE) = Mass x Gravitational Force × Vertical Height

$$PE = m \times g \times h$$

where g = the force of gravity = 9.81 N/kg

h = vertical height, m

The units are $(kg \times \frac{N}{kg}) \times m$, or N × m, or joules (J), which are the units of work.

Kinetic Energy

Kinetic energy (KE) is the ability of a body to do work due to its motion.

$$\text{Kinetic Energy (J)} = \frac{1}{2} \times \text{mass (kg)} \times \text{velocity}^2 \left(\frac{m}{s}\right)^2$$

and the units are:

$$= kg \times \frac{m^2}{s^2}$$

$$= \frac{kgm}{s^2} \times m$$

$$= N \times m$$

$$= \text{Joule}$$

CHAPTER 9 - QUESTIONS

1. A body travels 1000 m in 65 seconds. What is its average velocity?

    a) 14.79 m/s

    b) 15.12 m/s

    c) 15.38 m/s

    d) 22.25 m/s

2. A body is moving north at 15 m/s and 7 seconds later it has a velocity of 40 m/s in the same direction. What was the acceleration of the body?

    a) 3.57 m/s^2

    b) 5.25 m/s^2

    c) 2.84 m/s^2

    d) 4.56 m/s^2

3. A mass of 250 kg is accelerated at 17 m/s^2. What force is required to achieve this acceleration?

    a) 34.2 kN

    b) 42.5 kN

    c) 425 N

    d) 4.25 kN

4. A body with a mass of 75 kg is allowed to fall freely to the ground. What gravitational force is acting on the mass?

    a) 539.45 N

    b) 1.39 kN

    c) 735.75 N

    d) 626.55 N

5. A hydraulic plunger has an area of 0.10 m^2 and a force of 200 N acts on it. What is the pressure exerted on the plunger?

    a) 1.64 kPa

    b) 750 Pa

    c) 1.84 kPa

    d) 2 kPa

6. Potential energy is the ability of a body to do work by virtue of its;

    a) pressure.

    b) position.

    c) force.

    d) acceleration.

CHAPTER 9 - ANSWERS

1. (c)

2. (a)

3. (d)

4. (c)

5. (d)

6. (b)

Forces & Moments

LEARNING OUTCOME

When you complete this chapter you should be able to:

Perform calculations involving forces and moments, and determine whether or not a system is in equilibrium.

LEARNING OBJECTIVES

Here is what you should be able to do when you complete each objective:

1. Define the moment of a force and its units.

2. Determine the direction and calculate the magnitude of the moment of a force.

INTRODUCTION

When a force is applied to an object that is either stationary or in motion, the force will change its motion. It may or may not change the direction of motion as well.

The term "moments" means the product of a force times the distance from a centre point.

This chapter deals with the forces producing moments on beams that are fixed at some point so they will rotate.

Students should refer to the chapter Scalars and Vectors, for additional information on forces moving objects in a specific direction.

OBJECTIVE 1

Define the moment of a force and its units.

FORCE

A force is the pull or push exerted on a body; it may make a body move or bring it to rest.

For example, the pulling force of a locomotive on a string of boxcars causes the train to move, whereas the pushing force exerted by the brake pads on the rotating wheels causes it to stop.

When several balanced forces act on a body, no change in movement will take place and the body and system of forces is said to be in equilibrium.

Figure 1 shows a simple pivot type balance with bodies of equal mass on each side. The system is in equilibrium and the cross arm remains horizontal. Each mass exerts a turning effect about the pivot. The mass on the right exerts a clockwise turning effect, while that on the left exerts a counterclockwise effect as shown by the dotted lines in the diagram. The magnitude of this twisting or turning effect depends upon the:

- size of the masses
- distance of the suspension points from the pivot or fulcrum

Figure 1	Simple Pivot Type Balance

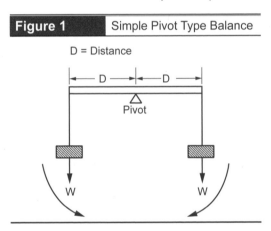

Moment of Force

A force, acting on a body at any distance from a point on that body, will tend to produce rotation around that point. The moment or turning moment of a force around a point is equal to the force multiplied by the perpendicular distance from the line of force to the point.

In Figure 2, the moment of force F about point A is F x d. Force is measured in newtons (or kN) and the distance in metres. Therefore, the moment of a force will be measured in newton metres (Nm) or kilonewton metres (kNm). The moment has a rotational direction also applied to it, expressed as clockwise or counterclockwise.

Figure 2	Moment of Force

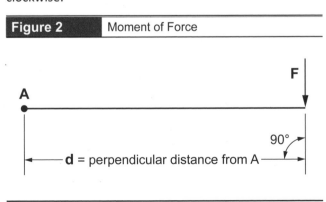

Example 1:

In Figure 2, a force of 300 N acts at a perpendicular distance of 2 m from point A. What turning moment will be produced? What is its direction?

Solution:

The force will produce a clockwise rotation.

Moment = Force x Perpendicular distance

= 300 N x 2 m

= **600 Nm clockwise (Ans.)**

Example 2:

A force of 200 N acts in the direction shown in Figure 3. What would be the turning moment of this force about point A?

Figure 3	Directional Force

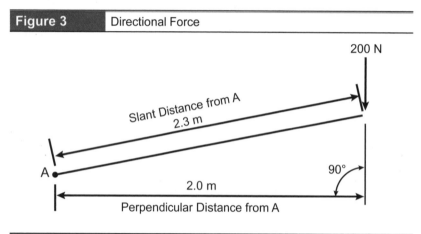

Solution:

Moment = Force x Perpendicular distance

= 200 N x 2 m

= **400 Nm (Ans.)**

OBJECTIVE 2

Determine the direction and calculate the magnitude of the moment of a force.

DIRECTION OF A MOMENT OF FORCE

A force, acting at a distance from a point, will produce or tend to produce rotation about a point, with the point as centre. This rotation will either be in a clockwise or counterclockwise direction, as shown in Figure 4. This direction can be determined by imagining what would happen if the force were free to rotate about the point.

Figure 4	Moment Directions

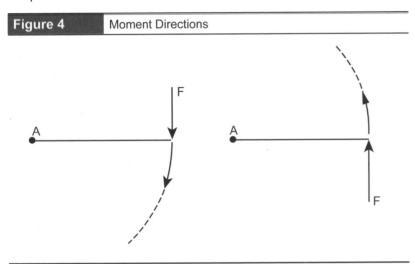

The bar shown in Figure 5 is pivoted at point P. The only forces applied are A and B at point E; they are equal in magnitude, but opposite in direction of action. Under this form of loading, the bar will be in equilibrium.

Figure 5	Rotational Equilibrium - Equal Forces

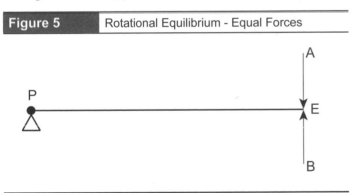

Fulcrum

A single support about which a bar is free to rotate is called a fulcrum. In Example 3 (see next page), the support at A would be the fulcrum.

Equilibrium

If the forces and moments of force are such that there is no movement or rotation of the bar, the system is said to be in equilibrium.

The conditions for equilibrium are:

- upward forces = downward forces
- forces acting to the right = forces acting to the left
- clockwise moments = counterclockwise moments

In Figure 6, the forces A and B are equal in magnitude and opposite in direction of action. The forces are acting at different distances from the pivot point. The moments that the forces are producing are not the same. The moment of force A about the pivot point is d_1 x A which will be less than the moment of force B about the pivot point which is d_2 x B. Therefore, the bar is not in equilibrium and will rotate in a counter-clockwise direction.

Figure 6   Rotational Equilibrium – Unequal Forces

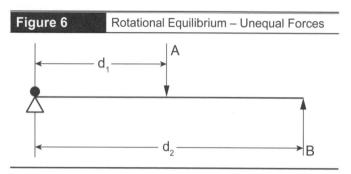

Figure 7 shows a bar with the same dimensions as that in Figure 6 but the values of forces A and B have been changed. The moments of the forces taken about the pivot are equal, so the bar is in equilibrium.

    1 m x 200 N = 200 Nm clockwise moment, due to force A

    2 m x 100 N = 200 Nm counterclockwise moment, due to force B

Figure 7   Rotational Equilibrium – Unequal Forces

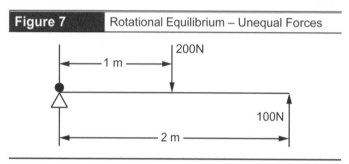

Example 3:

A bar of negligible mass is supported at A and loaded as shown in Figure 8. What are the clockwise and counterclockwise moments of force at the pivot point, and in which direction will the bar rotate?

Figure 8   Supported Bar

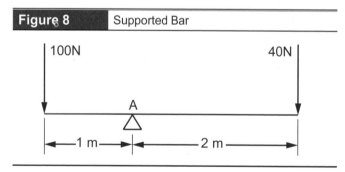

Solution:

Taking moments about A:

Clockwise moment = 40 N x 2 m

= **80 Nm (Ans.)**

Counterclockwise moment = 100 N x 1 m

= **100 Nm (Ans.)**

Since the counterclockwise moment is greater than the clockwise moment, **the bar would rotate in a counterclockwise direction. (Ans.)**

Example 4:

A bar of negligible mass is supported on a fulcrum as shown in Figure 9. What force (F) is required at the right hand end for equilibrium?

Figure 9	Negligible Mass Bar

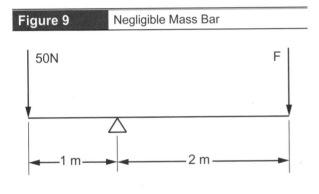

Solution:

Taking moments about the fulcrum, for **equilibrium**:

Clockwise moments = Counterclockwise moments

F x 2 m = 50 N x 1 m

$$F = \frac{50 \text{ Nm}}{2 \text{ m}}$$

= **25 N (Ans.)**

A downward force of 25 N at the right hand end of the bar is required for equilibrium.

It should also be noted that there must be an upward force of 50 N + 25 N = 75 N at the fulcrum, since upward forces must equal downward forces. Since there are no forces acting sideways to the left or right, the system is in equilibrium, because all the conditions for equilibrium are met.

Note: In solving moment problems, you should always:

- state that you are taking moments about the fulcrum
- state that clockwise moments = counterclockwise moments
- substitute known values and solve for the unknown value

BEAMS

A beam may be defined as a rigid member or bar supported in some way so that it is capable of carrying a load or system of loads.

Simply Supported Beams

If the beam rests on supports so that it is free to bend without restriction from the supports, it is called simply supported, as shown in Figure 10.

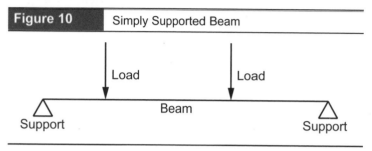

Figure 10 — Simply Supported Beam

Point Loads

If the loads on the beam can be considered to be concentrated at specific points, they are called point loads.

Reaction at Supports

For equilibrium, the external forces on the beam must be resisted by reaction forces at the supports.

Example 5:

A 6 m beam is simply supported at each end and carries point loads as shown in Figure 11. Calculate the reactions at each support to achieve equilibrium of the beam.

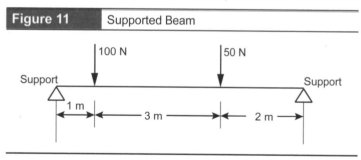

Figure 11 — Supported Beam

Solution:

The end reactions may be considered as upward forces to resist the downward forces; it is normal practice to draw the free body diagram (Fig. 12), where R_1 = reaction at left and R_2 = reaction at right.

Figure 12	Free Body Diagram of Beam

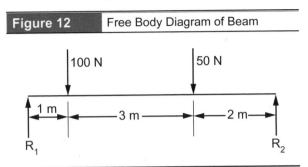

To find R_1 and R_2:

Take moments about either R_1 or R_2. Since the moment of a force is the product of the force and its perpendicular distance from the point about which moments are taken, R_1 or R_2 can be selected as the point about which moments are taken, allowing the other reaction to be calculated.

Let's take moments about R_1.. This will allow us to calculate R_2.

The 100 N force is 1 m from R_1, so its moment about R_1 is 100 N x 1 m = 100 Nm. If the beam were free to move about R_1, the 100 Nm moment would cause a clockwise rotation about R_1.

The 50 N force is 4 m from R_1, so its moment about R_1 is 50 N x 4 m = 200 Nm. It would also cause clockwise rotation about R_1

The reaction force R_2 is 6 m from R_1 so that its moment about R_1 is R_2 x 6 m = 6 R_2Nm. This moment would tend to cause a counterclockwise rotation of the beam about R_1.

For equilibrium:

Clockwise moments = Counterclockwise moments

$$100 \text{ Nm} + 200 \text{ Nm} = 6 \text{ m} \times R_2$$

$$300 \text{ Nm} = 6 \, R_2 \text{ m}$$

$$R_2 = \frac{300 \text{ Nm}}{6 \text{ m}}$$

$$= \textbf{50 N (Ans.)}$$

R_1 can now be found either by equating upward and downward forces or by taking moments about R_2.

For equilibrium:

Upward forces = Downward forces

$$R_1 + R_2 = 100 \text{ N} + 50 \text{ N}$$

$$R_1 + 50 \text{ N} = 150 \text{ N}$$

$$R_1 = 150 \text{ N} - 50 \text{ N}$$

$$= \textbf{100 N (Ans.)}$$

Check:

Taking moments about R_2:

Clockwise moments = Counterclockwise moments

$$R_1 \times 6 \text{ m} = (100 \text{ N} \times 5 \text{ m}) + (50 \text{ N} \times 2 \text{ m})$$

$$R_1 \times 6 \text{ m} = 500 \text{ Nm} + 100 \text{ Nm}$$

$$R_1 \times 6 \text{ m} = 600 \text{ Nm}$$

$$R_1 = \frac{600 \text{ Nm}}{6 \text{ m}}$$

$$= \textbf{100 N (Ans.)}$$

Example 6:

A beam 20 m long (Fig. 13) is simply supported at each end and carries a load of 10 000 N at the centre of the span. Calculate each reaction by taking moments.

| Figure 13 | 20 m Beam |

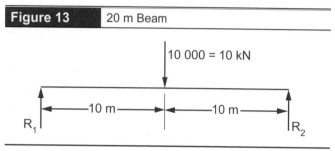

Taking moments about R_1:

Clockwise moments = Counterclockwise moments

$$10 \text{ kN} \times 10 \text{ m} = R_2 \times 20 \text{ m}$$

$$\frac{100 \text{ kNm}}{20 \text{ m}} = R_2$$

$$R_2 = \textbf{5 kN (Ans.)}$$

Taking moments about R_2:

Clockwise moments = Counterclockwise moments

$$R_1 \times 20 \text{ m} = 10 \text{ kN} \times 10 \text{ m}$$

$$= 100 \text{ kNm}$$

$$= \frac{100 \text{ kNm}}{20 \text{ m}}$$

$$= \textbf{5 kN (Ans.)}$$

R_1 could have been found by equating upward and downward forces:

Upward forces = Downward forces

$$R_1 + R_2 = 10 \text{ kN}$$

$$R_1 + 5 \text{ kN} = 10 \text{ kN}$$

$$R_1 = 10 \text{ kN} - 5 \text{ kN}$$

$$= \textbf{5 kN (Ans.)}$$

It should also be noted that since the 10 kN load is in the centre of the span, its support would be shared equally by R_1 and R_2, so that:

$$R_1 = R_2$$

$$= \frac{10 \text{ kN}}{2}$$

$$= 5 \text{ kN}$$

Example 7:

A beam 3 m long is simply supported at each end and carries loads as shown in Figure 14. Calculate the reactions.

| Figure 14 | 3 m Beam |

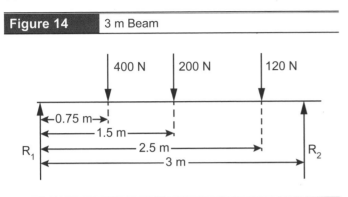

Solution:

Taking moments about R_1:

Clockwise moments = Counterclockwise moments

$(400 \text{ N} \times 0.75 \text{ m}) + (200 \text{ N} \times 1.5 \text{ m}) + (120 \text{ N} \times 2.5 \text{ m}) = R_2 \times 3 \text{ m}$

$300 \text{ Nm} + 300 \text{ Nm} + 300 \text{ Nm} = 3 R_2 \text{m}$

$900 \text{ Nm} = 3 R_2 \text{m}$

$$R_2 = \frac{900 \text{Nm}}{3 \text{m}}$$

$$= \textbf{300 N (Ans.)}$$

Upward forces = Downward forces

$R_1 + R_2 = 400 \text{ N} + 200 \text{ N} + 120 \text{ N}$

$R_1 + 300 \text{ N} = 720 \text{ N}$

$R_1 = 720 \text{ N} - 300 \text{ N}$

$$= \textbf{420 N (Ans.)}$$

Check:

Taking moments about R_2:

Clockwise moments = Counterclockwise moments

$R_1 \times 3 \text{ m} = (400 \text{ N} \times 2.25 \text{ m}) + (200 \text{ N} \times 1.5 \text{ m}) + (120 \text{ N} \times 0.5 \text{ m})$

$3 R_1 \text{m} = 900 \text{ Nm} + 300 \text{ Nm} + 60 \text{ Nm}$

$= 1260 \text{ Nm}$

$$R_1 = \frac{1260 \text{ Nm}}{3 \text{ m}}$$

$$= \textbf{420 N (Ans.)}$$

This page has intentionally been left blank.

CHAPTER 10 - QUESTIONS

1. The moment or turning moment of a force around a point is equal to the force _____ by the perpendicular distance from the line of force to the point.

   a) multiplied
   b) divided
   c) squared
   d) subtracted

2. A force is the pull or push exerted on a body which may make a body move or bring it to rest. For a body to remain at rest when several forces are acting upon it, the forces must _____ and the body is said to be in _____.

   a) counterbalance each other, rest
   b) balance, equilibrium
   c) attract, normal state
   d) oppose each other, motion

3. For the bar shown, what forces act on the bar and is it in equilibrium?

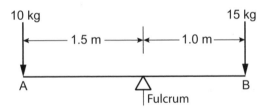

4. What forces are required at the right hand end so that the bar is in equilibrium?

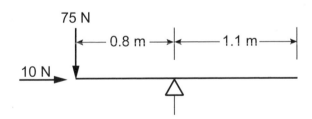

5. What is the moment of the force about Point A due to the 100 kg mass?

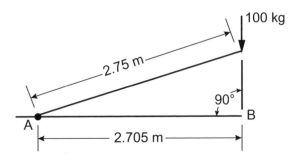

CHAPTER 10 - ANSWERS

1. (a)

2. (b)

3. Downward force at A = 98.1 N

   Downward force at B = 147.15 N

   Upward force at fulcrum = 245.25 N

   Bar is in equilibrium

4. 54.55 N vertically downward and 10 N horizontal to the left

5. 2654 Nm or 2.654 kNm

Simple Machines

LEARNING OUTCOME

When you complete this chapter you should be able to:

Define simple machines and perform calculations relating to them.

LEARNING OBJECTIVES

Here is what you should be able to do when you complete each objective:

1. Define the term 'simple machine' and calculate the mechanical advantage, velocity ratio and efficiency of simple machines.

Define the term 'simple machine' and calculate the mechanical advantage, velocity ratio and efficiency of simple machines.

SIMPLE MACHINES

A machine may be defined as a device that receives energy from some source and uses this energy to do work. A simple machine is one that receives energy by means of a single applied force and produces work by means of a single output force.

In all machines, the work output is always less than the work input, since work must be done by the machine to overcome internal friction and other resistive forces.

Lifting machines, in particular, are often arranged so that a relatively small effort can raise a relatively large load. The machine has a mechanical advantage.

ACTUAL MECHANICAL ADVANTAGE (MA)

In any machine, the ratio of the load to the effort is called the actual mechanical advantage of the machine.

$$\text{Actual mechanical advantage (MA)} = \frac{\text{Load}}{\text{Effort}}$$

Since the load and effort have the same units, MA is simply a unitless number, which indicates the advantage of using the machine.

Example 1:
A lever is used to move a load of 1000 N by applying an effort of 100 N. What is the mechanical advantage of the lever?

Solution:

$$\text{Actual MA} = \frac{\text{Load}}{\text{Effort}}$$

$$= \frac{1000 \text{ N}}{100 \text{ N}}$$

$$= \textbf{10 (Ans.)}$$

That is, this lever gives an advantage of 10:1.

Levers
A lever is a straight bar or other rigid structure supported at a fulcrum in such a way that a small force (or effort) can balance or move a much larger load.

Forces at Fulcrum (Reaction)
In a horizontal lever system, there must be a force or reaction at the fulcrum which opposes and balances the other forces (upward and downward) on the system.

Example 2:

Find the force necessary to just move the 100 kg mass on the end of the lever shown in Figure 1. Find the magnitude and direction of the reaction at the fulcrum. Find the mechanical advantage of the system. Neglect the mass of the lever itself.

Figure 1	Lever

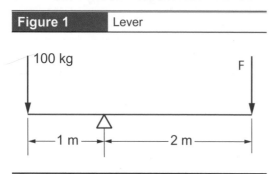

Solution:

Note: The mass of 100 kg must be converted to a load in newtons:

$$100 \text{ kg} \times \frac{9.81 \text{ N}}{\text{kg}} = 981 \textbf{ N}$$

Taking moments about the fulcrum:

Clockwise moments = Counterclockwise moments

F x 2 m = 981 N x 1 m

$$F = \frac{981 \text{ Nm}}{2 \text{ m}}$$

= **490.5 N acting downward on the right end (Ans.)**

Upward forces = Downward forces

Force at fulcrum = 490.5 N + 981 N

= **1471.5 N upwards (Ans.)**

$$\text{Actual MA} = \frac{\text{Load}}{\text{Effort}}$$

$$= \frac{981 \text{ N}}{490.5 \text{ N}}$$

= **2 (Ans.)**

Example 3:

A small hand pump is shown in Figure 2. If an effort of 500 N applied to the right end of the lever is required to overcome the resistance of the water plunger, calculate the force exerted by the plunger on the lever and the mechanical advantage of the lever.

Figure 2	Small Hand Pump

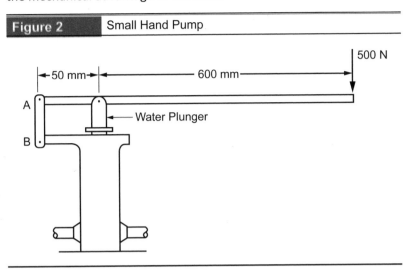

Solution:

The system may be simplified to a lever system, as shown in Figure 3, with the fulcrum at the left hand end.

Figure 3	Lever System

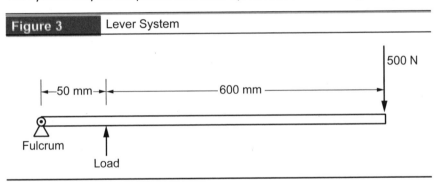

Taking moments about the fulcrum:

Clockwise moments = Counterclockwise moments

500 N x 0.65 m = Load x 0.05 m

$$\text{Load} = \frac{500 \text{ N} \times 0.65 \text{ m}}{0.05 \text{ m}}$$

= 6500 N in an upward direction (Ans.)

$$\text{Actual MA} = \frac{\text{Load}}{\text{Effort}}$$

$$= \frac{6500 \text{ N}}{500 \text{ N}}$$

= 13 (Ans.)

VELOCITY RATIO (VR)

The velocity ratio of a machine is the ratio of the distance moved by the effort to the distance moved by the load.

$$\text{Velocity ratio (VR)} = \frac{\text{Distance moved by effort}}{\text{Distance moved by load}}$$

SInce the same units appear on the top and bottom of the equation, VR is a number without units.

Example 4:

In a lifting machine, the effort applied moves a distance of 1 m while the load moves 100 mm. What is the velocity ratio?

Solution:

$$VR = \frac{\text{Distance moved by effort}}{\text{Distance moved by load}}$$

$$= \frac{1 \text{ m}}{0.1 \text{ m}}$$

$$= 10 \text{ (Ans.)}$$

Therefore, the effort moves 10 times further than the load.

Note: The units must be the same when determining velocity ratio.

EFFICIENCY

The efficiency of a machine is determined by the ratio of the output work to the input work.

$$\text{Efficiency} = \frac{\text{Output work}}{\text{Input work}}$$

$$\text{Output work} = \text{Load x Distance moved by load}$$

$$\text{Input work} = \text{Effort x Distance moved by effort}$$

Therefore:

$$\text{Efficiency} = \frac{\text{Load x Distance moved by load}}{\text{Effort x Distance moved by effort}}$$

$$= \frac{\text{Load}}{\text{Effort}} \text{ x } \frac{\text{Distance moved by load}}{\text{Distance moved by effort}}$$

$$= \text{Actual MA x } \frac{1}{\text{VR}}$$

$$= \frac{\text{Actual MA}}{\text{VR}}$$

$$\text{Percentage efficiency} = \frac{\text{Actual MA}}{\text{VR}} \text{ x } 100$$

Ideal Machine

If a machine had no losses, then the efficiency would be 100% (MA = VR). This would be the ideal mechanical advantage and would indicate a perfect machine:

Ideal MA = VR

Example 5:

A machine is used to lift a load of 1000 N through a distance of one metre. If the effort applied is 100 N, what is the MA? What distance will the effort move if the efficiency of the machine is 75%?

Solution:

$$Load = 1000 \text{ N}$$

$$Distance \text{ moved by the load} = 1 \text{ m}$$

$$Effort = 100 \text{ N}$$

$$Efficiency = 75\% \ (0.75)$$

$$Actual \ MA = \frac{Load}{Effort}$$

$$= \frac{1000 \text{ N}}{100 \text{ N}}$$

$$= \textbf{10 (Ans.)}$$

$$Efficiency = \frac{Actual \ MA}{VR}$$

$$VR = \frac{Actual \ MA}{Efficiency}$$

$$= \frac{10}{0.75}$$

$$= 13.33$$

$$= \frac{Distance \text{ moved by effort}}{Distance \text{ moved by load}}$$

$$Distance \text{ moved by effort} = Distance \text{ moved by load} \times VR$$

$$= 1 \text{ m} \times 13.33$$

$$= \textbf{13.33 m (Ans.)}$$

Example 6:

An effort of 200 N is required to raise a mass of 200 kg in a certain machine. If the mass is raised one metre while the effort moves 10 m, calculate the following:

    a) VR

    b) Actual MA

    c) Efficiency

Solution:

a) $VR = \dfrac{\text{Distance moved by effort}}{\text{Distance moved by load}}$

       $= \dfrac{10\ m}{1\ m}$

       = 10 (Ans.)

b) $Actual\ MA = \dfrac{\textbf{Load}}{\textbf{Effort}}$

       $= \dfrac{200\ kg \times 9.81\ N/kg}{200\ N}$

       = 9.81 (Ans.)

c) $Efficiency = \dfrac{\text{Actual MA}}{\text{VR}}$

       $= \dfrac{9.81}{10}$

       $= 0.981$

       = 98.1% (Ans.)

PULLEY SYSTEMS

Pulley systems, comprised of pulleys or wheels with ropes or chains, are lifting machines designed to lift heavy loads by the application of a relatively small effort.

The simplest arrangement is a single pulley or wheel with a single rope (shown in Fig. 4). Although this system has no actual mechanical advantage, it is often used because it allows a load to be lifted vertically by a downward effort. In the single pulley system, using Figure 4 as an example, the force on the rope that supports the pulley (200N) is equal to the sum of the load (100N) plus the effort (100N). That is, upward forces = downward forces.

Figure 4	Single Pulley

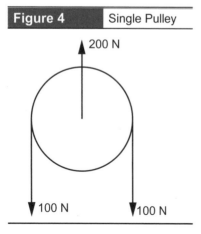

Block and Tackle System

Figure 5 shows a block and tackle system, which consists of top and bottom pulley blocks, each carrying a number of pulleys that rotate on a common axle. There may be an equal number of pulleys in each block or one more pulley in one than in the other. The rope passes over each pulley in turn from top to bottom, one end of the rope being fastened to the block opposite the last pulley and the other end being free to apply the effort. Both top and bottom blocks have hooks, the top hook to support the system and the bottom hook to support the load.

$$MA = \frac{Load}{Effort}$$

$$VR = \frac{Distance\ moved\ by\ effort}{Distance\ moved\ by\ load}$$

As before, if losses are neglected:

VR = Ideal MA

The velocity ratio of a pulley block system is equal to the number of ropes supporting the load block. If the blocks are used, with the effort pulling downward, to lift a load vertically, the number of ropes supporting the bottom block is equal to the total number of pulleys in the system. In Figure 5, there are 5 pulleys; therefore, the VR = 5.

Figure 5	Block and Tackle

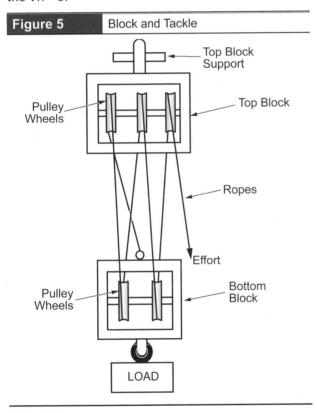

Downward Effort Versus Upward Effort

Figure 6 demonstrates alternative arrangements for a pulley system. The same block and tackle, with four pulleys, is used in both Figure 6(a) and 6(b); however, in 6(b) the system is inverted so that the effort must be directed upwards. This upward arrangement is very common, particularly in large cranes where the effort motor is located at the top of the crane.

The significant difference in operation between these two arrangements lies in the number of cable sections that are actually supporting (that is, applying upward lift to) the load. Notice that, in Figure 6(a), there are four cable sections supporting the load. The effort is acting downwards from the top block so is not supplying any upward force to the load. However, in Figure 6(b), the effort cable is applying upward force to the load block, so the total number of cable sections supporting the load becomes five.

Figure 6	Block and Tackle Systems

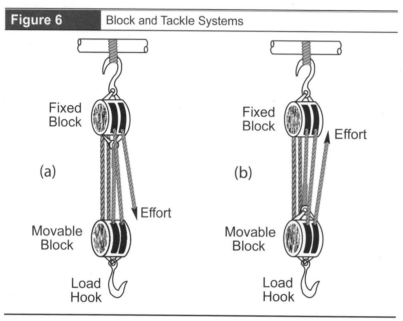

The significance of the above two arrangements becomes important when determining the velocity ratio for a pulley system.

Figure 7 shows some common block and tackle arrangements and the lifting force required for the given load forces, assuming 100% efficiency.

Figure 7	Block and Tackle Systems

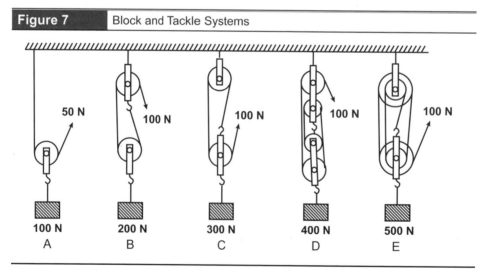

Example 7:

A block and tackle system has 3 pulleys in each block. If an effort of 100 N is required to raise a load of 480 N, calculate the efficiency of the system. (Normal hookup with effort pulling down.)

Solution:

Total number of pulleys = 6

$$VR = 6 \text{ (normal hookup, pulling down)}$$

$$MA = \frac{Load}{Effort}$$

$$= \frac{480 \text{ N}}{100 \text{ N}}$$

$$= 4.8$$

$$Efficiency = \frac{MA}{VR}$$

$$= \frac{4.8}{6}$$

$$= \textbf{0.8 (Ans.)}$$

$$\% \text{ Efficiency} = 0.8 \times 100$$

$$= \textbf{80\% (Ans.)}$$

Simple Wheel and Axle

A simple wheel and axle is shown in Figure 8. The load is applied to the smaller diameter axle and the effort to the wheel. The wheel and axle ropes are wound in opposite directions.

If the radius of wheel = R   and diameter = D

Radius of axle = r   and diameter = d

Taking moments about centre O and neglecting losses:

Clockwise moments = Counterclockwise moments

$$Load \times r = Effort \times R$$

from which, $Load = \dfrac{Effort \times R}{r}$

and $\dfrac{Load}{Effort} = \dfrac{R}{r}$

Also,   Actual Mechanical Advantage, $MA = \dfrac{Actual\ load}{Actual\ effort}$

Velocity Ratio, $VR = \dfrac{R}{r} \text{ or } \dfrac{D}{d}$

If there are losses, so efficiency is less than 100%;

$$\% \text{ Efficiency} = \frac{MA}{VR} \times 100$$

Figure 8	Wheel and Axle

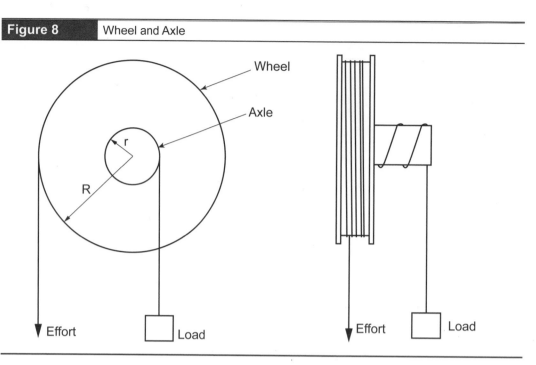

Example 8:

A simple wheel and axle has a wheel diameter of 250 mm and axle diameter of 50 mm. Calculate the following:

    a) VR

    b) MA if the efficiency is 90%

    c) Effort to raise a load of 500 N

Solution:

    a)

$$VR = \frac{D}{d}$$

$$= \frac{250 \text{ mm}}{50 \text{ mm}}$$

$$= \textbf{5 (Ans.)}$$

    b) $\% \text{ Efficiency} = \frac{MA}{VR} \times 100$

$$90 = \frac{MA}{5} \times 100$$

$$MA = \frac{90}{100} \times 5$$

$$= \textbf{4.5 (Ans.)}$$

    c) $MA = \frac{\text{Load}}{\text{Effort}}$

$$\text{Effort} = \frac{\text{Load}}{MA}$$

$$= \frac{500 \text{ N}}{4.5}$$

$$= \textbf{111.11 (Ans.)}$$

Inclined Plane

An inclined plane is a simple machine. An example is the a 5 m long ramp, which is used to raise a barrel of oil having a mass of 180 kg a vertical distance of 1 m, as shown in Figure 9.

Figure 9	Inclined Plane

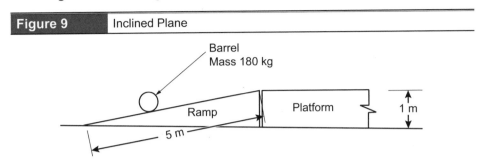

When the barrel of oil has been rolled up the ramp to the platform level, it will have a potential energy of:

180 kg x 9.81 N/kg x 1 m = 1765.8 Nm or 1765.8 J

If there is no friction, then the work done by rolling the barrel up the ramp will be equal to the output work, that is 1766 Nm. If there is friction, then some of the work done by rolling the barrel up the ramp will be turned into heat energy along the ramp. In this case, the input work will be greater than 1766 Nm.

The law of conservation of energy can be applied to simple machines and is written as:

Input work = Output work + Wasted work

Work in overcoming friction can be considered as wasted work.

Other simple machines that use the inclined plane principle are the screw jack and the wedge.

The screw jack is a special type of inclined plane. It is an inclined plane that has been wrapped around a cylinder. This simple machine is frequently used as part of a car's tool kit. The wedge is used to raise a heavy load a small distance so as to insert some other device under it or to promote or restrain movement.

This page has intentionally been left blank.

CHAPTER 11 - QUESTIONS

1. In any machine, the ratio of the load to the effort is called the

    a) forward thrust ratio.

    b) mechanical unity.

    c) redistribution of forces.

    d) actual mechanical advantage.

2. The velocity ratio of a machine is 10. The machine lifts 2000 N a distance of 2 m with an effort of 400 N. Find the following:

    a) Mechanical advantage

    b) % Efficiency

    c) Distance moved by the effort

3. In the pulley block assembly shown below, assuming a system efficiency of 95%, find the following:

    a) Force to raise the load 4 m

    b) Amount of rope that will pass through your hands to raise the load

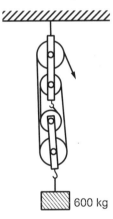

600 kg

4. What is the work input per person if 3 people are required to roll a 400 kg barrel up a ramp 6 m long to raise it 1.5 m? The roughness of the ramp's surface increases the work required by 15%.

5. The velocity ratio of a pulley block system is equal to the _____ of ropes supporting the block.

    a) diameter

    b) length

    c) number

    d) composition

CHAPTER 11 - ANSWERS

1. (d)

2. a) 5
   b) 50%
   c) 20 m

3. a) 1549 N
   b) 16 m

4. 2256.3 J

5. (c)

Scalars & Vectors

LEARNING OUTCOME

When you complete this chapter you should be able to:

Define and identify scalar and vector quantities and solve simple vector problems graphically.

LEARNING OBJECTIVES

Here is what you should be able to do when you complete each objective:

1. Define scalar and vector quantities and draw a vector diagram to scale.

OBJECTIVE 1

Define scalar and vector quantities and draw a vector diagram to scale.

SCALAR QUANTITIES

A scalar quantity is one that has magnitude only and can be completely described by a number with the necessary unit. Quantities such as length, area, volume, time and mass are scalars. For example, 3 metres describes a scalar quantity of length, 5 minutes a scalar quantity of time and 4 cubic centimeters, a scalar quantity of volume.

VECTOR QUANTITIES

A vector quantity is a quantity that has magnitude and direction:

- Magnitude, the numerical size of the quantity must be specified
- Direction, the direction of the action must be specified to describe a vector and can be stated in degrees, points of the compass, right, left, up or down

A vector is often represented by an arrow, where the length of the line is a scale representation of the magnitude and the direction in which the head points represents the direction of action. Some examples of vector quantities are:

- Force
- Velocity
- Displacement

Force
A force of 3 newtons (magnitude) acting at 45° to the horizontal (direction) can be represented as shown in Figure 1.

Figure 1	Vector Representation of a Force

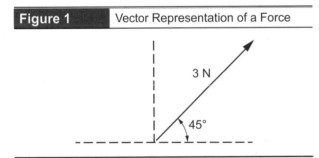

Velocity
An aircraft flying west (direction) at a speed of 400 kilometers per hour (magnitude) could be represented by a vector as shown in Figure 2.

Figure 2	Vector Representation of a Velocity

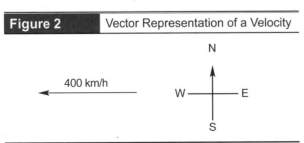

Displacement

If a man walks east (direction) a distance of 200 m (magnitude) from point A to point B, this act could be represented by a displacement vector as shown in Figure 3.

Figure 3	Displacement Vector

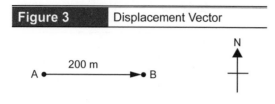

Space Diagrams

A space diagram illustrates a system of vectors. To draw a space diagram, a convenient scale is chosen so the diagram is a suitable size. The angles must be accurately drawn. In problems where the compass points are used to specify direction, the student should always state which direction is north. Figure 4 illustrates a common method.

Figure 4	Space Diagram

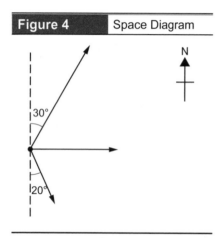

Example 1:

Draw a space diagram for three forces (in the same plane) all acting outwards from one point. The forces are 90 N due east, 120 N at 30° east of north and 60 N at 20° east of south.

Solution:

Specifying which direction is to be taken as north, choose a suitable scale for the length of the force vectors (be sure to state the scale used) and draw the space diagram.

Figure 5	Space Diagram for Example 1

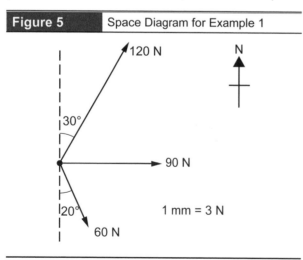

Coplanar Vectors

If the vectors are all in the same plane, they are called coplanar vectors.

Concurrent Vectors

Vectors whose lines of action meet at one point are called concurrent vectors. The forces shown in Figure 5 are coplanar, concurrent forces.

Resultant

The resultant of a system of vectors is the single vector that can replace the system of vectors and have the same effect. The resultant may be found by drawing a vector diagram and measuring the resultant (graphical method), or by calculation (analytical method).

Drawing a Vector Diagram

A vector diagram shows the vectors to scale with the angles accurately drawn, as in a space diagram. However, the positions of the vectors are shifted so that the head of one vector joins the tail of the next vector to form a continuous path.

To draw a vector diagram:

a) Select a suitable scale.

b) Take the vectors in order and draw them head to tail in a continuous path.

Example 2:

Find the resultant of 3 concurrent coplanar forces of:

- 120 N acting 30° east of north

- 90 N acting east

- 60 N acting 20° east of south

These are shown in the space diagram in Figure 6.

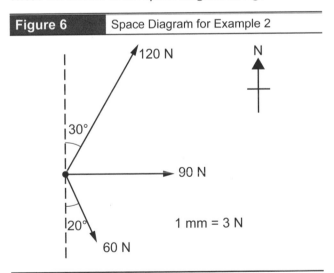

Figure 6	Space Diagram for Example 2

Figure 7	Vector Diagram for Example 2

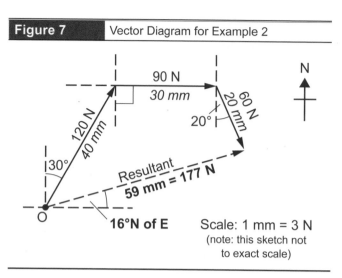

16°N of E

Scale: 1 mm = 3 N
(note: this sketch not
to exact scale)

Solution:

Refer to Figures 6 and 7 for illustrations of the solution for Example 2.

1. A scale of 1 mm = 3 N is chosen for the vector diagram.

2. Show which direction is north in the diagram.

3. To draw the vector diagram, start at point O. A line is drawn angled 30° east of north and a distance of 40 mm is marked off to represent the 120 N force. An arrowhead is placed at the end of the vector to show the direction. The end of this arrow is the starting point for the next vector.

4. The next force is the 90 N force. A line is drawn, directed to the east, starting from the finishing point of the 120 N vector. A length of 30 mm is marked off to represent 90 N, and the arrowhead is drawn to show the direction of the force.

5. A line is then drawn starting from the finishing point of the 90 N vector and directed at an angle of 20° south of east. A length of 20 mm is marked off to represent 60 N. The arrowhead is drawn to show the direction of the force.

6. The resultant (shown dashed) is drawn from the starting point O, to the head of the last vector. Its measured length is 59 mm, which represents a magnitude of 177 N(59 x 3 N = 177 N). Its direction is 16° north of east from O, as measured with a protractor. The resultant's arrowhead must meet the last force's arrowhead, while the resultant's tail must be at the point of origin.

Note: Any of the forces could have been selected to start the vector diagram and the forces could have been taken in any order. As long as the arrows follow head to tail, the result will be the same.

This method of finding the resultant by drawing a scale diagram is useful when checking the value of a resultant; however, it is not sufficiently accurate in most cases for problem solving.

CHAPTER 12 - QUESTIONS

1. By definition, vectors whose lines of action meet at one point are called _____ vectors.

   a) resultant

   b) concurrent

   c) coplanar

   d) unidirectional

2. A boat is traveling on a bearing of 25° east of north at a speed of 5 knots (a knot is 1.852 km/h). After traveling for 3 hours, the boat heading is changed to due south and it travels for a further 2 hours at 5 knots. What is the boat's bearing from its original position?

3. Using a vector diagram drawn to scale, find the magnitude and direction of the following 4 concurrent coplanar forces of

   a) 100 N acting 50° west of north.

   b) 40 N acting west.

   c) 60 N acting 20° east of south.

   d) 15 N acting east.

CHAPTER 12 - ANSWERS

1. (b)

2. 60.5° east of north OR 29.5° north of east

   (**Note:** since your answer is only found by drawing, it may not match exactly, but should be very close to these figures).

3. 81.4 N at 84° west of north OR 6° north of west.

   (**Note:** since your answer is only found by drawing, it may not match exactly, but should be very close to these figures)

Linear Velocity & Acceleration

LEARNING OUTCOME

When you complete this chapter you should be able to:

Define terms and solve simple problems involving speed, velocity, distance, displacement, and acceleration

LEARNING OBJECTIVES

Here is what you should be able to do when you complete each objective:

1. Solve problems involving distance, displacement, speed and velocity.

2. Draw graphs of velocity as a function of time and use to verify velocity calculations.

3. Define acceleration, state its units, and solve simple acceleration problems.

4. Use the mathematical formulae relating acceleration, velocity, distance and time to solve problems.

INTRODUCTION

There are two main areas of study involving motion. They are motion in a straight line (called linear motion) and motion in a circular path. This chapter will concentrate on linear motion only.

Acceleration, an important consideration when dealing with forces, is the relationship between change in velocity and time and is a result of some force.

When dealing with velocity and acceleration, it is important to distinguish between scalar and vector quantities and to fully understand Newton's laws of motion.

A scalar quantity is defined as a quantity that has magnitude only, while a vector quantity has magnitude and direction.

OBJECTIVE 1

Solve problems involving distance, displacement, speed and velocity.

DISTANCE & DISPLACEMENT

Distance is a quantity that has magnitude only; therefore, it is a scalar quantity. For example, 100 km only refers to the length of the path over which a body travels; the direction is irrelevant.

Displacement refers to the change in position of a body, relative to a reference point (usually the initial staring point). Displacement has magnitude and direction; therefore, it is a vector quantity.

Example 1:

A body moves along a path from point A to point D as shown in Figure 1.

- a) What distance does the body travel?

- b) What is the displacement of the body when it moves to B from A?

- c) What is the displacement of the body when it moves to D from A?

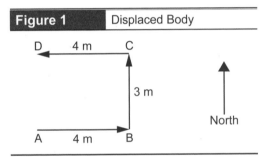

| Figure 1 | Displaced Body |

Solution:

- a) Total distance traveled from A to D:

    4 m + 3 m + 4 m = **11 m (Ans.)**

- b) Displacement of B from A:

    4 m to the right of A, or due east (Ans.)

- c) Displacement of D from A:

    3 m above A, or due north (Ans.)

Note: that the distance traveled does not always equal the displacement.

SPEED & VELOCITY

Speed is the rate at which a body moves, which can also be stated as the distance moved in a given time. It is a scalar quantity since it is not concerned with the direction. The usual units of speed are metres per second (m/s) and kilometres per hour (km/h).

It is unlikely that speed will remain constant during a specific journey. The journey may be interrupted by stops and/or the speed may increase or decrease along the way. Thus, it is usual to calculate the average speed in most cases.

$$\text{Average speed} = \frac{\text{Distance traveled}}{\text{Total time taken}}$$

Example 2:

A vehicle travels a total distance of 300 km. The journey involves a total driving time of 6 hours plus various stops taking up 2 hours. What is the average journey speed?

Solution:

$$\text{Journey time} = 6 \text{ hours} + 2 \text{ hours}$$

$$= 8 \text{ hours}$$

$$\text{Average journey time} = \frac{300 \text{ km}}{8 \text{ hrs}}$$

$$= \textbf{37.5 km/h (Ans.)}$$

No direction, starting point or destination was given in this problem so it would not be possible to represent this journey graphically (by vectors). The term average speed is used to indicate that a scalar quantity is being dealt with.

Velocity refers to the speed of an object in a given direction, and is therefore a vector quantity, having magnitude (speed) and direction.

$$\text{Velocity} = \text{Speed} + \text{Direction}$$

An advantage of vector quantities is that they can be drawn to scale (in a diagram) and then added or subtracted graphically. Vector quantities contain more information than scalar quantities.

When considering velocities, it is normal to account for variations which may occur by considering average velocity.

$$\text{Average velocity} = \frac{\text{Displacement}}{\text{Time}}$$

This formula can be rearranged as:

$$\text{Displacement} = \text{Average velocity} \times \text{Time}$$

The units of velocity are the same as the units of speed (m/s, km/h), with a direction added.

Note: When there is no change in the direction of a body in motion, then displacement and distance will be the same; average speed and average velocity will also be the same.

Example 3:

A body moves along the path shown in Figure 2 from Point A to Point B in a time of 10s. Determine:

a) the average speed

b) the average velocity

Figure 2	Path of Body

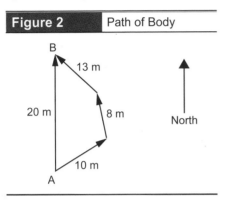

Solution:

$$\text{Distance traveled} = 10 \text{ m} + 8 \text{ m} + 13 \text{ m}$$

$$= 31 \text{ m}$$

$$\text{Displacement of B to A} = 20 \text{ m due north}$$

a) Average speed $= \dfrac{\text{Distance traveled}}{\text{Time}}$

$$= 31 \text{ m}/10 \text{ s}$$

$$= \textbf{3.1 m/s (Ans.)}$$

b) Average velocity $= \dfrac{\text{Displacement}}{\text{Time}}$

Average velocity $= \dfrac{20 \text{ m}}{10 \text{ s}}$

Average velocity $= \textbf{2 m/s north (Ans.)}$

Example 4:

A vehicle travels 60 km due east in a time of 45 minutes. What is its average velocity in km/h?

Solution:

$$\text{Displacement} = 60 \text{ km east}$$

$$\text{Time} = 45 \text{ minutes} = \frac{45 \text{ min}}{60 \text{ min/h}} = 0.75 \text{ h}$$

Average velocity $= \dfrac{\text{Displacement}}{\text{Time}}$

$$= \frac{60 \text{ km}}{0.75 \text{ h}}$$

$$= \textbf{80 km/h east (Ans.)}$$

Example 5:

A coal train travels 127 km from city A to city B which is 100 km due north of city A. If the average velocity of the train is 90 km/h north, how long will it take to make the journey?

Solution:

$$\text{Average velocity} = \frac{\text{Displacement}}{\text{Time}}$$

$$\text{Time} = \frac{\text{Displacement}}{\text{Average velocity}}$$

$$= \frac{100 \text{ km north}}{90 \text{ km/h north}}$$

$$= \textbf{1.11 h (Ans.)}$$

OBJECTIVE 2

Draw graphs of velocity as a function of time and use to verify velocity calculations.

GRAPHICAL REPRESENTATION

A velocity versus time graph can be plotted to represent the movement of a body as follows:

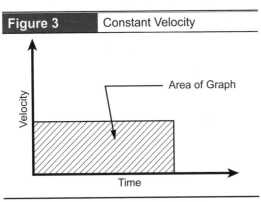

Figure 3	Constant Velocity

Area under graph = Velocity x time

= Displacement

The area under the line of a velocity-time graph represents displacement.

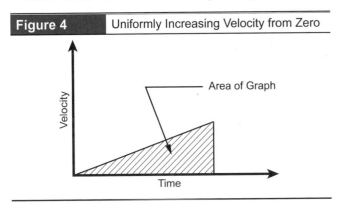

Figure 4	Uniformly Increasing Velocity from Zero

Area under graph = $\frac{1}{2}$ base x height

= Average velocity x time

= Displacement

Again, the area under the velocity-time graph is equal to the displacement.

Note: Not withstanding the technical definitions and distinction between speed and velocity, it is often common practice to use the term, "velocity" interchangeably with the term, "speed". Where motion occurs in a straight line and where consideration of direction is not important, that is, it does not affect the results of a calculation, the term velocity may be used in place of speed. However, if direction is important, then the velocity will, or should, include a direction (e.g. 50 m/sec, 45° north of east) and the student must take the direction into account.

Also, if direction is a straight line, then the velocity-time graph could be called a speed-time graph. The area under the graph would then represent distance traveled. Remember that for linear travel (straight line) distance equals displacement.

13-7

Example 6:

A train starts off from rest and reaches a velocity of 120 km/h in 10 minutes. If the velocity increased uniformly, how far will the train travel in the first 10 minutes? Check your calculation using a velocity-time graph.

Solution:

Since the acceleration was uniform:

$$\text{Average velocity} = \frac{\text{Initial velocity + final velocity}}{2}$$

$$= \frac{0 + 120 \text{ km/h}}{2}$$

$$= 60 \text{ km/h}$$

$$\text{Time taken} = 10 \text{ min}$$

$$= \frac{10 \text{ min}}{60 \text{ min/h}}$$

$$= \frac{10}{60} \text{ h}$$

$$\text{Average velocity} = \frac{\text{Displacement}}{\text{Time}}$$

$$\text{Displacement} = \text{Average velocity} \times \text{Time}$$

$$= 60 \text{ km/h} \times \frac{10}{60} \text{ h}$$

$$= \frac{600}{60} \text{ km}$$

$$= \textbf{10 km (Ans.)}$$

Drawing a velocity-time graph (Fig. 5)

$$\text{Area of graph} = \text{Displacement}$$

$$\text{Area of graph} = \frac{1}{2} \text{ base} \times \text{height}$$

$$= \frac{1}{2} \times \frac{10}{60} \text{ h} \times 120 \text{ km/h}$$

$$= \frac{1200}{120} \text{ km}$$

$$= \textbf{10 km (Ans.)}$$

Note: When drawing the graph, velocity and time plotted on the time scale must be the same: km/h and hours, m/s and seconds.

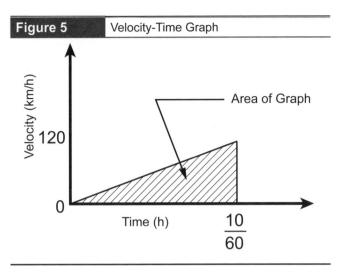

Figure 5 | Velocity-Time Graph

Mathematical Formula for Linear Velocity

A formula can be derived for bodies moving with uniform linear velocity as follows:

Let: Initial velocity = u (m/s)

   Final velocity = v (m/s)

   Time = t (s)

   Displacement = s (m)

From previous work:

   Displacement = Average velocity x Time

   Average velocity = $\frac{u + v}{2}$

Therefore:

$$s = \frac{u + v}{2} \times t$$

Example 7:

A vehicle starts from rest and reaches a velocity of 60 km/h in 20 seconds. If it increases velocity uniformly, how far will it travel in the first 20 seconds?

Solution:

   Initial velocity, u = 0

   Final velocity, v = 60 km/h

   Time, t = 20 s

$$60 \text{ km/h} = \frac{60 \text{k m/h x } 1000 \text{ m/km}}{60 \text{ s/min x } 60 \text{ min/h}}$$

$$= \frac{60\,000}{3600} \text{ ms}$$

$$= 16.67 \text{ ms}$$

$$s = \frac{u + v}{2} \times t$$

$$= \frac{0 \text{ m/s} + 16.67 \text{ m/s}}{2} \times 20 \text{ s}$$

$$= \frac{16.67 \text{ m/s}}{2} \times 20 \text{ s}$$

$$= 8.335 \text{ m/s} \times 20 \text{ s}$$

   Distance traveled = **166.7 m (Ans.)**

Example 8:

A vehicle traveling at 100 km/h decelerates uniformly to 60 km/h in 10 seconds. How far will the vehicle travel in this time?

Solution:

$$u = 100 \text{ km/h}$$

$$= \frac{100 \text{ km/h x 1000 m/km}}{60 \text{ s/min x 60 min/h}}$$

$$= \frac{100\,000}{3600} \text{ m/s}$$

$$= 27.78 \text{ m/s}$$

$$v = 60 \text{ km/h}$$

$$= \frac{60 \text{ km/h x 1000 m/km}}{60 \text{ s/min x 60 min/h}}$$

$$= \frac{60\,000}{3600} \text{ m/s}$$

$$= 16.67 \text{ m/s}$$

$$t = 10 \text{ s}$$

$$s = \frac{u + v}{2} \text{ x t}$$

$$= \frac{27.78 \text{ m/s} + 16.67 \text{ m/s}}{2} \text{ x 10 s}$$

$$= \frac{44.45 \text{ m/s}}{2} \text{ x 10 s}$$

$$= 22.225 \text{ m/s x 10 s}$$

$$= \textbf{222.25 m (Ans.)}$$

OBJECTIVE 3

Define acceleration, state its units, and solve simple acceleration problems.

ACCELERATION

Acceleration may be defined as the rate of change of velocity or the change in velocity per unit time.

$$\text{Acceleration} = \frac{\text{Change in velocity}}{\text{Time taken to change}}$$

$$= \frac{m/s}{s}$$

$$= m/s^2 \text{ (metres per second per second)}$$

A body is said to be accelerating if its velocity is changing with time. The change can be in speed (magnitude), direction or both.

An increase in speed is usually considered positive acceleration while a decrease in speed is negative acceleration or deceleration.

Example 9:

A car traveling at 20 km/h increases its velocity uniformly to 60 km/h in 10 seconds. What is the acceleration?

Solution:

$$\text{Change in velocity} = 60 \text{ km/h} - 20 \text{ km/h}$$

$$= 40 \text{ km/h}$$

$$40 \text{ km/h} = \frac{40 \text{ km/h} \times 1000 \text{ m/km}}{60 \text{ s/min} \times 60 \text{ min/h}}$$

$$= \frac{40\,000}{3600} \text{ m/s}$$

$$= 11.1 \text{ m/s}$$

$$\text{Acceleration} = \frac{\text{Change in velocity}}{\text{Time}}$$

$$= \frac{11.1 \text{ m/s}}{10 \text{ s}}$$

$$= \textbf{1.11 m/s}^2 \textbf{ (Ans.)}$$

Mathematical Formula for Linear Acceleration

Initial velocity = u (m/s)

Final velocity = v (m/s)

Time = t (s)

Acceleration = a (m/s²)

$$\text{Acceleration} = \frac{\text{Change in velocity}}{\text{Time}}$$

$$a = \frac{v - u}{t}$$

Using this formula to solve the problem in Example 9:

Change in velocity = v - u

= 60 km/h - 20 km/h

= 40 km/h

= 11.1 m/s

$$a = \frac{v - u}{t}$$

$$= \frac{11.1 \text{ m/s}}{10 \text{ s}}$$

= **1.11 m/s² (Ans.)**

A more familiar form for the equation, $a = \frac{v - u}{t}$, is found by transposing:

a x t = v - u

at + u = v

and   v = u + at

Example 10:

A car traveling at 60 km/h is brought to rest over a distance of 100 m. What is the acceleration?

Solution:

u = 60 km/h

$$= \frac{60 \text{ km/h x 1000 m/km}}{60 \text{ s/min x 60 min/h}}$$

$$= \frac{60\,000}{3600} \text{ m/s}$$

= 16.67 m/s

v = 0 m/s

$$s = \frac{v + u}{2} \times t$$

$$100 \text{ m} = \frac{0 \text{ m/s} + 16.67 \text{ m/s}}{2} \times t$$

Transpose to find time, t:

$$100 \text{ m} = \frac{0 \text{ m/s} + 16.67 \text{ m/s}}{2} \times t$$

$$t = \frac{100 \text{ m} \times 2}{16.67 \text{ m/s}}$$

$$= 12 \text{ s}$$

Now using the acceleration equation:

$$a = \frac{v - u}{t}$$

$$= \frac{0 \text{ m/s} - 16.67 \text{ m/s}}{12 \text{ s}}$$

$$= \frac{-16.67 \text{ m/s}}{12 \text{ s}}$$

$$= \textbf{-1.39 m/s}^2 \textbf{ (Ans.)}$$

The minus sign indicates deceleration.

OBJECTIVE 4

Use the mathematical formula relating acceleration, velocity, distance and time to solve problems.

OTHER MATHEMATICAL FORMULAE

Various formulae for velocity and uniform acceleration calculations can be derived from the two basic formulae:

$$s = \frac{u + v}{2} \times t$$

$$v = u + at$$

These formulae can be used to simplify many calculations.

Derived Formulae

$$s = \frac{u + v}{2} \times t$$

$$t = \frac{2s}{u + v}$$

Substituting this value for t in the formula v = u + at:

$$v = u + a \times \frac{2s}{u + v}$$

$$= u + \frac{2as}{u + v}$$

$$v - u = \frac{2as}{u + v}$$

$$(v - u)(v + u) = 2as$$

$$v^2 - u^2 = 2as$$

$$v^2 = u^2 + 2as$$

Formula for Distance

$$v = u + at \qquad \text{Equation (1)}$$

$$s = \frac{u + v}{2} \times t \qquad \text{Equation (2)}$$

Substituting u + at for v in Equation (2):

$$s = \frac{u + v}{2} \times t$$

$$= \frac{u + u + at}{2} \times t$$

$$s = \frac{2u + at}{2} \times t$$

$$= (u + \frac{1}{2} at) t$$

$$= ut + \frac{1}{2} at^2$$

Summary of Formulae for Uniform Linear Motion

$$s = \frac{u + v}{2} \times t$$

$$v = u + at$$

$$v^2 = u^2 + 2\,as$$

$$s = ut + \frac{1}{2}\,at^2$$

Example 11:

An object is dropped from a height of 30 m. What will its velocity be on impact?

Solution:

$$v^2 = u^2 + 2\,as$$

a = Acceleration due to gravity

   $= 9.81 \text{ m/s}^2$

u = Initial velocity

   $= 0 \text{ m/s}$

s = Distance traveled

   $= 30 \text{ m}$

$$v^2 = u^2 + 2\,as$$

$$v^2 = 0 + 2 \times 9.81 \text{ m/s}^2 \times 30 \text{ m}$$

$$v^2 = 588.6 \text{ m}^2/\text{s}^2$$

$$v = \sqrt{588.6 \text{ m}^2\text{s}^2}$$

Velocity on impact = **24.26 m/s (Ans.)**

Example 12:

A car has an initial speed of 20 km/h; and in 1 minute and 30 seconds, it accelerates to 100 km/h. What is the distance traveled during the acceleration period?

Solution:

$u = 20$ km/h

$$= \frac{20 \text{ km/h} \times 1000 \text{ m/km}}{60 \text{ s/min} \times 60 \text{ m/h}}$$

$$= \frac{20\,000}{3600} \text{ m/s}$$

$$= 5.56 \text{ m/s}$$

$v = 100$ km/h

$$= \frac{100 \text{ km/h} \times 1000 \text{ m/km}}{60 \text{ s/min} \times 60 \text{ min/h}}$$

$$= \frac{100\,000}{3600} \text{ m/s}$$

$$= 27.78 \text{ m/s}$$

$t = 1$ minute, 30 seconds $= 90$ seconds

$$s = \frac{u + v}{2} \times t$$

$$= \frac{5.56 \text{ m/s} + 27.78 \text{ m/s}}{2} \times 90 \text{ s}$$

$$= \frac{33.34 \text{ m/s}}{2} \times 90 \text{ s}$$

$$= 16.67 \text{ m/s} \times 90 \text{ s}$$

$$= \mathbf{1500.3 \text{ m}} \quad \textbf{(Ans.)}$$

For an alternate method, use:

$v = u + at$

Transpose this formula for 'a':

$$a = \frac{v - u}{t}$$

$$= \frac{27.78 \text{ m/s} - 5.56 \text{ m/s}}{90 \text{ s}}$$

$$= \frac{22.22 \text{ m/s}}{90 \text{ s}}$$

$$= 0.2469 \text{ m/s}^2$$

$$s = ut + \frac{1}{2}at^2$$

$$= (5.56 \text{ m/s} \times 90 \text{ s}) + (\frac{1}{2} \times 0.2469 \text{ m/s}^2 \times 90^2 \text{ s}^2)$$

$$= 500.4 \text{ m} + 999.9 \text{ m}$$

$$= \mathbf{1500.3 \text{ m (Ans.)}}$$

CHAPTER 13 - QUESTIONS

1. A train is traveling at 90 km/h. Find the following:

   a) Its speed in m/s

   b) How far it will travel in 7 seconds

   c) How long it takes to cover 4 km

   d) The average speed in km/h, if the time to travel 130 km is one hour and 40 minutes

2. A car traveling at a speed of 140 km/h decelerates for 20 seconds. During this time it travels 500 m.

   a) What is its deceleration?

   b) What is its speed after the deceleration?

3. A train starts from rest and increases its speed uniformly for three minutes. In that time it reaches a speed of 150 km/h. What is its acceleration in m/s^2?

4. A car traveling at an initial speed of 40 km/h accelerates uniformly to 120 km/h in two minutes. What distance is traveled during the acceleration period?

5. Acceleration is defined as the rate of change of

   a) velocity.

   b) speed.

   c) distance.

   d) time.

CHAPTER 13 - ANSWERS

1. a) 25 m/s
   b) 175 m
   c) 2 minutes, 40 seconds
   d) 78 km/h

2. a) 1.389 m/s^2
   b) 40 km/h

3. 0.23 m/s^2

4. 2.67 km

5. (a)

Force, Work, Pressure, Power & Energy

LEARNING OUTCOME

When you complete this chapter you should be able to:

Differentiate between force, work, pressure, power, and energy and perform calculations involving the relationships between these mechanical terms.

LEARNING OBJECTIVES

Here is what you should be able to do when you complete each objective:

1. Perform calculations involving force and work.

2. Differentiate between and perform calculations involving gauge, atmospheric and absolute pressure.

3. Differentiate between and perform calculations involving power and different forms of mechanical energy.

OBJECTIVE 1

Perform calculations involving force and work.

FORCE

A force is a push or pull exerted on an object. When a force is applied to an object, it may change the state of motion or rest, the location, the shape or the size of it. For example, sufficient force on a door will cause it to open; greater force causes it to open faster. If the door does not have a spring type closer or a doorstop, another force will have to be applied to stop the door from banging into a fixed object such as the wall. A bowling ball can apply a force to stationary bowling pins which sends them flying. The force of brakes can reduce the speed of an automobile. The force of a finger pressed against an inflated balloon can cause the balloon to become deformed.

In the SI system, the unit of force is called the newton (N).

$$1 \text{ N} = 1 \text{ kgm/s}^2$$

Variable Force

In practice, the magnitude of the force is not always constant, but may vary during the movement. The force required to keep a vehicle moving will be constant when all conditions are constant, but considering a typical highway, there will be level sections and there will be hills. The added force required to move a vehicle up a hill is evidenced by the need to press on the accelerator. Downhill travel requires less force and in extreme cases, braking. Pedaling a bicycle into a strong head wind requires more force than pedaling with the wind behind. These are examples of situations that involve variable force.

WORK

If force is applied to a body and causes it to move through a distance, work is done by the force. Work done by a force is the product of the force applied and the distance through which the force moves.

Work done = Force x Distance

The work done when a force of one newton moves through a distance of 1 metre is one newton metre (Nm). This unit of work is called the joule (J).

1 joule = 1 Newton metre (Nm)

If a graph of force against distance moved is plotted, then the work done is represented by the area of the graph (Fig. 1). Graphical representation very often simplifies work calculations.

Example 1:

A force is uniformly increased from 0 N to 100 N to keep a body moving a distance of 20 m at uniform velocity. Calculate the work done and check the result graphically.

Numerical Solution:

$$\text{Average force} = \frac{0 \text{ N} + 100 \text{ N}}{2}$$

$$= \frac{100 \text{ N}}{2}$$

$$= 50 \text{ N}$$

$$\text{Work done} = \text{Force x Distance}$$

$$= 50 \text{ N x 20 m}$$

$$= 1000 \text{ Nm}$$

$$= 1000 \text{ J}$$

$$= 1 \text{ kJ (Ans.)}$$

Graphical Solution:

Figure 1	Force Distance Graph for Example 1

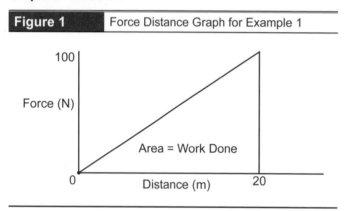

$$\text{Area of graph (triangle)} = \frac{1}{2} \text{ base x height}$$

$$= \frac{1}{2} \text{ x 20 m x 100 N}$$

$$= \frac{2000}{2} \text{ Nm}$$

$$= 1000 \text{ J}$$

$$= 1 \text{ kJ (Ans.)}$$

Example 2:

A force of 100 N acting on a body moves it a distance of 10 m. What is the work done by the force on the body?

Solution:

$$\text{Work done} = \text{Force x Distance}$$

$$= 100 \text{ N x 10 m}$$

$$= 1000 \text{ Nm}$$

$$= 1 \text{ kJ (Ans.)}$$

Example 3:

A mass of 50 kg is moved a vertical distance of 20 m. What work will be required?

Solution:

The force applied is the force necessary to overcome the force of gravity. (50 kg × 9.81 m/s²)

Work done = Force (N) x Distance (m)

$\qquad$ = (50 kg x 9.81 m/s²) x 20 m

$\qquad$ = (490.5 N) x 20 m

$\qquad$ = 9810 Nm

$\qquad$ = **9.81 kJ (Ans.)**

Example 4:

A pump is required to raise 500 litres of fresh water a vertical distance of 100 m.

a) How much work will be done by the pump in raising the water?

b) If the pump has an efficiency of 50%, how much work must be done on the pump to raise the water?

Solution:

a) 1 litre of fresh water has a mass of 1 kg. 500 litres have a mass of 500 kg which exert a "weight" or gravitational force of 500 kg × 9.81 m/s² = 4905 N downwards.

$\qquad$ Work done = Force (N) x Distance (m)

$\qquad$ = 4905 N x 100 m

$\qquad$ = 490 500 Nm

$\qquad$ = **490.5 kJ (Ans.)**

b) $\quad$ % Efficiency $= \dfrac{\text{Work output (Work done by the pump)}}{\text{Work input (Work done on the pump)}}$ x 100%

$\qquad$ Work input $= \dfrac{\text{Work output}}{\text{\% Efficiency}}$ x 100%

$\qquad\qquad = \dfrac{490.5 \text{ kJ}}{50}$ x 100

$\qquad$ = **981 kJ (Ans.)**

Note: Twice as much work is put into the pump as is done by the pump.

It should be noted here that the work done in pumping water uphill (Fig. 2) is not a function of how long the pipe is, but only of the height of the point of pipe discharge measured vertically above the pump outlet.

Excessively long pipes or high velocity may reduce the efficiency of the system because of friction in the pipe.

Figure 2 Work Done by Pump

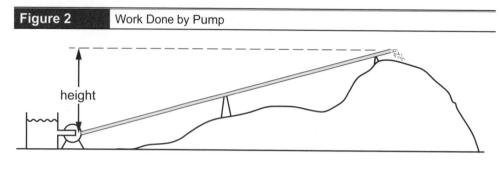

height

The actual work done by raising an oil drum from the floor to a loading dock is a function of the drum's mass and the vertical height of the dock above the floor. A ramp from the floor could be four times as long as the vertical height of the dock, but the actual work performed in rolling a drum up the ramp is not four times as much as the vertical lift. The inclined plane of the ramp helps to raise the drum more slowly and with less force, but the work accomplished is still the same (neglecting small frictional losses).

A heavily loaded truck may travel at 100 km/h along flat countryside. When the truck comes to a steep hill, the driver uses lower gears to move the heavy load up the hill, but at a much slower rate. Road, mechanical and wind resistance all play a part in how efficiently the truck changes elevation. The end result is still that the mass is raised the vertical height of the hill regardless of how long the road is.

OBJECTIVE 2

Differentiate between and perform calculations involving gauge, atmospheric and absolute pressure.

PRESSURE

The pascal (Pa) is the SI unit for pressure measurement; pressure is a measure of force per unit area. Since force is measured in newtons and area is measured in m², one newton per square metre equals one pascal:

$$1 \text{ N/m}^2 = 1 \text{ Pa}$$

Or $\quad 1 \text{ kN/m}^2 = 1 \text{ kPa}$

Example 5:

If 350 N acts on an area of 0.25 m², what is the resulting pressure?

Solution:

$$\text{Pressure} = \frac{\text{Force}}{\text{Area}}$$

$$= \frac{350 \text{ N}}{0.25 \text{ m}^2}$$

$$= 1400 \text{ Pa}$$

$$= \mathbf{1.4 \text{ kPa (Ans.)}}$$

Example 6:

What force is exerted on a rectangular tank wall 1.3 m long and 0.75 m high when a pressure of 150 kPa acts upon it?

Solution:

$$F = P \times A$$

$$= 150 \text{ kPa} \times (1.3 \text{ m} \times 0.75 \text{ m})$$

$$= 150 \text{ kPa} \times 0.975 \text{ m}^2$$

$$= 150 \text{ kN/m}^2 \times 0.975 \text{ m}^2$$

$$= \mathbf{146.25 \text{ kN (Ans.)}}$$

ABSOLUTE & GAUGE PRESSURE

The force due to the weight of the atmosphere above us produces **atmospheric pressure**. Assuming that the atmosphere forms an almost perfect sphere around the earth, the higher the elevation, the less atmosphere is above us. Thus, atmospheric pressure decreases with elevation. Obviously, this pressure will also be affected by a number of other factors relating to air conditions, such as:

- Moisture content (humidity)
- Density
- Temperature

However, on average, the pressure due to the atmosphere at sea level has been measured as 101.3 kPa. This pressure is measured relative to a theoretical "absolute zero" of pressure and to be precise, atmospheric pressure is 101.3 kPa **absolute**, although, in practice, this term is usually omitted. Since atmospheric pressure is always present on earth, this presence is discounted. Usually, pressure gauges are calibrated to a value of 0 kPa; pressures measured with these gauges are actually **gauge** pressures. Thus, if the absolute pressure of a substance is required, the following equation can be applied:

Absolute pressure = Gauge pressure + Atmospheric pressure

In thermodynamics, it is important to know the absolute pressure of a system as all pressure tables are quoted in these units.

Example 7:

If the pressure gauge on a steam drum reads 1200 kPa, what is the absolute pressure inside the drum?

Solution:

Absolute pressure = Gauge pressure + Atmospheric pressure

= 1200 kPa + 101.3 kPa

= **1301 kPa (Ans.)**

OBJECTIVE 3

Differentiate between and perform calculations involving power and different forms of mechanical energy.

POWER

Power is the rate of doing work or the quantity of work done per unit of time.

$$\text{Power} = \frac{\text{Work done}}{\text{Time}}$$

$$= \frac{\text{Nm}}{\text{s}}$$

$$= \frac{\text{Joule}}{\text{s}}$$

The unit of power, J/s is called the watt (W).

1 J/s = 1 watt

Since the watt is a small unit of power, the usual unit of power for most applications is the kilowatt.

1 kilowatt (kW) = 1000 watts

A megawatt is used for very large power outputs.

1 megawatt (MW) = 1 000 000 watts

= 1 000 kW

Example 8:

A mass of 50 kg is moved a vertical distance of 20 m in 10 s. What is the power developed?

Solution:

Work done = Force (N) x Distance (m)

$$= (50 \text{ kg} \times 9.81 \text{ m/s}^2) \times 20 \text{ m}$$

$$= (490.5 \text{ N}) \times 20 \text{ m}$$

= 9810 Nm

= 9810 J

$$\text{Power developed} = \frac{\text{Work done}}{\text{Time}}$$

= 9810 J/10 s

= 981 J/s

= 981 W (Ans.)

Example 9:

A pump raises 200 tonnes of fresh water a height of 10 m in 1 hour. What is the power output of the pump?

Solution:

$$1 \text{ h} = 60 \text{ min} \times 60 \text{ s/min}$$
$$= 3600 \text{ s}$$

Distance moved = 10 m

$$\text{Work done} = \text{Force (N)} \times \text{Distance (m)}$$
$$= (200\ 000 \text{ kg} \times 9.81 \text{ m/s}^2) \times 10 \text{ m}$$
$$= 1\ 962\ 000 \text{ N} \times 10 \text{ m}$$
$$= 19\ 620\ 000 \text{ Nm}$$
$$= 19\ 620\ 000 \text{ J}$$
$$= 19\ 620 \text{ kJ}$$

$$\text{Power output} = \frac{\text{Work done}}{\text{Time}}$$
$$= \frac{19\ 620 \text{ kJ}}{3600 \text{ s}}$$
$$= 5.45 \text{ kJ/s}$$
$$= \mathbf{5.45 \text{ kW (Ans.)}}$$

Example 10:

If the efficiency of the pump in Example 9 is 80%, what is the power required to drive the pump?

Solution:

$$\% \text{ Efficiency} = \frac{\text{Power output}}{\text{Power input}} \times 100\%$$

$$\text{Power input} = \frac{\text{Power output}}{\% \text{ Efficiency}} \times 100\%$$

$$= \frac{5.45 \text{ kW}}{80\%} \times 100\%$$

$$= \mathbf{6.81 \text{ kW (Ans.)}}$$

In the Imperial system, the unit of power is called the horsepower. This unit is still often used to rate electric motors.

$$1 \text{ horsepower} = 746 \text{ W}$$

Since $\qquad \text{Power} = \dfrac{\text{Work}}{\text{Time}}$, then

$$\text{Work} = \text{Power} \times \text{Time}$$

Work is sometimes expressed in terms of Power x Time.

For example:

1 Kilowatt hour = Work done when 1 kilowatt of power is exerted for 1 hour

$$1 \text{ kWh} = 1 \text{ kW} \times 1 \text{ h}$$
$$= 1000 \text{ W} \times 3600 \text{ s}$$
$$= 1000 \text{ J/s} \times 3600 \text{ s}$$
$$= 3\ 600\ 000 \text{ J}$$
$$= 3.6 \text{ MJ}$$

ENERGY

A body possesses energy when it is capable of doing work; thus, energy is the capacity to do work. The basic SI unit of energy is the joule, the unit of work when dealing with such forms of energy as:

- Thermal
- Mechanical

Thermal Energy

Thermal energy is expressed in J, kJ, MJ or GJ in the SI system.

Mechanical Energy

There are two forms of mechanical energy:

- Potential
- Kinetic

Potential Energy

Potential energy (PE) is the ability of a body to do work due to its position. For example, water stored in a dam contains potential energy due to its position and can be made to do such work as turning a hydroelectric alternator. If the water is released, it will flow to a lower point due to the force of gravity.

PE = Gravitational force (newtons) x Vertical height (metres)

= Mass x g x h,   where g is the acceleration due to gravity

Example 11:

An object with a mass of 100 kg is at a height of 10 m above the ground. What is its potential energy?

Solution:

PE = Mass x Acceleration due to gravity x height

= 100 kg x 9.81 m/s^2 x 10 m

= 9810 Nm

= **9810 J (Ans.)**

Kinetic Energy

Kinetic energy (KE) is the ability of a body to do work due to its motion.

Mass of the body = m(kg)

Velocity of the body = v(m/s)

Then $KE = \frac{1}{2} mv^2 (J)$

Example 12:

A body with a mass of 100 kg is moving at a velocity of 100 km/h. What is the kinetic energy?

Solution:

$m = 100$ kg

$$v = \frac{100 \text{ km} \times 1000 \text{ m/km}}{1 \text{ h} \times 60 \text{ min/h} \times 60 \text{ s/min}}$$

$$= \frac{100 \times 1000 \text{ m}}{3600 \text{ s}}$$

$$= 27.78 \text{ m/s}$$

$$KE = \frac{1}{2} mv^2$$

$$= \frac{1}{2} \times 100 \text{ kg} \times (27.78 \text{ m/s})^2$$

$$= \frac{1}{2} \times 100 \text{ kg} \times 771.73 \text{ m}^2/\text{s}^2$$

$$= 38\,586.5 \text{ J}$$

$$= \mathbf{38.5865 \text{ kJ} \textbf{ (Ans.)}}$$

Transformation of Mechanical Energy

Potential energy can be transformed to kinetic energy; the law of conservation of energy states that energy cannot be created or destroyed but can change its form.

Loss in PE = Gain in KE (or vice versa)

This is a useful relationship for solving many problems.

Example 13:

A resting block with a mass of 50 kg is allowed to fall from rest from a height of 10 m. What will be its velocity upon striking the ground?

Solution:

Potential energy = Mass x Acceleration due to gravity x Height

$$= 50 \text{ kg} \times 9.81 \text{ m/s}^2 \times 10 \text{ m}$$

$$= 4905 \text{ Nm}$$

$$= \mathbf{4905 \text{ J} \textbf{ (Ans.)}}$$

After falling, its entire PE is transformed into KE due to the block being at zero height above the ground.

Loss in PE = Gain in KE

$$4905 \text{ J} = \frac{1}{2} mv^2$$

$$= \frac{1}{2} \times 50 \text{ kg} \times v^2$$

$$\frac{4905 \text{ J} \times 2}{50 \text{ kg}} = v^2$$

$$\frac{9810 \text{ J}}{50 \text{ kg}} = v^2$$

$$v^2 = 196.2 \text{ J/kg}$$

$$= 196.2 \text{ Nm/kg}$$

$$= 196.2 \text{ kgm}^2/\text{s}^2/\text{kg}$$

$$= 196.2 \text{ m}^2/\text{s}^2$$

$$v = \sqrt{196.2 \text{ m}^2/\text{s}^2}$$

$$= \textbf{14.01 m/s (Ans.)}$$

At the moment of striking the ground, the PE will be zero and the KE at maximum. The velocity will be 14.01 m/s when the block strikes the ground.

At 5 m above the ground, half of its PE will have been converted into KE. Thus, at 5 m:

PE = KE

$$PE = \frac{1}{2} \times 4905 \text{ J}$$

PE = 2452.5 J

Example 14:

A 60 kg mass falls freely to the ground from rest. It hits the ground at 10 m/s. From what height did it fall?

Solution:

Mass = 60 kg

Loss in PE = Gain in KE

$$KE = \frac{1}{2} mv^2$$

$$= \frac{1}{2} \times 60 \text{ kg} \times (10 \text{ m/s})^2$$

$$= 3000 \text{ J}$$

$$PE = m \times g \times h = 3000 \text{ J}$$

$$h = \frac{PE}{m\,g}$$

$$= \frac{3000 \text{ J}}{60 \text{ kg} \times 9.81 \text{ m/s}^2}$$

$$= \frac{3000 \text{ kgm/s}^2\text{m}}{60 \times 9.81 \text{ kgm/s}^2}$$

$$= \frac{3000 \text{ m}}{588.6}$$

$$= \textbf{5.10 m (Ans.)}$$

This page has intentionally been left blank.

CHAPTER 14 - QUESTIONS

1. A hoist system raises a mass of 750 kg a vertical distance of 80 m. Calculate the work done and the quantity of work input to the system if the hoist is 85% efficient.
   a) 455.6 kJ, 724.77 kJ
   b) 588.6 kJ, 692.47 kJ
   c) 525.4 kJ, 655.75 kJ
   d) 501.5 kJ, 597.78 kJ

2. If the hoist in question 1 raises the load in 10 seconds, what is the power developed and what is the power input?
   a) 58.86 kW, 69.25 kW
   b) 62.55 kW, 74.26 kW
   c) 55.25 kW, 64.25 kW
   d) 77.87 kW, 91.44 kW

3. A cylindrical tank, 1 m in diameter, has flat ends. What force is exerted against each end if a pressure of 350 kPa is contained in the tank?
   a) 350 kN
   b) 274.89 kN
   c) 167.25 kN
   d) 215.54 kN

4. A 75 kg boiler drum manhole falls from the top of the boiler to the boiler room floor. If this distance is 25 m, what is its velocity at the point of impact?
   a) 83.75 m/s
   b) 12.95 m/s
   c) 34.25 m/s
   d) 22.15 m/s

5. Potential energy is the ability of a body to do work due to its
   a) pressure.
   b) position.
   c) mass.
   d) distance traveled.

6. River water with a mass of 100 tonnes is moving at 12.5 km/h. What is its kinetic energy?
   a) 345 kJ
   b) 602.7 kJ
   c) 552.2 kJ
   d) 481.2 kJ

CHAPTER 14 - ANSWERS

1. (b)

2. (a)

3. (b)

4. (d)

5. (b)

6. (b)

CHAPTER 15

Friction

LEARNING OUTCOME

When you complete this chapter you should be able to:

Explain friction and solve problems involving friction.

LEARNING OBJECTIVES

Here is what you should be able to do when you complete each objective:

1. Define the types of friction and the laws governing them.

2. Define the coefficient of friction and solve problems involving friction forces on a horizontal plane.

OBJECTIVE 1

Define the types of friction and the laws governing them.

FRICTION

The 'force of friction' can be defined as a force that opposes motion of one surface over another. This opposition to motion is due to the irregularities of the two surfaces. The direction of this force of friction is opposite to the direction of any force trying to move or is moving an object.

The control of friction is necessary in many situations. Friction may be reduced by lubrication, which separates the two surfaces and results in only the resistance of the lubricant itself causing friction. An example of this is a rotating shaft, supported by an oil-supplied bearing. The oil, which is under pressure, causes the shaft to ride on a cushion of oil instead of allowing metal to metal contact. Friction may be necessary in some cases and an increase in friction may be achieved by the proper selection of materials and by applying forces in the proper direction. An example is two pulleys joined by a belt. The selection of the belt material and belt tension may increase the friction. Friction can be an asset or a liability, depending upon the application.

TYPES OF FRICTION

Friction occurs in several different forms:

1. **Standing or static friction** is the resistance that opposes the initial movement of a body at rest. In other words, to start an object moving, a certain amount of frictional resistance must be overcome; this resistance is called static friction.

2. **Sliding or kinetic friction** is the resistance that opposes the continued movement of an object. To keep an object moving at a constant speed requires a constant force to overcome the kinetic friction.

3. **Rolling friction** is the resistance that opposes the motion of a wheel or roller as it rolls along a surface. An example of this is a tire rolling over concrete.

4. **Fluid friction** is the resistance to movement within the layers of a fluid.

Friction always exists to some extent and a percentage of the energy input to any machine is consumed in overcoming frictional forces. The two main types of friction examined here will be static friction and kinetic friction.

LAWS GOVERNING FRICTION

The laws governing friction are not precise; however, they have been experimentally determined to hold true for any situation encountered:

1. The force of friction is proportional to the force that presses the two surfaces together. For static or kinetic friction, this will depend upon the mass of an object on a horizontal surface, or more precisely the total force normal (perpendicular) to the surface. If the downward force is doubled, the frictional force between the two surfaces is doubled.

2. Static friction (standing friction) is always greater than kinetic friction (moving friction). The amount of force required to start an object moving is greater than that required to keep the object moving at a constant speed.

3. The force of friction, whether static or kinetic, is not affected by the area of the two surfaces in contact. If the same downward force is distributed over twice as much area, there is no change in the frictional forces between the two surfaces.

4. Kinetic friction is not affected by the speed of the body. Within reasonable limits, the forces of kinetic friction between two surfaces will remain unchanged as the speed of the object is increased or decreased.

5. The force of friction (either static or kinetic) is affected by the relative roughness of the two surfaces in contact; the rougher the surfaces, the greater the forces required to overcome friction. If a greater force of friction is desired, it is only necessary to increase the roughness on one of the surfaces.

6. Kinetic friction (sliding friction) is greater than rolling friction. Which explains why roller type bearings are extensively used.

OBJECTIVE 2

Define the coefficient of friction and solve problems involving friction forces on a horizontal plane.

COEFFICIENT OF FRICTION

The coefficient of friction (μ) is the ratio of the frictional force opposing a body's motion on a surface to the normal (i.e. perpendicular) reaction force between the body and the surface. The coefficient of friction is a ratio and, therefore, has no units. Stated mathematically,

$$\mu = F_F / R_N$$

Where:

μ is the coefficient of friction.

F_F is the friction force (parallel to the surface). This is also equal to the force required to start an object moving or keep it moving at a constant speed. At the instant the object moves or is kept moving at a constant speed, the applied force (F_A) equals the friction force (F_F), when dealing with horizonal forces and surfaces.

R_N is the reaction force between the surfaces, normal (perpendicular) to the surface. R_N is opposite in direction and numerically equal to the downward force of the object due to gravity, when dealing with horizontal surfaces.

Note: F_F and R_N must be at right angles to each other.

Table 1 shows some examples of the coefficient of friction between two surfaces. These values have been determined experimentally and should be considered as typical ranges.

Table 1	Examples of Coefficient of Friction
Surfaces	**Coefficient of Friction**
metal on metal	0.15 to 0.65
greased metal on metal	0.02 to 0.06
metal on wood	0.20 to 0.60
wood on wood - dry	0.25 to 0.55
wood on wood - wet	0.10 to 0.45
rubber on concrete	0.60 to 0.95

Figure 1(a) shows the forces acting on a block under static friction conditions. If force F_A is less than force F_F, then the block will not move. When force F_A is equal to force F_F, then the block will just start to move. If force F_A is increased, then the block will accelerate.

Figure 1(a)	Static Friction

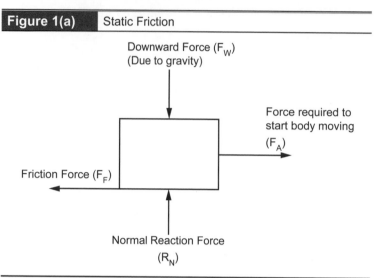

Figure 1(b) shows the forces acting on a block under kinetic friction conditions. If the force F_A is equal to the force F_F, then the block will move at constant velocity. If the force F_A is increased, then the block will accelerate.

Figure 1(b)	Kinetic Friction

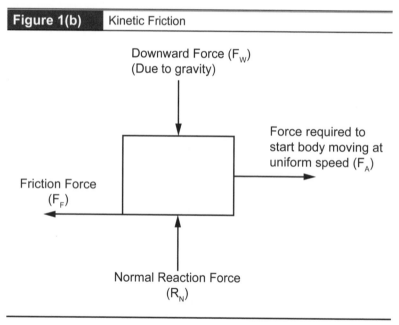

Example 1:

Find the coefficient of friction between a 100 kg box (Fig. 2) and a horizontal concrete floor if a horizontal force of 460 N is required to start the box moving.

Figure 2	Coefficient of Friction Example

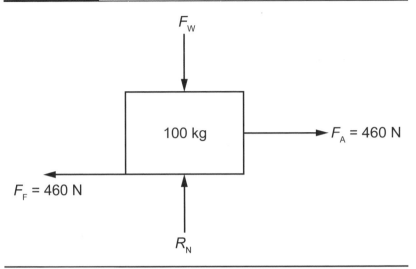

Solution:

First, R_N must be calculated from the 100 kg mass. The mass (m), multiplied by the acceleration due to gravity (g), will be equal to the downward force (F_W). R_N is numerically equal to the downward force when the surface and applied force are both horizontal.

Therefore:

$$F_W = mg$$
$$= 100 \text{ kg} \times 9.81 \text{ m/s}^2$$
$$= 981 \text{ N}$$

Then:

$$R_N = 981 \text{ N}$$

And:

$$F_F = F_A = 460 \text{ N}$$

$$\text{Coefficient of static friction } (\mu_S) = \frac{F_F}{R_N}$$

$$\mu_S = \frac{460 \text{ N}}{981 \text{ N}}$$

$$= 0.47 \text{ (Ans.)}$$

Example 2:

Find the coefficient of sliding (kinetic) friction if the box in Figure 2 requires a force of 430 N to keep it moving at constant speed.

Solution:

$$R_N = 981 \text{ N}$$

$$F_F = F_A = 430 \text{ N}$$

Coefficient of sliding friction (μ_K) $= \dfrac{F_F}{R_N}$

$$= \dfrac{430 \text{ N}}{981 \text{ N}}$$

$$= \textbf{0.44 (Ans.)}$$

Note: The coefficient of static friction is greater than the coefficient of kinetic friction.

$$\mu_S > \mu_K$$

The subscripts "s" and "k" are not always included with "μ" since the wording of a problem often indicates whether the frictional forces are static or kinetic.

Example 3:

Find the horizontal force required to move a pump and the skid on which it rests. The total mass is 2000 kg. The coefficient of static friction between the horizontal floor and the skid is 0.26.

Solution:

First find the value of R_N:

$$F_W = \text{Mass x acceleration due to gravity}$$

$$= 2000 \text{ kg x } 9.81 \text{ m/s}^2$$

$$= 19\ 620 \text{ N}$$

Thus:

$$R_N = 19\ 620 \text{ N}$$

Now substitute in the equation:

$$\mu_S = \dfrac{F_F}{R_N}$$

$$F_F = R_N \times \mu_S$$

$$= 19\ 620 \text{ N x } 0.26$$

$$= \textbf{5101.2 N (Ans.)}$$

Example 4:

Find the mass of an object when a horizontal force of 2100 N just starts to move the object along a horizontal surface. The coefficient of static friction is 0.40.

Solution:

$$\mu_S = 0.40$$

$$F_F = 2100 \text{ N}$$

$$\mu_S = \frac{F_F}{R_N}$$

$$R_N = \frac{F_F}{\mu_s}$$

$$= \frac{2100 \text{ N}}{0.40}$$

$$= 5250 \text{ N}$$

The downward force (F_W) is numerically equal to R_N, since the surface and applied force are horizontal.

Therefore:

$$F_W = 5250 \text{ N}$$

And:

$$F_W = mg$$

$$m = \frac{F_W}{g}$$

$$= \frac{5250 \text{ N}}{9.81 \text{ m/s}^2}$$

$$= \textbf{535.2 kg (Ans.)}$$

This page has intentionally been left blank.

CHAPTER 15 - QUESTIONS

1. a) Find the coefficient of static friction of a crate on a wooden floor if the crate has a mass of 400 kg and the horizontal force being applied is 1600 N.

   b) Find the coefficient of kinetic friction if a force of 1400 N is required to keep the same crate moving at constant speed.

   c) Find the coefficient of kinetic friction between the same crate and the floor if water is used as a lubricant and the force required to move the crate at a constant speed is 1100 N.

2. Find the force required to keep a wooden block moving along a horizontal surface if the block has a mass of 25 kg and the coefficient of friction between the two surfaces is 0.19.

3. The coefficient of friction is the ratio of the _____ required to move a body to the normal reaction force.

   a) force
   b) motion
   c) horsepower
   d) rhythm

4. The direction of the force of friction is _____ to the direction of any force that is trying to move or is moving an object.

   a) in a vertical plane
   b) in a horizontal plane
   c) opposite
   d) in the same direction

CHAPTER 15 - ANSWERS

1. a) Coefficient of static friction (μ_S) = 0.41

   b) Coefficient of kinetic friction (μ_S) = 0.36

   c) Coefficient of kinetic friction (μ_S) = 0.28

2. Force required = 46.6 N

3. (a)

4. (c)

Stress & Strain

LEARNING OUTCOME

When you complete this chapter you should be able to:

Discuss the deformation of bodies caused by externally applied forces, and the internal forces that resist these deformations; discuss the physical properties of materials and explain how these properties affect their behaviour when external forces are applied.

LEARNING OBJECTIVES

Here is what you should be able to do when you complete each objective:

1. Describe the significant characteristics of materials, including elasticity, stiffness, plasticity, ductility, toughness, brittleness and hardness.

2. Define stress and calculate tensile, compressive and shear stresses in rigid body members due to external loads.

3. Calculate the strain of members under load.

INTRODUCTION

External forces applied to a body have a tendency to deform it. But the body develops an internal resistance against the deforming forces. The external forces acting on a rigid body are termed loads, the deformation is known as strain and the internal resistance to the external force is called stress. The stress increases with additional external force up to a certain limit, beyond which will cause permanent deformation, or failure, of the body. All materials subjected to stress will change their shape and become strained, though the amount of strain may be too small to measure.

OBJECTIVE 1

Describe the significant characteristics of materials, including elasticity, stiffness, plasticity, ductility, toughness, brittleness and hardness.

MECHANICAL PROPERTIES OF MATERIALS

When considering the strength of materials, the internal effects produced and the deformations of bodies caused by externally applied forces are studied. The ability of a material to withstand stress and strain depends on the characteristics of the material itself. To correctly specify a material for a certain application, a designer must know the following important mechanical properties of the material.

Elasticity
Elasticity is the ability of a material to return to its original shape after the force or load that caused its deformation is removed.

Stiffness
Stiffness is the ability of a material to resist a change in shape or size when a load is applied.

Plasticity
Plasticity is the ability of a material to retain its deformed shape when the load causing deformation is removed.

Ductility
Ductility is the ability of a material to be stretched and reduced in cross section without breaking. Ductile materials will undergo large deformations before breaking.

Toughness
Toughness is the ability of a material to absorb energy before breaking. Tough materials will absorb and dissipate energy by bending, twisting, and changing shape considerably before they break.

Brittleness
Brittle materials break without much deformation occurring before fracture.

Hardness
Hardness is the ability of a material to resist penetration.

OBJECTIVE 2

Define stress and calculate tensile, compressive and shear stresses in rigid body members due to external loads.

STRESS

Stress is defined as the internal resistance of a material to an external force (load) that is being applied. The amount of stress is indicated by the applied load (force) per unit area that is resisting the force.

$$\text{Stress} = \frac{\text{Load (N)}}{\text{Area (m}^2)}$$

In SI units, stress is indicated in pascals, Pa.

$$1 \text{ N/m}^2 = 1 \text{ pascal}$$

Since pascals are very small units, larger units, such as kilopascals (kPa), megapascals (MPa) and gigapascals (GPa), are commonly used.

Theoretically, stresses act in all directions, but, for simplicity, the stresses are resolved into two components, with one having a direction perpendicular to the surface being considered and the other being parallel to this surface.

Perpendicular forces cause compressive or tensile stress, depending on whether they push or pull on the surface being considered. Forces that are parallel to a surface cause shear stress.

Mathematically, stresses are expressed as:

$$\sigma = \frac{P}{A}$$

Or

$$\tau = \frac{P}{A}$$

Where: σ = Normal stress intensity - pascals

τ = Parallel (shear) stress intensity - pascals

P = Perpendicular or parallel load applied - newtons

A = Cross-sectional area of the section being considered - square metres

The ultimate stress, (the stress at which the material breaks) is defined as the maximum load, at which breakage occurs, divided by the original cross-sectional area of the material.

Tensile Stress

Consider a straight bar of uniform cross section (Fig. 1) subjected to a pair of forces acting in opposite directions and coinciding with the axis of the bar. If the forces are directed away from the bar, they tend to increase the length of the bar, which is said to be in tension. The internal stress developed (tensile stress) is normal to the cross-section and the bar is often called a tie.

Figure 1	Member under Tension

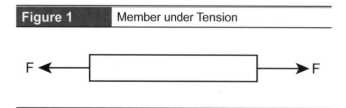

Example 1:

A round tie bar is subjected to an axial (along its length) load of 100 kN. If the diameter of the tie is 0.050 m, what will the stress be in the tie?

Solution:

a) Load = 100 kN or 100 000 N

Calculate the area of the tie:

$$A = \frac{\pi d^2}{4}$$

$$= \frac{3.1416 \times (0.05)^2 m^2}{4}$$

$$= \frac{3.1416 \times 0.0025 m^2}{4}$$

$$= \frac{0.0079 m^2}{4}$$

$$= 0.001\ 963\ m^2$$

b)   Calculate the stress, σ:

$$\sigma = \frac{Load}{Area}$$

$$= \frac{100\ 000\ N}{0.001\ 963\ m^2}$$

$$=\ 50\ 942\ 435\ Pa$$

$$=\ \mathbf{50\ 942.435\ kPa\ (Ans.)}$$

Compressive Stress

If the forces described in Figure 1 are directed towards the bar as in Figure 2, they will tend to compress the material. Then the bar is said to be in compression; the internal stress will be a compressive stress and the member is often called a strut.

Figure 2	A Member under Compression

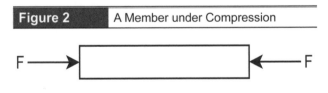

Example 2:

A compressive load of 107 kN is resisted by a rectangular strut that is 50 mm × 75 mm. What is the stress in the strut?

Solution:

Area, A = 0.05 m x 0.075 m

$$= 0.003\ 75\ m^2$$

Stress, $\sigma = \frac{Load}{Area}$

$$= \frac{107\ 000\ N}{0.003\ 75\ m^2}$$

$$=\ 28\ 533\ 333\ Pa$$

$$=\ \mathbf{28\ 533\ kPa\ (Ans.)}$$

Shear Stress

If the external forces act parallel to one another, but are not in the same plane, a shear stress will result. Consider two plates, A and B, (Fig. 3) joined together by a rivet, C. If a tensile load, F, is applied to the plates, the force or load is exactly parallel to the cross-section of the rivet (x-x) and if overloaded, the rivet would shear along its cross section (x-x). If d is the diameter of the rivet, the cross-sectional area of the rivet resisting the shear force P is:

$$A = \frac{\pi d^2}{4}$$

Figure 3   Single Shear

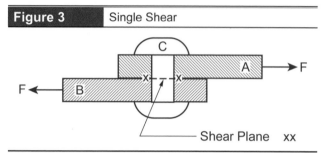

Shear Plane xx

In Figure 3, the rivet C would only shear across a single cross-sectional plane, x-x, and it is said to be in single shear. In Figure 4, the bolt shown could shear across two cross-sectional planes (xx and yy). Both these planes resist the shearing force, F. Therefore, both areas are added together and then used in the formula for stress. Because two planes resist the shear, the bolt is said to be in double shear.

Figure 4   Double Shear

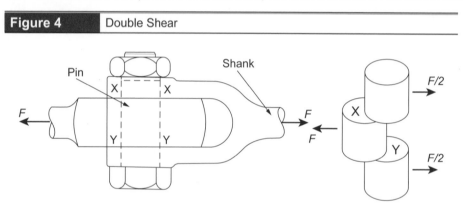

Example 3:

A tie rod made up of two parts, as shown in Figure 4, is to carry a tensile load of 350 kN. Determine the minimum diameter for the connecting bolt if the allowable working stress in shear is limited to 300 MPa.

Solution:

The bolt in this case is in double shear. The area resisting shear is two times the cross-sectional area of the bolt.

$$A = \frac{\pi d^2}{4} \times 2$$

$$= 0.5 \, \pi \, d^2$$

$$\tau = \frac{Load}{Area}$$

$$= \frac{350 \times 10^3 \, N}{0.50 \pi d^2 \, m^2}$$

Since the allowable stress, τ, is known, it can be placed into the equation which can be solved to determine the diameter. This value of d will be the minimum diameter required to keep the stress below the allowable 300 MPa.

$$\text{Allowable stress } (\sigma) = \frac{\text{Load}}{\text{Area}}$$

$$300 \times 10^6 \text{N/m}^2 = \frac{350 \times 10^3 \text{ N}}{0.5\pi d^2 \text{ m}^2}$$

$$0.5\pi d^2 = \frac{350 \times 10^3 \text{ N}}{300 \times 10^6 \text{ N/m}^2}$$

$$d^2 = \frac{350 \times 10^3 \text{ N}}{0.5 \times 3.1416 \times 300 \times 10^6 \text{ N/m}^2}$$

$$d^2 = \frac{350\,000 \text{ N}}{4.7124 \times 10^8 \text{ N/m}^2}$$

$$d^2 = 7.43 \times 10^{-4} \text{m}^2$$

$$d = 0.0273 \text{ m} = \textbf{27.3 mm (Ans.)}$$

Example 4:

An angle bracket on a steel column (Fig. 5) supports a load of 400 kN. If the bracket is bolted to the column with two 16 mm diameter bolts, find the shear stress in each bolt.

Figure 5	Angle Bracket

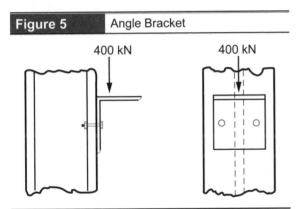

400 kN   400 kN

Solution:

In this case, the bolts are in single shear, but there are two of them. The diameter of each bolt is 16 mm or 0.016 m.   The cross-sectional area of each bolt is:

$$A = \frac{\pi d^2}{4}$$

$$= \frac{\pi \times 0.016^2 \text{m}^2}{4}$$

$$= \frac{3.1416 \times 0.016^2 \text{m}^2}{4}$$

$$= \frac{3.1416 \times 0.000256 \text{ m}^2}{4}$$

$$= \frac{0.000804 \text{ m}^2}{4}$$

$$= \textbf{0.000201 m}^2 \textbf{ (Ans.)}$$

Assume the load of 400 kN is shared equally by the two bolts. Therefore, the load carried by each bolt is:

P = 200 kN

The average shear stress in each bolt is:

$$\tau = \frac{P}{A}$$

$$= \frac{200\ kN}{0.000\ 201\ m^2}$$

$$= 995\ 025\ kN/m^2$$

$$= 995\ 025\ kPa$$

= 995 MPa (Ans.)

Example 5:

A hole 10 mm square is to be punched out of a plate that is 9 mm thick. The shear stress of the material is 300 MPa. What force is required on the punch?

Solution:

The area resisting the force on the punch is the perimeter of the hole times the thickness of the plate

$$Resisting\ area = (10\ mm\ x\ 4)\ x\ 9\ mm$$

$$= 40\ mm\ x\ 9\ mm$$

$$= 360\ mm^2$$

$$Stress = 300\ MPa$$

$$= 300\ 000\ 000\ N/m^2$$

$$= 300\ N/mm^2$$

$$Stress = \frac{Force}{Area}$$

so:

$$Force\ on\ punch = Stress\ x\ Area$$

$$= 300\ N/mm^2\ x\ 360\ mm^2$$

$$= 108\ 000\ N$$

= 108 kN (Ans.)

Terms Related to Stress

Ultimate Stress

The ultimate stress or strength of a material is the stress at the instant it breaks. It is based on the force required to break the material and its original cross-sectional area.

Allowable Stress

The allowable stress or working stress is the amount of stress that a material is allowed to carry. This stress is usually well within the elastic limit for safety reasons.

Elastic Limit

The elastic limit of a material is the maximum stress to which it can be subjected and still return to its original size and shape when the deforming load is removed.

Maximum Allowable Load

The maximum allowable load is the greatest load that can be applied to a material under its design conditions; it is the load which corresponds to the allowable stress.

Factor of Safety

The factor of safety is the ratio of the ultimate stress to the allowable stress.

$$\text{Factor of safety} = \frac{\text{Ultimate stress}}{\text{Allowable stress}}$$

When designing a component, the value of the factor of safety is selected after considering several factors, including:

- Mechanical properties of the material
- Loading conditions (e.g. steady, shock, vibration)
- Possibility of corrosion or erosion
- Degree of safety required

OBJECTIVE 3

Calculate the strain of members under load.

STRAIN

Strain is a measure of the deformation produced in a member by a load. Normal stresses (tensile or compressive) produce a change in length in the direction of the stress. If Δl is the change in length of a member of original length, l, then:

$$\text{Strain } (\varepsilon) = \frac{\Delta l}{l}$$

Strain is defined as the change in length of a member in a given length and thus has no units. However, it is usually expressed in units of metres per metre or millimetre per millimetre (i.e. consistent units).

Tensile stress will cause an increase in length, while compressive stress will decrease the length. Strain is normally considered positive for an increase in length and negative for a decrease in length.

Example 6:

A steel bar 2 m long shortens by 4 mm under a compressive load. What will be the strain?

Solution:

$$\text{Strain } (\varepsilon) = \frac{\Delta l}{l}$$

$$= \frac{-4 \text{ mm}}{2000 \text{ mm}}$$

$$= \textbf{-0.002 (Ans.)}$$

CHAPTER 16 - QUESTIONS

1. A hollow cylinder with an outside diameter of 100 mm and an inside diameter of 30 mm supports a load of 100 kN. What is the compressive stress in the material in megapascals?

    a) 25.75 MPa

    b) 1.41 MPa

    c) 15.55 MPa

    d) 13.99 MPa

2. A tie bar is made of a material having an ultimate tensile strength of 231 MPa and must carry a load of 255 kN. What is the diameter of the bar if a factor of safety of 7 is required?

    a) 46.8 mm

    b) 25.75 mm

    c) 10.75 mm

    d) 99.2 mm

3. A bar 36.5 mm in diameter and 1.5 m long stretches 1.2 mm when a load of 240 kN is applied. What are the stress and strain?

    a) 229.4 MPa , 0.0008

    b) 175.25 MPa, 0.0014

    c) 204.68 MPa, 0.0005

    d) 292.77 MPa, 0.0021

4. A round steel bar, 5 cm in diameter, is placed in tension by a load of 1 tonne. What is the stress in the bar?

    a) 509.29 kPa

    b) 496.25 kPa

    c) 4996.18 kPa

    d) 5225.65 kPa

CHAPTER 16 - ANSWERS

1. (d)

2. (d)

3. (a)

4. (c)

Power Transmission

LEARNING OUTCOME

When you complete this chapter you should be able to:

Describe the major types of drive systems for power transmission and perform calculations.

LEARNING OBJECTIVES

Here is what you should be able to do when you complete each objective:

1. *Describe belt drive systems and calculate pulley speeds, transmitted power and efficiency.*

2. *Describe gear and chain drive systems and calculate gear speeds.*

INTRODUCTION

Mechanical power may be transmitted by belts, chains, or gears. Linear motion is motion that takes place in a straight line. For example, a piston moving in a cylinder is moving with linear motion. Circular motion is motion that takes place by rotation about a fixed center. For example, consider a point on the wheel of a vehicle, or the crankpin of an engine.

OBJECTIVE 1

Describe belt drive systems and calculate pulley speeds, transmitted power and efficiency.

BELT DRIVES

A belt drive moves a pulley (follower or driven pulley) from another pulley (driver) by means of a friction force between the surface of the belt and the pulleys.

If there is no slippage between the belt and the pulleys, the linear speed of a point on each pulley will be the same and equal to the linear speed of the belt. If the pulleys are the same diameter, the rotational speeds (r/min) of the pulleys will be equal. If the driver pulley is smaller in diameter than the follower, the follower will rotate at a lower r/min than the driver, and vice versa.

Considering the belt driven pulley shown in Figure 1, the belt drive should be arranged so that the tension (force F_1) in the bottom belt is always greater than the tension (force F_2) in the top belt. This increases the angle of contact of the belts with the pulleys and reduces slippage, with a resulting increase in the power transmitted from the driver to the follower. Belt drives are used to transmit power, or to change rotational speeds, or both.

Figure 1	Belt Driven Pulley

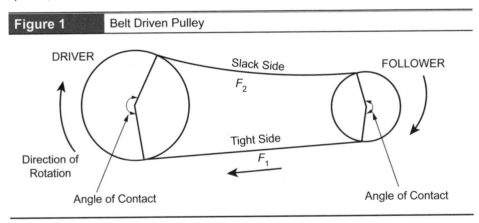

Rotational Speed of Pulleys

If the belts do not slip (efficiency = 100%), then any point on the rim of each pulley will travel at the same linear speed (r/min) as the belt itself, although the rotational speed (m/s) of the pulleys will vary if they are different diameters. This is illustrated in Figure 2.

For each revolution of the driver, if there is no belt slippage, any point on the belt will travel a distance equal to the circumference of the driver.

Figure 2	Belt Drive

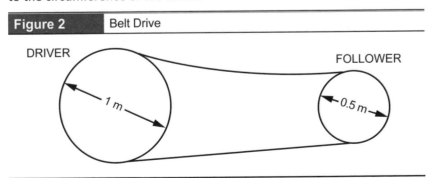

Referring to Figure 2, for one revolution of the driver, the distance moved by any point on the belt

$$\text{Distance} = \pi D$$
$$= \pi \times 1 \text{ m}$$
$$= 3.1416 \text{ m}$$

This would be the distance traveled by a point on the belt and also by a point on the rim of the follower.

For one revolution of the follower,

$$\text{Circumference} = \pi D$$
$$= \pi \times 0.5 \text{ m}$$
$$= 3.1416 \times 0.5 \text{ m}$$
$$= 1.5708 \text{ m}$$

But for one revolution of the driver, a point on the rim of the follower moves 3.1416 m. That is, the follower rotates:

$$3.1416 \text{ m}/1.5708 \text{ m} = 2 \text{ times for each revolution of the driver}$$

Since π is a constant, the revolutions of the pulleys are inversely proportional to the diameters. In the last case:

$$\text{Driver diameter} = 1 \text{ m}$$
$$\text{Follower diameter} = 0.5 \text{ m}$$
$$\text{Revolutions of follower} = 1 \text{ m}/0.5 \text{ m}$$
$$= 2 \times \text{revolution of driver}$$

Summary:

If D_1 = Diameter of pulley 1

N_1 = r/min of pulley 1

D_2 = Diameter of pulley 2

N_2 = r/min of pulley 2

then $\qquad D_1N_1 = D_2N_2$

or $\qquad \dfrac{N_1}{N_2} = \dfrac{D_2}{D_1}$

Also, the linear velocity of a belt being driven without slippage by a rotating drive wheel of radius R (in m) is:

$$\text{Linear velocity (m/s)} = \frac{\text{r/min} \times \pi D \text{ m/r}}{60 \text{ s/m}}$$

Example 1:

A pulley with a diameter of 1 m is driven at (a) 200 r/min, (b) 150 r/min, (c) 120 r/min. What will be the linear speed in m/s of a point on the rim of the pulley for each rotational speed?

Solution:

a) Linear speed (m/s) $= \dfrac{r/min \times \pi D\ m/r}{60 s/min}$

$\quad\quad\quad\quad = \dfrac{200 r/min}{60 s/min} \times 3.1416 \times 1.0\ m/r$

$\quad\quad\quad\quad = 3.33\ r/s \times 3.1416 \times 1.0\ m/r$

$\quad\quad\quad\quad = \mathbf{10.46\ m/s\ (Ans.)}$

b) Linear speed (m/s) $= \dfrac{r/min \times \pi D\ m/r}{60 s/min}$

$\quad\quad\quad\quad = \dfrac{150\ r/min}{60\ s/min} \times 3.1416 \times 1.0\ m/r$

$\quad\quad\quad\quad = 2.5\ r/s \times 3.1416 \times 1.0\ m/r$

$\quad\quad\quad\quad = \mathbf{7.85\ m/s\ (Ans.)}$

c) Linear speed (m/s) $= \dfrac{r/min \times \pi D\ m/r}{60\ s/min}$

$\quad\quad\quad\quad = \dfrac{120\ r/min}{60\ s/min} \times 3.1416 \times 1.0\ m/r$

$\quad\quad\quad\quad = 2\ r/s \times 3.1416 \times 1.0\ m/r$

$\quad\quad\quad\quad = \mathbf{6.28\ m/s\ (Ans.)}$

Example 2:

A pulley with a diameter of 1.5 m is driven at 50 r/min by a belt drive from a pulley of 0.5 m diameter. What will be the r/min of the driving pulley?

Solution:

$D_1 = 1.5\ m$

$N_1 = 50\ r/min$

$D_2 = 0.5\ m$

$\dfrac{N_1}{N_2} = \dfrac{D_2}{D_1}$

$N_2 = \dfrac{N_1 D_1}{D_2}$

$\quad = \dfrac{50\ r/min \times 1.5\ m}{0.5\ m}$

$\quad = \dfrac{75\ r/min/m}{0.5\ m}$

$\quad = \mathbf{150\ r/min\ (Ans.)}$

Power Transmitted by Belts

Power transmitted (watts) = $(F_1 - F_2)$ x Speed of belt

Where F_1 = Tension on tight side (N)

F_2 = Tension on slack side (N)

Speed of belt = Speed, m/s

Example 3:

The tensions in the tight and slack side of a belt drive system are 2000 N and 500 N, respectively. If the belt speed is 5 m/s, what power will be transmitted if there is no belt slippage?

Solution:

Power transmitted (watts) = $(F_1 - F_2)$ x Speed of belt

= (2000 N - 500 N) x 5 m/s

Power = 1500 N x 5 m/s

= 7500 Nm/s

= 7500 J/s

= 7500 W

= **7.5 kW (Ans.)**

Belt Slippage

In practice, belts slip on pulley drives and there is a resulting loss of energy or power transmitted, so that the efficiency is less than 100%.

$$\% \text{ Efficiency} = \frac{\text{Power output}}{\text{Power input}} \times 100\%$$

Example 4:

In a belt drive system, the input to the driver pulley is 75 kW and the output from the follower is 70 kW. What is the % efficiency of the drive?

Solution:

$$\% \text{ Efficiency} = \frac{\text{Power output}}{\text{Power input}} \times 100\%$$

$$= \frac{70 \text{ kW}}{75 \text{ kW}} \times 100\%$$

$$= 0.9333 \times 100\%$$

$$= \textbf{93.33\% (Ans.)}$$

Pulley Trains

A pulley train consists of a series of pulleys connected by belts. Pulley trains are used to change speeds and/or to transmit power at varying speeds to different shops or machines. When considering pulley trains, the principles for simple pulley arrangements can be applied.

Example 5:

Find the linear speed of the 2 m diameter pulley in the train shown in Figure 3 if there is:

a) No belt slippage

b) Overall belt slippage of 10%

Figure 3	Pulley Train

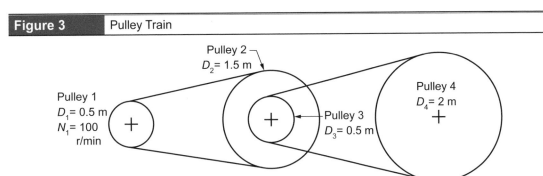

Solution:

a) If N_1 = 100 r/min

$$N_2 = N_1 \times \frac{D_1}{D_2}$$

$$= 100 \text{ r/min} \times \frac{0.5 \text{ m}}{1.5 \text{ m}}$$

$$= 100 \text{ r/min} \times 0.3333$$

$$= 33.33 \text{ r/min}$$

If pulley #2 rotates at 33.33 r/min, then pulley #3 must also rotate at 33.33 r/min, since it is on the same shaft.

Thus: $\dfrac{N_4}{N_3} = \dfrac{D_3}{D_4}$

$$N_4 = \frac{N_3 \times D_3}{D_4}$$

$$= \frac{33.33 \text{ r/min} \times 0.5 \text{ m}}{2 \text{ m}}$$

$$= \textbf{8.33 r/min (Ans.)}$$

b) Assuming 10% belt slippage overall:

N_4 (with belt slippage) = 8.33 r/min - (0.10 x 8.33 r/min)

$$= 8.33 \text{ r/min} - 0.833 \text{ r/min}$$

$$= \textbf{7.50 r/min (Ans.)}$$

Linear speed of 2 m diameter pulley = 7.5 r/min x πd

$$= 7.5 \text{ r/min} \times 3.1416 \times 2 \text{ m/r}$$

$$= \frac{47.12 \text{ m/min}}{60 \text{ s/min}}$$

$$= \textbf{0.785 m/s (Ans.)}$$

Note: With belt drives, the pulleys all rotate in the same direction.

OBJECTIVE 2

Describe gear and chain drive systems and calculate gear speeds.

GEAR DRIVES

In gear drives, teeth in mating gear wheels mesh together to transmit power from one to the other. For single gears meshing together, the direction of rotation becomes reversed, as shown in Figure 4. .

| Figure 4 | Gear Drive |

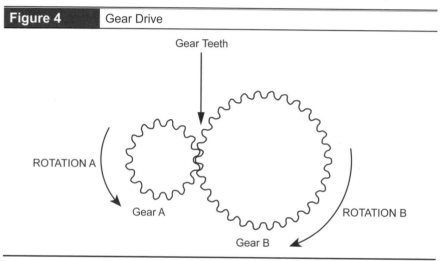

The ratio of the rotational speeds of the gears is inversely proportional to the number of teeth on each gear, such that (referring to Figure 4):

$$\frac{\text{Rotational speed A (r/min)}}{\text{Rotational speed B (r/min)}} = \frac{\text{Number of teeth on B}}{\text{Number of teeth on A}}$$

Example 6:

A gear wheel having 20 teeth and rotating at 200 r/min drives a gear having 40 teeth. What will be the r/min of the driven gear?

Solution:

$$\text{Speed of driven gear} = \text{speed of driver gear} \times \frac{\text{Number of teeth on driver gear}}{\text{Number of teeth on driven gear}}$$

$$= 200 \text{ r/min} \times \frac{20 \text{ teeth}}{40 \text{ teeth}}$$

$$= 200 \text{ r/min} \times 0.5$$

$$= \textbf{100 r/min (Ans.)}$$

Intermediate Gears

Intermediate gears, also called idler gears, are used to transmit power between gears that are some distance apart. Intermediate gears do not affect the speed of the driven gear, since the same number of teeth mesh with both the driven gear and driver.

If two intermediate gears were used, then the rotation of the driver and driven gears would be in opposite directions. The intermediate gears do not affect the speed ratio.

Example 7:

An idler gear is used as shown in Figure 5. The driver rotates at 200 r/min and has 20 teeth. If the driven gear has 30 teeth and the idler gear has 40 teeth, what will be the r/min of the driven gear?

Figure 5	Idler Gear

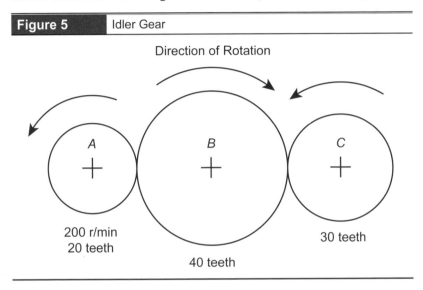

Direction of Rotation

200 r/min
20 teeth

40 teeth

30 teeth

Solution:

$$\text{r/min B} = \text{r/min A} \times \frac{\text{Number of teeth on A}}{\text{Number of teeth on B}}$$

$$= 200 \text{ r/min} \times \frac{20 \text{ teeth}}{40 \text{ teeth}}$$

$$= 200 \text{ r/min} \times 0.5$$

$$= 100 \text{ r/min}$$

$$\text{r/min C} = \text{r/min B} \times \frac{\text{Number of teeth on B}}{\text{Number of teeth on C}}$$

$$= 100 \text{ r/min} \times \frac{40 \text{ teeth}}{30 \text{ teeth}}$$

$$= 100 \text{ r/min} \times 1.3333$$

$$= \textbf{133.33 r/min (Ans.)}$$

If there was no intermediate gear:

$$\text{r/min C} = \text{r/min A} \times \frac{\text{Number of teeth on A}}{\text{Number of teeth on C}}$$

$$= 200 \text{ r/min} \times \frac{20 \text{ teeth}}{30 \text{ teeth}}$$

$$= 200 \text{ r/min} \times 0.6667$$

$$= 133.33 \text{ r/min as before}$$

The idler gear does cause gear C to rotate in the same direction as A. An advantage of gear drives over belt drives is that there is no slippage. However, badly meshing or poorly lubricated gears result in excessive friction and low efficiency. Gears are able to transmit more power than belt systems of comparable size.

CHAIN DRIVES

Chain drives use special gears called sprockets, which are driven by chains. An advantage of chain drives is that the gears do not have to mesh together and a positive drive can be obtained over a longer distance. The speeds of chain drives are calculated in the same way as for gear drives.

Gear Trains

A number of gears may mesh together in a train, to produce variations in shaft speeds and directions of rotation. Gear trains are considered in a similar manner to pulley trains.

Backlash

Because clearance is necessary between teeth that have to mesh, gears can be moved slightly when not driving. This movement is called backlash and, if excessive, can cause extreme forces on the teeth during starting or reversing.

CHAPTER 17 - QUESTIONS

1. A drive gear rotates at 200 r/min in a counterclockwise direction and has 20 teeth. The drive gear meshes with the first intermediate gear having 40 teeth, which meshes with the second intermediate gear having 20 teeth. The second intermediate gear meshes with the driven gear, which has 30 teeth. Find the rotational speed and the direction of rotation for each of the intermediate gears and the driven gear.

2. A belt pulley has a diameter of 0.855 m and is driven at 305 r/min.

    a) What is the linear speed in m/s of a point on the rim of the pulley?

    b) If the pulley hub is 200 mm in diameter, what is the linear speed of a point on the hub?

3. The tension in the tight side of a belt is 2500 N and in the slack side it is 475 N. The drive pulley is 0.9 m in diameter and turns at 150 r/min. If the efficiency of the drive is 95%, what is the:

    a) Power output

    b) Power input

4. The gear train shown has a driver speed of 150 r/min in a clockwise direction. Find the speed of the driven shaft and its direction of rotation.

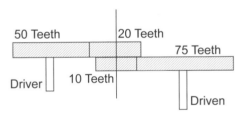

5. A chain drive has a drive sprocket of 300 mm diameter and a driven sprocket of 1000 mm diameter. What is the speed of the driven shaft if the driver shaft turns at 890 r/min?

CHAPTER 17 - ANSWERS

1. r/min B = 100 r/min in a clockwise direction

    r/min C = 200 r/min in a counterclockwise direction

    r/min D = 133.33 r/min in a clockwise direction

2. a) 13.65 m/s

    b) 3.19 m/s

3. a) 13.6 kW

    b) 14.31 kW

4. 50 r/min in a clockwise direction

5. 267 r/min

ELEMENTARY THERMODYNAMICS

Introduction to Thermodynamics

LEARNING OUTCOME

When you complete this chapter you should be able to:

Explain the principles of thermodynamics, including the laws of thermodynamics and the modes of heat transfer.

LEARNING OBJECTIVES

Here is what you should be able to do when you complete each objective:

1. Define various terms associated with the study of thermodynamics.

2. Describe the laws of thermodynamics and the different temperature scales.

3. Define heat and specific heat and perform sensible heat calculations.

4. Describe the expansion of solids and liquids.

5. Describe the three modes of heat transfer.

INTRODUCTION

Thermodynamics is a branch of physics that deals with the conversion of heat into other forms of energy, or other forms of energy into heat, and with the transfer of heat from one substance to another.

A Power Engineer is involved with heat transfer in many aspects of the job. For example, in boilers, heat energy is transferred from the burning fuel to water and then is used to produce steam. In internal combustion engines, fuel is burned with air in a cylinder to perform work on a piston. In refrigeration systems, heat is extracted from the substance to be cooled and transferred to other systems for utilization or disposal.

The efficient transfer and utilization of heat energy is of major importance to the Power Engineer. Therefore, it is essential to have a good understanding of thermodynamics.

To understand energy conversion, it is necessary to understand the concepts of temperature, heat, expansion of liquids and solids, pressure, the general laws of thermodynamics and certain other topics fundamental to the study of thermodynamics.

OBJECTIVE 1

Define various terms associated with the study of thermodynamics.

DEFINITIONS

The following definitions are for terms used throughout this chapter:

Absolute pressure: The pressure measured above a perfect vacuum. It is the sum of atmospheric and gauge pressures and is expressed as kPa (abs).

Absolute zero: The temperature at which all molecular vibrational motion ceases.

Atmospheric pressure: This pressure, exerted by the earth's atmosphere, can be expressed as follows:

- As kPa, mm of mercury (mmHg), or metres of water (mH_2O).

- The standard atmospheric pressure expressed in SI units is 101.3 kPa, 760 mm Hg or 10.33 mH_2O. It is the average atmospheric pressure at sea level. Actual atmospheric pressure varies from location to location on the earth's surface and from time to time at each specific location.

Change of state: The altering of a substance from solid to liquid, liquid to gas or vice-versa.

Conduction: The flow of heat from molecule to molecule within a substance or from molecules of one body to those of another body in direct contact with it.

Convection: The transfer of heat within a fluid by movement of the fluid, whereby warm fluid is displaced by cooler fluid.

Cooling: The process of removing heat from a substance, resulting in a decrease in temperature and/or a change in state.

Density: The mass per unit volume of a substance expressed in kg/m^3.

Enthalpy or heat content: The amount of heat, expressed, in kJ/kg, contained in a substance relative to a base temperature at which the enthalpy is defined to be zero. For example, in calculating the enthalpy of steam, the base temperature of water is taken as 0°C and the enthalpy of the steam is the sum of the heat required to raise a unit mass of the water to its boiling point (sensible heat) and the heat required to evaporate this water into steam (latent heat). Should the steam be superheated, the heat required to raise the temperature of the steam above the boiling point (sensible heat) must also be added to arrive at the enthalpy. The enthalpy of refrigerants is determined in a similar way; however, the base temperature is taken as -40°C or as absolute zero.

Gauge pressure: The pressure as registered on a pressure gauge. This is pressure above atmospheric pressure, expressed as kPa (gauge).

Heat: This is a form of energy, which, when supplied to a body or substance, will increase the internal energy of that body or substance.

Heating: The process of increasing the heat energy of a substance, resulting in an increase in temperature and/or a change of state.

Heat transmission: The movement of heat from a warmer (higher temperature) substance to a colder (lower temperature) substance.

Latent heat: Heat that causes a change in the state of a substance without changing its temperature.

Latent heat of evaporation: The amount of heat required to change a unit mass of a substance from liquid to vapour without changing its temperature.

Latent heat of fusion: The amount of heat required to change a unit mass of a substance from solid to liquid without changing its temperature.

Pressure: Force per unit area. The unit of pressure is the pascal (Pa). One pascal is equal to one newton (N) of force acting uniformly over an area of 1 m^2. The pascal is a very small unit, so the kilopascal (kPa), which equals 1000 Pa, is commonly used to express pressure.

Radiation: The transfer of heat by electromagnetic waves, causing a rise in temperature in the body by increasing the motion of the molecules of that body.

Saturated steam: Steam that is fully saturated with latent heat and has no water particles present.

Saturation temperature: The temperature at which a liquid reaches its boiling point, which is dependant upon the pressure on the surface of the liquid. For example, at atmospheric pressure at sea level (101.3 kPa absolute), the saturation temperature or boiling point of water is 100°C. When the pressure is raised to 198.53 kPa, the boiling point rises to 120°C.

Sensible heat: Heat that causes a change in the temperature of a substance without changing its state.

Specific heat: The amount of heat required to increase the temperature of a unit mass of a substance by 1°C without changing the state of the substance.

Specific Volume: The volume of a unit mass of a substance, expressed in m^3/kg. For gases, specific volume will depend on the temperature and pressure of the gas.

Superheat: The temperature increase, expressed in °C, of a gas or vapour above its saturation temperature after all the liquid has been evaporated. It is expressed in °C, as in 50°C of superheat.

Temperature: A relative measure of the intensity of heat (ie. the "hotness") in a body.

Unit of heat energy: The unit used to measure heat energy is the joule (J) or kilojoule (kJ, which equals 1000 J). It requires approximately **1 kJ** of heat to raise the temperature of **1 kg** of air by **1°C** at standard atmospheric pressure.

Vacuum: The reduction in pressure below atmospheric pressure. It is usually expressed in mm Hg.

Wet Steam: Steam that does not have its full quantity of latent heat energy and, therefore, contains unvaporized water.

OBJECTIVE 2

Describe the laws of thermodynamics and the different temperature scales.

LAWS OF THERMODYNAMICS

There are two laws of thermodynamics that the student must fully understand:

First Law of Thermodynamics

The first law of thermodynamics states that heat and work are mutually convertible.

This law can be stated in the general form (with no losses):

> Work = Heat

In practice, usually only a part of the heat is converted to work or only a part of the work generates heat.

For example, when considering the expansion of a gas in a cylinder moving a piston (called a nonflow process), then the heat supplied does work in moving the piston and the internal energy of the gas also increases so that:

> Heat supplied (Q) = Increase internal energy + Work done
>
> $Q = \Delta U + W$

In a steam boiler, the same relationship applies. As the water is heated, the internal energy increases and work is done in increasing the volume of the water. When steam is produced, the internal energy increases and work is done to increase the volume during the change from water to steam at constant temperature.

Second Law of Thermodynamics

The second law of thermodynamics states that, unaided, heat will flow only from a hot substance to a colder substance. If it is required to transfer heat from a cold substance to a hotter substance (as in refrigeration), then external work must be performed.

TEMPERATURE

The temperature of a body is a measure of the speed at which the body's molecules vibrate. A high temperature indicates an increased molecular velocity, while a low temperature indicates a decreased molecular velocity. A body at high temperature will have the ability to transfer heat to one of lower temperatures, so the temperature determines the direction of the heat flow between a body and its surroundings.

For example, a piece of metal is lifted from the heat of a forge and set on an anvil; heat will flow from the red hot metal to the anvil.

Alternatively, a block of ice is removed from a refrigerated locker and placed into an ice box. Heat will then flow from the contents of the ice box to the block of ice.

Heat flows naturally from a point of high temperature toward one of low temperature; as heat transfers, the temperature difference between the points gradually decreases.

Heat is a measure of the quantity of internal vibrational energy in a substance.

Temperature is a measure of the intensity or "hotness" of heat in a body. For example, a red hot rivet will contain a small quantity of high grade (high temperature) heat as compared to the water in a low pressure firetube boiler which could be said to contain a large quantity of low grade (low temperature) heat.

Temperature is measured by means of a scaled instrument known as a thermometer. The scale on the thermometer is established with reference to two fixed points: the boiling point of water and the melting point of ice. The space between these fixed points is divided into equal parts; each division is called a degree (°). The divisions are also extended above and below the fixed points in order to measure temperatures above the boiling point of water and below the melting point of ice.

Two different temperature scales are used in the SI system; the Celsius and the Kelvin. Two additional scales are also seen; the Fahrenheit and the Rankine scales.

Celsius

The Celsius scale (previously called the Centigrade scale) considers the boiling point of water as 100° and the melting point of ice as 0°C, giving 100 divisions or degrees between these points.

Kelvin

The Kelvin scale, based upon degrees Celsius, considers -273° as the lowest possible temperature (absolute zero). Note that the degree symbol is not used with the Kelvin scale, the one used principally in thermodynamics.

Fahrenheit

The Fahrenheit scale considers the boiling point of water as 212° and the melting point of ice as 32°, given 180 divisions or degrees between these points.

Rankine

The Rankine scale is based on Fahrenheit divisions and considers 0° as the lowest possible temperature that may be theoretically achieved (absolute zero). This point is -460° on the Fahrenheit scale.

These four scales are shown in relation to each other in Figure 1.

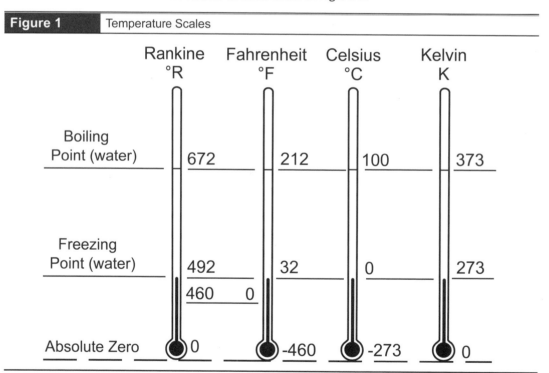

Figure 1 Temperature Scales

The three fixed points used to compare the scales are:

- the boiling point of water
- the freezing point of water
- absolute zero

Note: The Celsius scale shows 100 degrees between freezing point and boiling point of water, while the Fahrenheit scale shows 180 degrees between the same points. Thus 100 Celsius degrees = 180 Fahrenheit degrees, so a change of 1°C = a change of 1.8°F.

The relationships to convert temperatures between °C and °F are as follows:

To convert from °C to °F:

$$°F = 9/5 °C + 32$$

To convert from °F to °C :

$$°C = 5/9 (°F - 32)$$

Absolute Scales

It is useful in engineering and scientific work to have a range of temperatures beginning at absolute zero, the temperature at which all molecular motion is said to completely cease. The temperature scales beginning at absolute zero are called absolute scales and are particularly useful in the calculation of the behaviour patterns of gases and vapours.

The Fahrenheit absolute scale is called the Rankine scale and begins at 492° below the melting point of ice or 460° below zero on the Fahrenheit scale.

The relationship between Fahrenheit and Rankine temperatures can be expressed as:

$$°R = °F + 460$$

Note: That the size of the degrees or divisions on both Fahrenheit and Rankin scales are the same.

The Celsius absolute scale is called the Kelvin Scale and begins at 273° below the melting point of ice or 273° below zero on the Celsius scale.

The relationship between Celsius and Kelvin temperatures can be expressed as:

$$K = °C + 273$$

Note: That the degrees or divisions on both Celsius and Kelvin scales are the same.

From absolute zero to the melting point of ice (freezing point of water) measures a span of 492 Rankine degrees and 273 Kelvin. The ratio 492 to 273 is the same as 9 to 5. Hence 9 Rankine degrees denotes the same temperature difference as 5 K.

The relationship between Rankine and Kelvin temperatures can be expressed as:

$$°R = 9/5 \times K$$

$$K = 5/9 \times °R$$

MEASURING TEMPERATURE

There is a considerable range of instruments available for the measurement of temperature. The particular type chosen depends upon the temperatures to be measured and the conditions under which the measurements will be made. Some of the types used in measurement of temperature are:

- Liquid-in-glass thermometers
- Bi-metal thermometers
- Pyrometers

Liquid-in-Glass Thermometers

The mercury or alcohol thermometer is constructed of a thick-walled glass tube with a small bore. A bulb is on one end and the other end is sealed. Before sealing, the bulb and glass tube are completely filled with liquid at the highest temperature of the thermometer. The liquid cools, the level drops and a vacuum is created above the liquid.

The thermometer is calibrated by immersing the bulb in melting ice to obtain the freezing point of water and then exposing the bulb to steam rising from boiling water to obtain the boiling point. These points are marked on the stem or on a separate scale and the space between is divided into 100 equal divisions. The scale is then extended above and below the freezing and boiling points.

Bimetal Thermometers

Bimetal thermometers consist of two dissimilar metals rigidly fixed together. Due to their different coefficients of linear expansions, these bimetal strips will bend when subjected to temperature changes. This movement can be transmitted, by linkages or directly, to a pointer to read the temperature on a graduated scale.

Pyrometers

The term pyrometer is used to describe instruments made for measuring temperatures in the range above that suitable for the mercury thermometer.

There are several types of pyrometer, using different principles of operation. Two common types are the thermoelectric and the optical.

Thermoelectric Pyrometer

The thermoelectric pyrometer makes use of a thermocouple that produces an electrical voltage which is proportional to temperature.

A thermocouple consists of two wires made of different metals. The two wires are joined together at each of their ends and if one of the joints is at a higher temperature than the other then a voltage is produced in the wires. The high temperature joint is called the hot junction and the other joint is called the cold junction.

The voltage produced is proportional to the temperature difference between the junctions and this voltage is measured by means of a millivoltmeter which is calibrated to read in degrees of temperature. Figure 2 is a simplified sketch of a thermoelectric pyrometer.

Figure 2	Thermoelectric Pyrometer

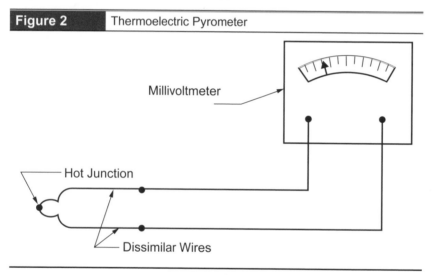

Optical Pyrometer

This instrument is suitable for measuring extremely high temperatures. Its operation is based upon the fact that the intensity of light emitted from a hot surface will vary with the temperature of that surface. In the pyrometer, the brightness of the object to be measured is compared to the brightness of a filament.

The filament brightness is produced by an electric current which heats the filament. The amount of current required to produce the necessary brightness is measured and will be proportional to the temperature of the object.

OBJECTIVE 3

Define heat and specific heat and perform sensible heat calculations.

HEAT

Heat is a form of energy which may be transferred from one body to another by virtue of a difference in temperature. Under normal circumstances, heat can only be transferred from a hot body to a colder body. If it is required to transfer heat from a cold body to a hot body (as in refrigeration), then external work is required to make the transfer.

It should be noted that, if there is no temperature difference between the heat source and the substance, there can be no heat transfer.

Heat Units
The joule is the basic unit of all energy, including heat. Therefore, units of heat are expressed in joules or multiples of joules.

$$1 \text{ kilojoule (kJ)} = 1000 \text{ J or } 10^3 \text{ J}$$

$$1 \text{ megajoule (MJ)} = 1\ 000\ 000 \text{ J or } 10^6 \text{ J}$$

Mechanical Equivalent of Heat
It has been shown by experiment that one joule is equivalent to the work done by a force of one newton moving through a distance of one metre in the direction in which the force is applied; thus, the work done is one newton metre which is equal to one joule.

$$1 \text{ Nm} = 1 \text{ J}$$

In other words, the unit of work is numerically equal to the unit of heat.

Specific Heat
The specific heat of a substance is the quantity of heat required to raise the temperature of a unit mass of the substance by one degree. Expressed in SI units, the specific heat of a substance is the quantity of heat (in kJ) required to raise **1 kg** of the substance 1K or 1°C. For example, the specific heat of fresh water is 4.2 kJ/kg°C (4.2 kilojoules per kilogram per degree Celsius).

Other substances require different amounts of heat energy to have one kg of their mass raised one degree Celsius in temperature. For instance, brass has a specific heat of 0.383 kJ/kg°C, aluminum 0.909 kJ/kg°C and ice 2.135 kJ/kg°C .

Heat Quantities
The quantity of heat absorbed by a substance when it is increasing in temperature depends on three factors:

- Temperature rise
- Mass of the substance
- Specific heat of the substance

Heat quantity can be expressed in the form of a formula as follows:

$$Q = mc\,(t_2 - t_1)$$

Where:

Q = Heat absorbed by the substance (kJ)

m = Mass of the substance (kg)

c = Specific heat of the substance (kJ/kg°C)

t_1 = temperature of the substance before heating (°C)

t_2 = temperature of the substance after heating (°C)

Note: Temperature can be expressed in either Celsius or Kelvin, but both t_1 and t_2 must be in the same units.

Example 1:

Find the quantity of heat required to raise the temperature of one litre of fresh water from 10°C to 60°C, if the specific heat of fresh water is 4.2 kJ/kg°C. Assume that 1 litre of fresh water has a mass of 1 kg.

Solution:

$$Q = mc\,(t_2 - t_1)$$

$$= 1\ kg \times 4.2\ kJ/kg°C \times (60°C - 10°C)$$

$$= 4.2\ kJ/°C \times 50°C$$

$$= 4.2\ kJ \times 50$$

$$= \textbf{210 kJ (Ans.)}$$

The quantity of heat required to raise the temperature of the water is 210 kJ.

Example 2:

Find the quantity of heat required to raise the temperature of one kilogram of copper from 10°C to 60°C, if the specific heat of copper is 0.39 kJ/kg°C.

Solution:

$$Q = mc\,(t_2 - t_1)$$

$$= 1\ kg \times 0.39\ kJ/kg°C \times (60°C - 10°C)$$

$$= 0.39\ kJ/°C \times 50°C$$

$$= 0.39\ kJ \times 50$$

$$= \textbf{19.5 kJ (Ans.)}$$

The quantity of heat required to raise the temperature of the copper is 19.5 kJ.

A comparison of Examples 1 and 2 shows that the mass and temperature rise were the same in both cases, but the copper only required 19.5 kJ of heat compared to 210 kJ for the water. In other words, the water required over ten times the amount of heat that the copper did.

Obviously, the higher the value of the specific heat of a substance, the greater the amount of heat required to raise the temperature of a given mass of the substance.

Table 1 lists the specific heat of some common substances.

Table 1	Specific Heat
Water	4.2 kJ/kg°C
Ice	2.04 kJ/kg°C
Copper	0.39 kJ/kg°C
Aluminum	0.912 kJ/kg°C

⚠ CAUTION

When using the formula, $Q = mc(t_2 - t_1)$, it is vitally important that the substance not change state (from solid to liquid, or liquid to gas, or vice versa) in the temperature range from t_1 to t_2. In other words, the formula only works in a temperature range within which the substance does not melt, freeze, vapourize or condense.

OBJECTIVE 4

Describe the expansion of solids and liquids.

LINEAR EXPANSION OF SOLIDS

Almost all solids will expand when their temperature increases. If a rod or pipe of a given length is raised in temperature, its increase in length will be directly proportional to its initial length and to the rise in temperature.

The increase in length due to heating is referred to as **linear expansion**. The change in length per unit length per degree rise in temperature is known as the **coefficient of linear expansion**.

That is:

> Change in length = Original length x Coefficient of linear expansion x Temperature rise

Example 3:

What is the increase in length of a steel bar 10 m long if its temperature is increased from 20°C to 70°C? The coefficient of linear expansion of steel is 0.000012/°C or 12×10^{-6}°C.

Solution:

> Change in the length = Original length x Coefficient of linear expansion x Temperature rise
>
> = 10 m x 0.000 012/°C x (70°C - 20°C)
>
> = 10 m x 0.000 012/°C x 50°C
>
> = **0.006 m (Ans.)**

The bar increases in length by 0.006 m or 6 mm.

It should be noted that the coefficient of linear expansion gives the change in length per unit length per degree change in temperature. That is, if the length of the steel bar is given in metres (m), the change of length will be in metres. If the length of the steel bar is expressed in millimetres (mm), then the change of length would be in millimetres.

The answer to the above problem is 0.006 m; this value does not give the student a physical feel for the increase, so it would be better to express the answer as 6 mm which the student can readily visualize by looking at a ruler or tape measure.

This linear expansion is of interest to an engineer when assembling metal parts of equipment that will be subjected to temperature change, as different materials possess different coefficients. Coefficients of linear expansion for some common materials are listed in Table 2.

Table 2	Coefficients of Linear Expansion
Material	**Coefficient of Linear Expansion Per °C**
Steel	12×10^{-6}
Copper	16.5×10^{-6}
Brass	18.4×10^{-6}

Since materials expand or contract by different amounts for the same temperature change, allowance must be made to avoid interference of one part upon another at high temperatures. It will be noticed that brass and copper expand and contract considerably more than steel for the same temperature change.

When steam or feedwater piping is erected, the expected expansion is calculated and then allowance is made by the use of expansion bends or joints.

Example 4:

A large diameter steel steam pipe is erected at 20°C and is to carry steam at a temperature of 320°C. How much expansion would you expect in a 30 m straight section of this steam line?

Solution:

Change in length = Original length x Coefficient of linear expansion x Temperature rise

$$= 30 \text{ m x } 0.000\ 012/°C \text{ x } (320°C - 20°C)$$

$$= 30 \text{ m x } 0.000\ 012/°C \text{ x } 300°C$$

$$= 0.108 \text{ m}$$

$$= \textbf{108 mm (Ans.)}$$

The pipe will expand 108 mm.

VOLUMETRIC EXPANSION OF SOLIDS

When a body is heated, it will expand along all dimensions. That is, its linear dimensions of length, width and height will all increase due to the increase in temperature. In other words, the body's volume will increase due to the rise in temperature and the increase will depend upon the coefficient of volumetric expansion of that material, which may be taken as being equal to three times the coefficient of linear expansion of the same material.

VOLUMETRIC EXPANSION OF LIQUIDS

With the exception of water, all liquids will expand in direct proportion to their change in temperature when heated and will contract similarly when cooled.

Water is a special case. When cooled, its volume decreases until a temperature of about 4°C is reached. At this point, there is a large increase in volume as the water cools further to 0°C and turns to ice.

This peculiarity of water is the reason why the surface water of a lake will freeze while the water below the surface will not. As the lake water is cooled below 4°C, it will expand, become less dense and rise to the surface where it eventually freezes. The layer of ice formed then acts as an insulator and the below surface water remains between 0°C and 4°C.

In general, the coefficients of expansion of liquids are greater than those of solids.

Like solids, different liquids have different coefficients of expansion. However, unlike the coefficients for solids which are considered to be constant at all temperatures, the coefficients for liquids change in value as the temperature changes.

For example, the coefficient of expansion of alcohol between 0°C and 10°C is 0.0011, but between 10°C and 60°C it is taken as 0.0013.

OBJECTIVE 5

Describe the three modes of heat transfer.

TRANSFER OF HEAT

Heat will always flow between two bodies if they are at different temperatures. The flow will always be from the body with the higher temperature to the body with the lower temperature. The rate at which the heat flow takes place will depend upon the temperature difference and also upon the type of material through which the flow takes place.

There are three methods by which the transfer of heat energy from one location to another takes place: **conduction**, **convection** and **radiation**. Any particular heat transfer will involve one or more of these methods.

Conduction

This method involves the flow of heat from molecule to molecule within a substance or from the molecules of one body to those of another body which is in direct contact with the first body. Molecules at a high temperature are considered to be in rapid vibration which is transferred to adjacent molecules within the same body. This rapid vibration may also be transferred from the molecules of one body to those of another if the two bodies are in direct contact.

A good example of heat transfer by conduction is an iron bar having one end in contact with a flame. The other end will soon become hot due to the conduction of heat from molecule to molecule through the metal.

The amount of heat transferred by conduction will depend upon the:

- temperature difference
- kind of material through which the flow takes place
- time during which heat flow occurs
- thickness of the material
- surface area involved.

The highest rate of conductive heat transfer is obtained in dense materials because the molecules are in close contact with each other. For this reason solids, particularly metals, are good conductors of heat while gases, in general, are poor.

Convection

The transfer of heat by convection involves the movement of a fluid (liquid or a gas). If a fluid is in contact with a hot surface, the portion adjacent to the surface will be heated and will expand. Its density will therefore be decreased.

The lighter heated fluid will rise and be displaced by cooler and denser fluid which in turn is heated and displaced. In this manner, a circulation of the liquid or gas will be set up.

Water in a boiler is heated by means of convection currents. The part of the water in contact with the hot tube walls or shell will be heated and will be displaced by cooler water which in turn is heated and displaced.

Other examples of convection currents are:

- hot gases rising up in a stack
- air rising from a room radiator
- water heated in a heat exchanger and rising into a storage tank

Forced convection may also be used in the transfer of heat. In this case, the movement of the fluid is brought about by means of a pump or a fan. An example of forced convection is the use of a pump to circulate hot water through a building heating system. Another example is the use of a fan to force air through an automobile radiator.

The fact that convection currents occur within a fluid must be considered when attempting to prevent a flow of heat. For example, still air is a good insulator since it has a fairly low conductivity. However, moving air will transfer a considerable amount of heat. A cold storage room with large air spaces within its walls will gain heat by the convection currents set up in these air spaces.

By using an insulating material containing extremely small air spaces, convection currents are prevented because all the air is in extremely close proximity to the surface of the fibres or bubbles in the insulating material. Such surface air is bound to the surfaces of the insulating material in a layer called the boundary layer. Air in the boundary layer cannot move and hence cannot convect heat. Bound air is a good insulator.

Insulating material such as fibreglass, styrofoam or cellulose has many fine fibres or air cavities that increase the surface area of the material and hence, increase the amount of bound air. It is the bound air that insulates, not the material itself. Because of this fact, very fine steel wool will actually act as a good insulator, whereas solid steel is a good conductor of heat. Wet insulation will be a poor insulator because all the bound air has been replaced by water, an excellent conductor.

Radiation

Radiation refers to the transmission of electromagnetic waves. All bodies emit these waves and the higher the body's temperature, the greater will be this emission.

These waves are similar to light waves in that they travel in straight lines and are able to pass through a vacuum. When they strike another body, they will be absorbed, reflected or transmitted through, depending upon the material of the body. If the waves are absorbed by the body, they will be converted into heat. When the energy waves are absorbed, they increase the velocity of the molecules in the absorbing body and hence, the heat of the body.

The condition of a body's surface will determine the amount of electromagnetic radiation absorbed or reflected. If the surface is black and rough, then the body will readily absorb the radiant energy. If the surface is smooth and highly polished, most of the radiant energy will be reflected. In the case of a substance such as air, the radiant energy will be transmitted through it to a great extent and only a small portion will be absorbed.

A typical example of radiation is heat reaching the earth from the sun. The energy waves first pass through the vacuum above the earth's atmosphere and then through the atmosphere itself where a portion is absorbed. Upon striking the earth's surface, much of the remaining energy is absorbed and converted to heat.

Another example of radiation is the sun's rays hitting the windows of a building. Some of the rays are reflected back to the outside of the building, some are absorbed by the glass or the coatings on the glass, while others are transmitted through the glass where they are absorbed by the drapes, blinds or contents of the room.

Different window assemblies will reflect, absorb and transmit different proportions of the sun's radiation. Such considerations are of major concern when designing or replacing the windows in a building.

This page has intentionally been left blank.

CHAPTER 18 - QUESTIONS

1. The amount of heat required to raise the temperature of a unit mass of a substance 1 degree Celsius without changing the state of the substance is defined as

   a) sensible heat.
   b) specific heat.
   c) superheat.
   d) saturated.

2. _____ heat causes a change in the temperature of a substance without changing its state.

   a) Sensible
   b) Specific
   c) Superheat
   d) Saturated

3. The first law of thermodynamics states that heat and work are

   a) incompatible.
   b) unconvertible.
   c) mutually convertible.
   d) the same process.

4. The second law of thermodynamics states that if it is required to transfer heat from a cold substance to a hotter substance (as in refrigeration), then _____ must be supplied.

   a) pressure
   b) external heat
   c) external work
   d) R134-a

5. A bimetal thermometer consists of

   a) a filament that is compared to the object being measured.
   b) two dissimilar metals rigidly fixed together.
   c) two dissimilar wires connected to a battery.
   d) two copper wires connected together.

6. A 3 m copper bar is heated from 25°C to 175°C. After heating it increased in length by 1.45 mm. What is the coefficient of linear expansion?

   a) 0.000 003 2/°C
   b) 0.000 025 6/°C
   c) 0.000 001 2/°C
   d) 0.000 002 5/°C

CHAPTER 18 - ANSWERS

1. (b)

2. (a)

3. (c)

4. (c)

5. (b)

6. (a)

Thermodynamics of Steam

LEARNING OUTCOME

When you complete this chapter you should be able to:

Describe the principles of the thermodynamics of steam and the associated terms.

LEARNING OBJECTIVES

Here is what you should be able to do when you complete each objective:

1. *Define the various terms related to water (ice a& steam).*

2. *Explain the various columns of the steam tables.*

3. *Explain the principles of the thermodynamics of steam using the steam tables.*

OBJECTIVE 1

Define the various terms related to water (ice a& steam).

Sensible Heat

When heat is supplied or taken away and causes an immediate change in temperature without changing the state, the heat is known as sensible heat.

Latent Heat

When heat is supplied or taken away and causes a change in state without a change in temperature, then the heat is known as latent heat.

Latent Heat of Fusion

The latent heat of fusion is the heat required to change a unit mass of solid to a unit mass of liquid at the same temperature. For example, at atmospheric conditions, the latent heat of fusion of ice is 335 kJ/kg. That is, it requires 335 kJ of heat to change every kg of ice at 0°C into water at 0°C.

Latent Heat of Evaporation

The latent heat of evaporation is the heat required to change a unit mass of liquid to a unit mass of vapour or gas at the same temperature and pressure. For example, at atmospheric conditions, the latent heat of evaporation of water is 2257 kJ/kg. That is, it requires 2257 kJ of heat to change every kg of water at 100°C into steam at 100°C.

Note: Latent heat of fusion and evaporation are found by experiment. The latent heat of evaporation varies with pressure; it decreases in value as the pressure rises.

Example 1:

How much heat is required to convert 10 kg of ice at 0°C to steam at 100°C?

Solution:

Heat required to melt ice:

Heat required = Mass x Latent heat of fusion

= 10 kg x 335 kJ/kg

= 3350 kJ

Heat required to raise temperature of water from 0°C to boiling point:

Heat required = Mass x Specific heat x Temperature difference

= 10 kg x 4.2 kJ/kg°C x (100°C - 0°C)

= 42 kJ/°C x 100°C

= 4200 kJ

Heat required to convert water at 100°C into steam at 100°C:

Heat required = Mass x Latent heat of evaporation

= 10 kg x 2257 kJ/kg

= 22 570 kJ

Total heat required to convert the 10 kg of ice to steam at 100°C:

Total heat required = 3350 kJ + 4200 kJ + 22 570 kJ

= **30 120 kJ (Ans.)**

Thus, to convert the ice to water at its boiling point, it took 3350 + 4200 = 7550 kJ or 25% of the total 30 120 kJ of heat supplied. To convert the boiling water to steam, it took 22 570 kJ or 75% of the total 30 120 kJ of heat supplied.

In other words, it takes much less heat to change the ice to water and to raise the water to its boiling point than it does to boil all of the hot water into steam. **Steam contains much more heat per kg than hot boiling water**.

Saturation Temperature

The temperature at which the change from water to steam takes place is called the boiling point or saturation temperature; this temperature will depend on the pressure on the surface of the water. Examples of the boiling point at various pressures are shown in Table 1.

Table 1	Saturation Temperatures
Absolute Pressure	**Boiling Point or Saturation Temperature**
101.3 kPa	100°C
200 kPa	120.23°C
300 kPa	133.55°C
400 kPa	143.63°C

Calculations concerning steam are complex due to variations in temperature and pressure. All values of the properties of steam have been determined accurately and are listed in available and easy to use steam tables.

Similar tables are also available for most liquids and gases, such as: refrigerants and industrial gases.

Saturated Steam

As mentioned before, the change of state from water to steam takes place at the saturation temperature (or boiling point) corresponding to the pressure acting on the water surface. Water at the saturation temperature corresponding to a particular pressure is called saturated water because it is saturated with sensible heat. The steam produced is called saturated steam. If this steam does not contain any particles of water in suspension, it is called dry saturated steam. It is called wet steam if the steam has particles of water suspended in it.

Thus, saturated steam is just at the temperature of the change of state from liquid to vapour and if any heat is removed from it, it will immediately begin to condense.

Superheated Steam

Saturated steam may be perfectly dry; that is, it may contain no water particles in suspension as it leaves the boiler. But as it begins to lose heat and fall in temperature, there will be a certain amount of condensation loss in the steam line. To avoid or minimize these losses, the saturated steam can be heated to a higher temperature than that corresponding to its pressure by passing it through rows of tubes placed in the combustion chamber of the boiler before entering the main steam header. These tubes are known as a superheater. This heating of the steam to a higher temperature than its saturation temperature is called superheating; the steam produced is called superheated steam.

This steam will not condense until the temperature has dropped to the saturation temperature meaning that the superheated steam can be transmitted long distances to turbines or other equipment without encountering excessive condensation losses.

Buildings using steam for heating, almost always use saturated steam. Superheated steam is used mainly for steam turbines or very high temperature processes.

OBJECTIVE 2

Explain the various columns of the steam tables.

STEAM TABLES

Certain properties of steam, the volume per kilogram, the sensible and latent heat per kg, and the saturation temperature corresponding to certain absolute pressures, are known as the thermodynamic properties of steam. These values and others must be known to solve problems involving the use of steam. All these properties of steam have been obtained by careful experiments and the values are tabulated in **steam tables**.

Referring to the **Academic Supplement**, Table 1 of the **SI Steam Tables for Reference in Power Engineering** lists the **Properties of Saturated Steam (Pressure Table)** for various saturation pressures. For the discussion here, consider the columns as being numbered from left to right (note: they are not actually numbered in the steam table).

Columns 1, 2, 3 and 4
These columns list various pressures and their corresponding temperatures, plus the specific volumes of saturated liquids and vapours.

Column 1 lists the absolute pressure (p) in kPa .

It should be remembered that the absolute pressure is obtained using the following formula:

Absolute pressure = Gauge pressure + 101.3 kPa

Column 2 lists the corresponding saturation temperature (t) in °C for each absolute pressure.

By examining the values in columns 1 and 2, the student will see that the temperature of saturated steam increases as the pressure increases. That is, as Table 2 below illustrates, the boiling point of water increases as the pressure increases.

Table 2	Boiling Point, Pressure & Temperature Relationships
p	t
100 kPa	99.63°C
500 kPa	151.86°C
1500 kPa	198.32°C

Column 3 lists the specific volume (v_f) of the saturated liquid in cm³/gram at each saturation temperature and pressure. The specific volume is the volume occupied by 1 gram of water at that pressure and temperature). Referring to Table 3 below, note that the specific volume of saturated water (ie. water at its boiling point) increases as the pressure and temperature increase.

Table 3	Pressure, Temperature & Specific Volume of Saturated Liquid	
p	t	v_f
100 kPa	99.630C	1.0432 cm³/g
500 kPa	151.860C	1.0926 cm³/g
1500 kPa	198.320C	1.1539 cm³/g

Column 4 lists the specific volume (v_g) of the saturated vapour in cm^3/gram saturated steam for each pressure (that is, the volume occupied by 1 gram of steam at that pressure and temperature). As illustrated by Table 4, note that the specific volume of the saturated steam decreases with increasing pressure. For example:

Table 4	Pressure, Temperature & Specific Volume of Saturated Vapour	
p	t	V_g
100 kPa	99.63°C	1694.0 cm³/g
500 kPa	151.86°C	374.9 cm³/g
1500 kPa	198.32°C	131.77 cm³/g

It is interesting that one gram of saturated water at 100 kPa has a volume of 1.0432 cm^3 and that if this water is converted into saturated steam at the same pressure, the volume becomes 1694 cm^3. That is, the volume increases more than **1600 times** when the state changes from water to steam.

Columns 5, 6 and 7
These columns are concerned with internal energy, the sum of all of the energy in the atoms and molecules in a substance due to the fact that they are in constant motion. These three columns are not a direct concern to the student at this point.

Columns 8, 9 and 10
These columns of the steam tables indicate specific enthalpy. Enthalpy is a measure of heat added to a unit mass of a substance.

Column 8 lists the liquid enthalpy (h_f) in kilojoules/kilogram of the saturated water for each pressure. The term enthalpy refers to the amount of heat added to the water to raise its temperature from 0°C to the saturation temperature. This is sensible heat since it raises the temperature without changing the state.

Column 9 lists the enthalpy of evaporation (h_{fg}) in kilojoules/kilogram for each pressure. In this case, the enthalpy is the heat added to the water at saturation temperature to convert it to saturated steam at the same temperature. In other words, it is the latent heat of evaporation.

Column 10 lists the total enthalpy (h_g) in kilojoules/kilogram of the saturated steam for each pressure. Note saturated steam is steam that is fully saturated with latent heat and has no water particles present.

It should be noted that:

$$h_g = h_f + h_{fg}$$

h_g is the total heat necessary to produce saturated steam from water at 0°C and consists of the sensible heat plus the latent heat.

Columns 11, 12 and 13
These columns list values of entropy which are beyond the scope of this course.

OBJECTIVE 3

Explain the principles of the thermodynamics of steam using the steam tables.

Note: All pressures given in this module are absolute unless stated otherwise.

USING THE STEAM TABLES

Example 2:

From the steam tables find the following:

    a) The liquid enthalpy of one kilogram of saturated water at 200 kPa

    b) The enthalpy of evaporation of one kilogram of saturated steam at 200 kPa

    c) The total enthalpy of one kilogram of saturated steam at 200 kPa

Solution:

Using columns 8, 9 and 10:

    a) h_f = **504.7 kJ (Ans.)**

    b) h_{fg} = **2201.9 kJ (Ans.)**

    c) h_g = **2706.7 kJ (Ans.)**

Example 3:

    a) Find the sensible heat required to raise 5 kg of feedwater from 0°C to the boiling point at 300 kPa.

    b) What is the boiling point at this pressure?

Solution:

    a) h_f at 300 kPa = 561.47 kJ/kg

        h_f at 0°C = Zero

    Therefore, the sensible heat required to raise 5 kg of water to its boiling point at 300 kPa is:

        = (561.47 kJ/kg - 0) x 5 kg

        = **2807.35 kJ (Ans.)**

    b) From the steam tables, the boiling point or saturation temperature (t) at 300 kPa is:

        = **133.55°C (Ans.)**

The student should realize that values of sensible heat given in the steam tables are measured from 0°C. That is, at 0°C, the value of the enthalpy of water is zero.

Since feedwater is not usually supplied at this low temperature, it is necessary to determine the enthalpy of feedwater at the supply temperatures.

In the **Academic Supplement Book**, Table 2 of the **SI Steam Tables for Reference in Power Engineering** lists the **Properties of Saturated Steam Temperature Table** for various saturation temperatures. Again, consider the columns as being numbered from left to right. The first column gives the temperature and the enthalpy can be found in Columns 8, 9 and 10 as in the pressure table previously discussed.

Example 4:

How much heat will be required to convert 10 kg of water at 60°C into saturated steam at 200 kPa?

Solution:

Enthalpy of saturated steam at 200 kPa is found in Table 1 (pressure table):

h_g = 2706.7 kJ/kg

Enthalpy of water at 60°C is found in Table 2 (temperature table):

h_f = 251.13 kJ/kg

Therefore, heat required for 1 kg:

$$= h_g - h_f$$

$$= 2706.7 \text{ kJ/kg} - 251.13 \text{ kJ/kg}$$

$$= 2455.57 \text{ kJ/kg}$$

Heat required to convert the 10 kg of water at 60°C to saturated steam at 200 kPa is:

$$= 2455.57 \text{ kJ/kg} \times 10 \text{ kg}$$

$$= \textbf{24 555.7 kJ (Ans.)}$$

Temperature Enthalpy Chart

The process of changing water into wet, saturated steam can be shown by a temperature enthalpy chart, as in the following example:

Example 5:

Using information from the steam tables, plot the values of heat required to produce dry saturated steam from feedwater at 0°C at a pressure of 100 kPa.

At 100 kPa:

Saturation temperature = 99.63°C

h_f = 417.46 kJ/kg

h_{fg} = 2258 kJ/kg

h_g = 2675.5 kJ/kg

Plotting these values gives a graph similar to the one shown in Figure 1.

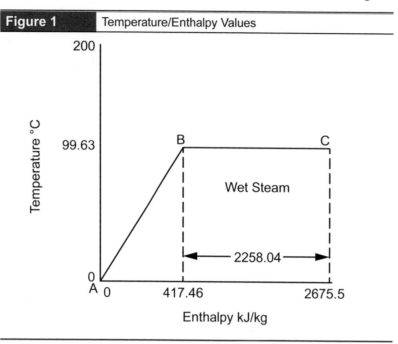

Figure 1 — Temperature/Enthalpy Values

If all the various pressures were plotted in the same manner and the points joined, a temperature-enthalpy chart would be produced as in Figure 2. Temperature-enthalpy charts have the advantage that the properties of steam at any pressure can be determined, whereas the steam tables are limited to the pressures listed.

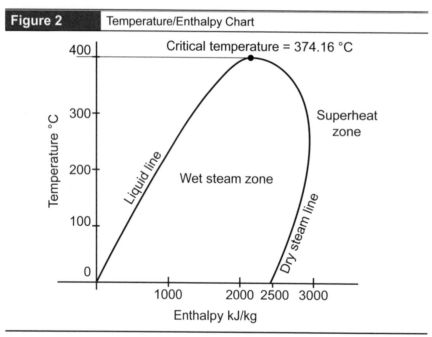

Figure 2 — Temperature/Enthalpy Chart

Wet Steam

The values given for saturated steam in the steam tables are not always obtained in an actual steam boiler.

The steam produced may contain particles of saturated water (that is, water at the same temperature as the steam) due to the vigorous boiling action at the water surface. Obviously if steam has 10% wetness, then the dryness portion must be 90%. Thus, 90% of a gram (or kilogram) of water has been converted into saturated steam, but the remaining 10% of the gram (or kilogram) remains as saturated water entrained as droplets in the steam. That is, a gram or kilogram of saturated water has only received 90% of the latent heat necessary to convert it all to steam. Only 90% of the water has been converted to saturated steam.

Example 6:

If steam with a dryness fraction of 90% is to be produced from saturated water at 200 kPa, what amount of heat must be supplied per kilogram?

The dryness fraction of wet steam can be used to calculate the actual enthalpy that the steam contains using the formula:

$$h = h_f + qh_{fg}$$

where q = dryness fraction (expressed as a decimal; eg. 90% = 0.90)

h = total enthalpy at the stated condition

h_{fg} = enthalpy of evaporation at the given pressure

h_f = enthalpy of the saturated liquid

Note: From the steam tables, it can be seen when $h_g = h_f + qh_{fg}$, $q = 1.0$, which means 100% dry, saturated steam. Also, for superheated steam, $q = 1.0$ or 100%

Solution:

Dryness fraction of 90% (or 0.9) means that only that portion has been converted to saturated steam. The remaining 10% is called the wetness fraction. Consider only the h_{fg} in this example:

Let q = Dryness fraction of the steam = 0.9

Heat (h) to convert water to steam   = 0.9 x 2201.9 kJ/kg

= **1981.71 kJ/kg (Ans.)**

Thus, 1981.7 kJ/kg of heat is required to convert saturated water at 200 kPa into wet steam with a dryness fraction of 90%.

Example 7:

How much heat must be supplied to water at 0°C to make wet steam at 200 kPa, having a dryness fraction of 90%?

Solution:

Since the water is raised from 0°C to saturation temperature, one kilogram of water receives its full sensible heat (h). However, since only 90% of the saturated water is converted to saturated steam, the latent heat received is only 90% of h_{fg}.

$$\begin{aligned} h &= h_f + qh_{fg} \\ &= 504.70 \text{ kJ/kg} + (0.9 \times 2201.9 \text{ kJ/kg}) \\ &= 504.70 \text{ kJ/kg} + 1981.7 \text{ kJ/kg} \\ &= \textbf{2486.41 kJ/kg (Ans.)} \end{aligned}$$

Therefore, 2486.41 kJ/kg of heat is required to convert water at 0°C into wet steam at 200 kPa, having a dryness fraction of 90%.

Boiler Efficiency

The efficiency of a steam boiler is the ratio of the heat energy required to make steam to the heat energy supplied by the combustion of the fuel.

$$\text{Boiler efficiency} = \frac{\text{Heat given to the steam}}{\text{Heat supplied by the fuel}}$$

Note:

(a) The "heat given to the steam" is the total heat that must be absorbed by the feedwater to convert it into steam. This involves knowing the total mass (kg) of steam produced, the initial enthalpy of the feedwater (kJ/kg), and the final enthalpy of the steam (kJ/kg). The "heat given to the steam" is then the product of the total mass of steam and the heat added to each kg. The heat added to each kg is the difference between the final and initial enthalpies.

(b) The "heat supplied by the fuel" is the total heat created in the boiler furnace by combustion of the fuel. This involves knowing the total mass (kg) of fuel burned and the heating value (kJ/kg) of the fuel. The "heat supplied by the fuel" is then the product of the mass and the heating value.

A more detailed equation, expressed as a percentage is as follows:

$$\text{Boiler efficiency} = \frac{m_s\,(h - h_w)}{m_f \times \text{Heating value of fuel}} \times 100\%$$

Where: m_s = mass of steam produced (kg)

m_f = mass of the fuel burned (kg)

h = Enthalpy of the steam (kJ/kg)

h_w = Enthalpy of the feedwater (kJ/kg)

Heating value of the fuel = kJ/kg of fuel

Example 8:

A boiler generates 7 kg of dry saturated steam per kg of fuel oil burned; the heating value of the oil is 30 000 kJ/kg. The feedwater is supplied at 60°C and the boiler pressure is 200 kPa. Calculate the boiler efficiency.

Solution:

h_W = Enthalpy of the feedwater (liquid enthalpy, h_f only)

= 251.13 kJ/kg

h = Enthalpy of dry saturated steam at 200 kPa(h_g)

= 2706.7 kJ/kg

$\dot{m}_s$ = 7 kg

$\dot{m}_f$ = 1 kg

$$\text{Boiler efficiency} = \frac{\dot{m}_s\,(h - h_w)}{\dot{m}_f \times \text{Heating value of fuel}} \times 100\%$$

$$= \frac{7 \text{ kg} \times (2706.7 - 251.13)\text{kJ/kg}}{1 \text{ kg} \times 30\,000 \text{ kJ/kg fuel}} \times 100\%$$

$$= \frac{7(2455.57 \text{ kJ/kg})}{30\,000 \text{ kJ/kg}} \times 100\%$$

= 57.3% (Ans.)

This means that 57.3% of the heat available in the fuel was effectively used in the production of steam. The remaining 42.7% of the heat is referred to as the boiler losses. These losses include such items as:

- sensible heat in dry gaseous products of combustion
- incomplete combustion
- moisture in fuel

The attainment of maximum efficiency in daily operation of boiler equipment is dependent upon keeping **boiler losses** to a minimum.

CHAPTER 19 - QUESTIONS

1. In column 1 of Table 1 of the Steam Tables, the unit used for pressure is
   a) PSI.
   b) kPa.
   c) kJ/kg.
   d) kPa(abs).

2. To avoid condensation loss in steam
   a) steam is heated to saturation temperature.
   b) wet steam is used.
   c) steam pressure is increased.
   d) super heated steam is used.

3. What is the liquid enthalpy of 2 kg of saturated steam at 1,100 kPa?
   a) 1562.68 kJ
   b) 2000.40 kJ
   c) 1525.62 kJ
   d) 1660.60 kJ

4. What is the enthalpy of 7.2 kg of saturated water at 700 kPa?
   a) 4675.24 kJ
   b) 4956.74 kJ
   c) 5019.98 kJ
   d) 5268.33 kJ

5. In a boiler, 23 600 kJ of heat are absorbed by the feedwater to produce a quantity of steam. This requires 33 500 kJ of heat to be supplied by the boiler fuel. What is the boiler efficiency? ?
   a) 84.78%
   b) 70.45%
   c) 56.25%
   d) 70.05%

6. Wet saturated steam at a pressure of 1500 kPa has a specific enthalpy of 2636.41 kJ/kg. What is the dryness fraction of the steam?
   a) 92.00%
   b) 84.85%
   c) 90.75%
   d) 94.42%

CHAPTER 19 - ANSWERS

1. (b)

2. (d)

3. (a)

4. (c)

5. (b)

6. (a)

Basic Concepts About Matter

LEARNING OUTCOME

When you complete this chapter you should be able to:

Discuss the basic types of matter and their properties.

LEARNING OBJECTIVES

Here is what you should be able to do when you complete each objective:

1. Describe the physical states of matter.

2. Define the properties of and distinguish between chemical and physical changes in matter.

3. Classify matter as a type of mixture or a pure substance.

4. Describe the purpose of the periodic table.

INTRODUCTION

Chemistry is the branch of science that describes matter and its:

- composition
- structure
- properties
- transformations

Matter can be defined as anything that has mass and occupies space. A substance need not be visible, even to the most powerful microscope, to be considered matter as long as it meets these two criteria.

Matter can be described in terms describing its state and its physical and chemical properties; transformations between states and properties are also possible.

OBJECTIVE 1

Describe the physical states of matter.

PHYSICAL STATES OF MATTER

Matter can exist in three different physical states: solid, liquid, or gas. Solids have an ordered arrangement of particles close together, giving them a rigid structure with a definite shape and volume. They have very little capability to compress or expand. Liquids have a definite volume, but no specific shape. They will flow and assume the shape of the container that holds them. Gases have no fixed volume or shape because their particles are in constant motion. They assume the shape and volume of their container. A gas consists mainly of empty space with the particles of gas far apart from each other. Therefore, they are easily compressible to occupy a smaller volume as well as expandable to fill a larger container. Figure 1 illustrates the three states of matter.

Figure 1	Solids, Liquids and Gases

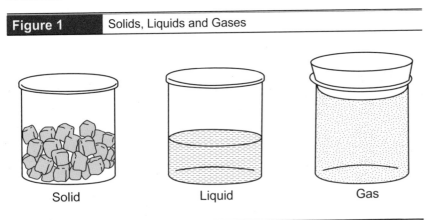

Solid   Liquid   Gas

The state of matter observed for a particular substance is dependent on the temperature and pressure. At room temperature, most substances are solid; however, some are liquids and a few exist in the gaseous state.

For example, at standard room-temperature conditions:

- oxygen, ammonia, carbon dioxide and methane are gases.
- water, mercury and bromine are liquids.
- iron and copper are solids.

Phases

A phase is one individual substance in one particular state. For example, a glass of water with ice cubes in it contains two phases: a liquid phase and a solid phase, or water in liquid state and water in solid state. (The separate ice cubes are all part of the one solid phase, even though they are dispersed through the liquid). A mixture of water and oil contains two phases, both of them liquid phases. One phase is liquid water, and the other is the separate distinguishable substance, liquid oil. Even if the mixture is stirred violently so that thousands of tiny droplets of each liquid are dispersed throughout the other, there are still only two phases present. All the water droplets are part of the one liquid water phase, and all of the oil droplets are part of the one liquid oil phase.

Distinction Between Gases and Vapours

In common use, a **gas** is a substance that remains in the gaseous state at room conditions. A **vapour** is the gaseous phase of a substance that is normally liquid or solid at room conditions. The word "vapour" rather than "gas" is also generally used for any case where the liquid or solid phase is also present, or could be made to appear by increasing the pressure or cooling the system slightly.

This distinction can be illustrated by the following examples:

- Oxygen and helium are called gases, not vapours since each are a separate compound in one phase.

- The gaseous phase of gasoline is called a vapour, not a gas since it is a mixture of a number of individual compounds

- Mothballs consist largely of the white solid, naphthalene, and the strong smell they emit is due to naphthalene vapour, not naphthalene gas.

OBJECTIVE 2

Define the properties of and distinguish between chemical and physical changes in matter.

PROPERTIES OF MATTER

Matter is classified according to different characteristics or properties. Since these properties are distinct, they are used to identify and distinguish between different substances. The properties of matter are classified as:

- Chemical or
- Physical

Chemical Properties

Chemical properties describe the way in which a substance can undergo change. They are those properties that matter exhibits as it undergoes a change in its composition. The change usually results from a chemical reaction leading to the formation of a new substance.

For example, iron will combine with oxygen to produce rust, a new substance. sulphur will combine with silver to produce tarnish; magnesium will react with oxygen to produce magnesium oxide, a white powder.

Physical Properties

Physical properties are those characteristics used to describe a substance, or those properties that can be observed without a change in the composition of the matter. Physical properties include:

- Colour
- Hardness
- Density
- Boiling point
- Electrical conductivity

Although the physical appearance of the substance may change, the chemical composition is still the same.

For example, a block of ice is composed of a hydrogen and oxygen compound in the solid state. When the ice melts, its physical state changes to a liquid, but it is still chemically composed of the same hydrogen and oxygen compound.

Table 1 shows some of the chemical and physical properties of water.

Table 1	Properties of Water
Chemical	**Physical**
Can be decomposed electrically into hydrogen and oxygen.	Colourless
Reacts violently with metallic sodium to produce hydrogen.	Boils at 100°C and freezes at 0°C
Doesn't react with gold.	Density is 1.0 g/mL

Physical properties can be further subdivided, as follows:

- An **intensive** property is one that is not dependent on the amount of matter. For example, the boiling point of water is normally 100°C, whether boiling one litre or one thousand litres, and the colour of iodine remains unchanged, regardless of its volume. All chemical properties are intensive.

- An **extensive** property is one that is dependent on the amount of matter. Volume and mass are both examples of extensive properties.

Since no two substances have identical physical and chemical properties under the same conditions, this information is used to distinguish between them. For instance, water is the only colourless liquid that has a density of 1.00 g/mL and boils at 100°C at standard pressure.

CHANGES IN MATTER

Changes in matter may involve the transformation from one form to another. These changes can be either chemical or physical and both require a change in energy.

Chemical Change

Chemical change involves a change in the chemical composition of a substance. The original substance (or substances) is used up and a new substance or substances formed. Each new substance is different both chemically and physically from the original.

Substances display their chemical properties whenever they undergo a chemical reaction. When fuel gases react with air in a combustion reaction, carbon dioxide and water are formed as products. Both differ chemically and physically from the original reactants (i.e. the fuel and the air).

Physical Change

Physical changes occur when physical properties are altered without a change in chemical composition. After the physical change, the original substances remain; therefore, no new substance is formed. A change in physical state (e.g. changes in water from a liquid to a solid or gaseous state) is perhaps the most common type of physical change.

Figure 2 depicts the six possible state changes that matter can undergo. The student should already be familiar with most of these terms, with the possible exception of sublimation (a change from a solid to a gas) and deposition (a change from a gas to a solid).

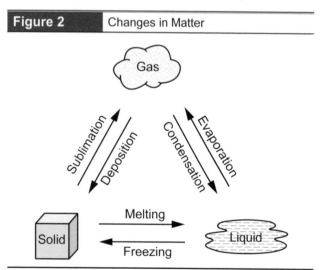

| Figure 2 | Changes in Matter |

There are other types of physical changes that don't involve a change of state including changes in the size, shape or subdivision of matter. The grinding of coal into fine particles is an example of this type of physical change.

THE BEHAVIOUR OF SUBSTANCES IN DIFFERENT STATES

Substances exist as huge numbers of small, discrete particles, called molecules.

Gas Molecules

Molecules of a gas are totally independent and move about rapidly in all directions, colliding with each other or the walls of the container, without slowing down or sticking together in clumps. This is why gases have no definite shape or volume, and can disperse to all corners of a container. Also, different kinds of gases can spread throughout the container, so all kinds of gases are completely miscible with each other; over time they always form a uniform mixture.

Moreover, the molecules are tiny and far apart, with lots of empty space between them. This allows the gas to easily be compressed to a small fraction of its original volume. The pressure exerted by a gas is due to the molecules colliding with the wall of the container. A compressed gas has more molecules per unit volume and a greater rate of collisions, so exerts more pressure. As the temperature of a gas increases, the velocity of the gas molecules also increases. As a result, if gas in a container of fixed volume is heated, an increase in pressure occurs.

Liquid Molecules

Liquid molecules are much less independent. They attract each other, due to intermolecular forces, and accumulate into clumps too large to "disperse" like gas molecules. This is why liquids settle to the bottom of a container. The molecules are very close together, loosely touching, but not rigidly attached. Thus, the liquid has a definite volume, since the molecules can't easily be pushed closer together; but no definite shape, since molecules can slither around and over each other.

Solid Molecules

Molecules of a solid are held together rigidly. The molecules are generally slightly closer together and more ordered than in liquids. They may become locked into a fixed position relative to their neighbours due to their shape, or to the strength of the attractive forces holding them against each other, so that they can't easily revolve or slide past each other.

OBJECTIVE 3

Classify matter as a type of mixture or a pure substance.

CLASSIFICATION OF MATTER

Matter can be classified into two main categories, mixtures and pure substances, then further divided into four distinct groups, as shown in Figure 3.

Figure 3	Classification of Matter

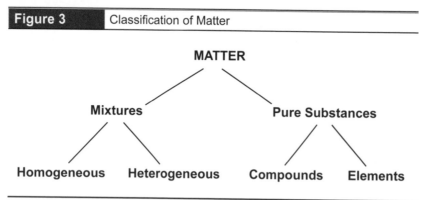

Mixtures

Most natural substances in the world are mixtures; that is, they are combinations of two or more pure substances that aren't chemically bound to each other. The components of a mixture can therefore be separated by physical means. Although the composition of a mixture can vary, thus leading to variation in properties, each component of the mixture retains its individual composition and properties. Two types of mixtures include:

- Homogenous
- Heterogeneous

Homogeneous Mixtures

A homogeneous mixture, also called a solution, exhibits uniform composition throughout; therefore, it has only one set of properties. Homogeneous mixtures are possible only when all the components are in the same physical state.

Flue gas is an example of a homogeneous mixture of a number of different gases while metal alloys are examples of homogeneous mixtures of solid elements.

Heterogeneous Mixtures

A heterogeneous mixture has a non-uniform composition as well as differing properties. The substances may or may not be in the same physical state.

An oil and water emulsion is a heterogeneous mixture of one physical state, both liquids. A mixture of sand and water is a heterogeneous mixture of two different physical states, solid and liquid.

Pure Substances

A pure substance can be defined as any type of matter having a constant composition and displaying identical properties under identical conditions. There are two types of pure substances: compounds and elements.

Elements

Elements are pure substances that cannot be decomposed into simpler forms of matter. As of 2011, there are 118 known elements in existence. They are the building blocks of all other forms of matter. They are distributed very unevenly in the universe, with only a few predominating. Ninety-four of the elements occur naturally, while the remainder are created by decay or by synthesis in a laboratory.

Note: The Periodic Table, shown on page 20-11 and in the Academic Supplement, shows only the first 112 elements. It will be updated when approved to do so. Elements 113 to 118 are new and have largely unknown chemical properties..

Compounds

A compound is a pure substance that consists of two or more elements, chemically bound together, in fixed proportions by mass. All samples of a given substance will contain the same elements in the same proportions. This is called the **Law of Constant Composition**. The compounds can only be separated into their constituent elements through chemical means by which the compound is destroyed.

There are millions of compounds known in the world today, but only a small number of elements. Water, for example, is a compound composed of hydrogen and oxygen in fixed proportions. It can be broken down into these two elements by passing an electric current through it which breaks the chemical bonds.

The physical and chemical properties of a compound are distinctly different from those of the elements from which it is composed. NaCl (table salt) is a white granular solid composed of the elements sodium (Na) and chlorine (Cl). Sodium is a silvery metal that reacts violently with water; chlorine is a green poisonous gas.

OBJECTIVE 4

Describe the purpose of the periodic table.

PERIODIC TABLE OF THE ELEMENTS

A few elements were known in ancient times. Over the centuries, as studies gathered more data on the known elements and identified new ones, scientists felt it necessary to organize the large amount of information that was being amassed. They noticed certain groups of elements possessed similar properties and grouped these elements together in a graphical format called a periodic table, which is shown in Figure 4.

The current table was developed by Jons Berzelius in 1814. The name of each element sometimes represents its discoverer and the symbols assigned to each are characteristic of the element's name. The symbol may consist of one, two or three letters, with the first letter capitalized. For example, calcium is symbolized Ca and hydrogen is symbolized H.

Some elements don't follow this pattern. For example, the symbol for tungsten is W because tungsten is derived from the German word wolfram. Other symbols come from Latin words, such as: Na (natrium) for sodium, Pb (plumbum) for lead and Fe (ferrum) for iron.

The only elements that use three letters for their symbol are those of the elements 110 to 112. These symbols have been derived from a Latin-Greek naming system.

The periodic table provides a great deal of information about the elements, such as their mass, ionic charge and nuclear particles.

Figure 4 Periodic Table of the Elements

PERIODIC TABLE OF THE ELEMENTS

Legend:
- 6 — Atomic Number
- C — Symbol
- 12.011 — Atomic Mass
- 2-4 — Electron Configuration
- -4+2+4 — Selected Oxidation States

GROUP IA	IIA	IIIB	IVB	VB	VIB	VIIB	VIIIB			IB	IIB	IIIA	IVA	VA	VIA	VIIA	VIIIA
1 H 1.00794 1 +1 -1																	2 He 4.00260 2 0
3 Li 6.9414 2-1 +1	4 Be 9.01218 2-2 +2											5 B 10.81 2-3 +3	6 C 12.011 2-4 -4+2+4	7 N 14.0067 2-5 -3-2+1+2+3+4+5	8 O 15.9994 2-6 -2	9 F 18.998403 2-7 -1	10 Ne 20.179 2-8 0
11 Na 22.98977 2-8-1 +1	12 Mg 9.01218 2-8-2 +2											13 Al 26.98154 2-8-3 +3	14 Si 28.0855 2-8-4 -4+2+4	15 P 30.97376 2-8-5 -3+3+5	16 S 32.06 2-8-6 -2+4+6	17 Cl 35.453 2-8-7 -1+1+3+5+7	18 Ar 39.948 2-8-8 0
19 K 39.0983 2-8-8-1 +1	20 Ca 40.08 8-8-2 +2	21 Sc 44.9559 2-8-9-2 +3	22 Ti 47.89 2-8-10-2 +2+3+4	23 V 50.9415 2-8-11-2 +2+3+4+5	24 Cr 51.996 2-8-13-1 +2+3+6	25 Mn 54.9380 2-8-13-2 +2+3+4+7	26 Fe 55.847 2-8-14-2 +2+3	27 Co 58.9332 2-8-15-2 +2+3	28 Ni 58.69 2-8-16-2 +2+3	29 Cu 63.546 2-8-18-1 +1+2	30 Zn 65.39 2-8-18-2 +2	31 Ga 69.72 2-8-18-3 +3	32 Ge 72.59 2-8-18-4 -4+2+4	33 As 74.9216 2-8-18-5 -3+3+5	34 Se 78.96 2-8-18-6 -2+4+6	35 Br 79.904 2-8-18-7 -1+1+5	36 Kr 83.80 2-8-18-8 0+2
37 Rb 85.4678 2-8-18-1 +1	38 Sr 87.62 2-8-18-8-2 +2	39 Y 88.9059 2-8-18-9-2 +3	40 Zr 91.224 2-8-18-10-2 +4	41 Nb 92.9064 2-8-18-12-1 +3+5	42 Mo 95.94 2-8-18-13-1 +3+6	43 Tc (98) 2-8-18-14-1 +4+6+7	44 Ru 101.07 2-8-18-15-1 +3	45 Rh 102.906 2-8-18-16-1 +3	46 Pd 106.42 2-8-18-18 +2+4	47 Ag 107.868 2-8-18-18-1 +1	48 Cd 112.41 2-8-18-18-2 +2	49 In 114.82 2-8-18-18-3 +3	50 Sn 118.71 2-8-18-18-4 +2+4	51 Sb 121.75 2-8-18-18-5 -3+3+5	52 Te 127.60 2-8-18-18-6 -2+4+6	53 I 126.905 2-8-18-18-7 -1+1+5+7	54 Xe 131.29 2-8-18-18-8 0+2+4+6
55 Cs 132.905 2-8-18-18-8-1 +1	56 Ba 137.33 2-8-18-18-8-2 +2	57 La 138.906 +3	72 Hf 178.49 -18-32-10-2 +4	73 Ta 180.948 -18-32-11-2 +5	74 W 183.85 -18-32-12-2 +6	75 Re 186.207 -18-32-13-2 +4+6+7	76 Os 190.2 -18-32-14-2 +3+4	77 Ir 192.22 -18-32-15-2 +3+4	78 Pt 195.08 -18-32-17-1 +2+4	79 Au 196.957 -18-32-18-1 +1+3	80 Hg 200.59 -18-32-18-2 +1+2	81 Tl 204.383 -18-32-18-3 +1+3	82 Pb 207.2 -18-32-18-4 +2+4	83 Bi 208.980 -18-32-18-5 +3+5	84 Po (209) -18-32-18-6 +2+4	85 At (210) -18-32-18-7 -1+1+5+7	86 Rn (222) -18-32-18-8 0
87 Fr (223) -18-32-18-8-1 +1	88 Ra 226.025 -18-32-18-8-2 +2	89 Ac 227.028 +3	104 Rf (261)	105 Db (262)	106 Sg (263)	107 Bh (264)	108 Hs (265)	109 Mt (268)	110 Uun (269)	111 Uuu (272)	112 Uub (277)						

Lanthanides:

58 Ce 140.12 +3+4	59 Pr 140.908 +3	60 Nd 144.24 +3	61 Pm (145) +3	62 Sm 150.36 +2+3	63 Eu 151.96 +2+3	64 Gd 157.25 +3	65 Tb 158.925 +3	66 Dy 162.50 +3	67 Ho 164.930 +3	68 Er 167.26 +3	69 Tm 168.934 +3	70 Yb 173.04 +2+3	71 Lu 174.967 +3

Actinides:

90 Th 232.038 +4	91 Pa 231.036 +4+5	92 U 238.029 +3+4+5+6	93 Np 237.048 +3+4+5+6	94 Pu (244) +3+4+5+6	95 Am (243) +3+4+5+6	96 Cm (247) +3	97 Bk (247) +3+4	98 Cf (251) +3	99 Es (252)	100 Fm (257)	101 Md (258)	102 No (259)	103 Lr (250) +3

Metals ← → Non-Metals

This page has intentionally been left blank.

CHAPTER 20 - QUESTIONS

1. Matter can best be defined as anything that has mass and

   a) can be chemically combined into other elements.
   b) occupies space.
   c) is dependent on its relative temperature.
   d) is visible to the naked eye.

2. Transformations between states and properties of a matter are

   a) impossible.
   b) difficult.
   c) possible.
   d) infrequent.

3. Which is not an example of a physical property of a material?

   a) Colour
   b) Boiling Point
   c) Odour
   d) Reactive Properties

4. An extensive (physical) property is one that is

   a) not dependent on the amount of matter.
   b) demonstrative of the way in which a substance can undergo change.
   c) dependent on the amount of matter.
   d) exhibiting uniform composition throughout and having only one set of properties.

5. An example of a physical change is:

   a) specific heat.
   b) melting of lead.
   c) burning of coal.
   d) rust on steel.

6. If a substance goes through a process that changes its composition so that it is no longer the same substance, then it is said that the substance has undergone a

   a) chemical change.
   b) physical change.
   c) change to a homogenous mixture.
   d) change to a heterogeneous mixture.

CHAPTER 20 - ANSWERS

1. (b)

2. (c)

3. (d)

4. (c)

5. (b)

6. (a)

SKETCHING & ADMINISTRATION

Sketching Fundamentals

LEARNING OUTCOME

When you complete this chapter you should be able to:

Make basic engineering sketches of plant equipment.

LEARNING OBJECTIVES

Here is what you should be able to do when you complete each objective:

1. *Set up a sketch using centre lines and dimensioning.*

2. *Recognize standard views of an object.*

3. *Apply simple techniques for drawing circles, ellipses and parallel lines.*

4. *Apply and recognize cross hatching methods in sectional drawings.*

INTRODUCTION

A technical sketch may be drawn by freehand or with the use of some simple drawing instruments. Its purpose may be to describe a machine part to the person responsible for making the part, or to illustrate an idea without making a formal drawing.

Whatever its particular purpose at the time, a sketch is always a valuable aid to effective communication between Power Engineers. To be able to sketch clearly is one of the most useful abilities a Power Engineer can possess.

OBJECTIVE 1

Set up a sketch using centre lines and dimensioning.

CENTRE LINES

During the operation of a plant, a special repair part may be required which must be made to certain specifications. By means of a sketch, all the necessary information regarding shape and size that is required for the making of the part can be conveyed in a few lines. Without a sketch, it may be a difficult matter to explain verbally or in writing just what is wanted. There will be a greater possibility of error.

Some hints on sketching freehand are included in this chapter. However, it may be just as quick to use a few simple drawing instruments which make a much better job. The following inexpensive instruments are all that are required:

- Two triangles (60° and 45°)

- Scale or ruler

- Compasses

- Pencil

- Eraser

The proper way to make a sketch can be summed up in the following simple instructions:

1. Make sketches large. It is easier to draw on a large scale which shows details more clearly.

2. Begin with the centre lines and take all necessary measurements from them.

3. Make the sketch in proper proportion so that it **looks like** the object it is supposed to represent.

4. Lines needed only for construction purposes, such as centre lines, should be drawn lightly but heavier lines should be used to outline the object being drawn.

5. Print the name of the article (typically) drawn beneath the sketch and put the names of the principal parts on the sketch.

Do not complicate a sketch with unnecessary detail. In answering a question show no more than is asked for but show that on a large scale.

Beginning a sketch by drawing the foundation or centre lines is illustrated by the in Figure 1. This sketch of a knuckle joint is accompanied by three preliminary steps or stages which illustrate how easily a freehand sketch of the right size and proportions can be made when the first half-dozen lines are placed where they belong.

In making this particular sketch, first draw the horizontal centre line and then four horizontal parallel lines spaced so that the inner part of the joint is somewhat wider than the outer sections of the forked member. Next draw a vertical centre line for the pin. The sketch is now as represented in the upper left hand corner of the illustration.

For the second stage, draw lines spaced to suit the pin diameter. Since these lines, excepting at the top, represent a part of the pin that is concealed, they may be drawn in lightly and dotted in afterwards. Draw vertical lines to locate the end of the fork.

The third and fourth stages are then achieved by adding the lines as shown. The resulting sketch shows good proportioning and has all prominent parts clearly drawn and ready for dimensioning.

Figure 1 Sketch of a Knuckle Joint

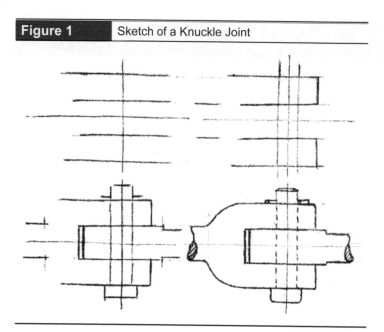

DIMENSIONING

The sketch so far (Fig. 1) only shows a shape. But to be a useful working tool, it must be given size. Figure 2 shows an example of dimensioning on a simple sketch. Note that the points at which the measurements are to be taken are brought out as "extension lines". The dimension line then extends the full distance between these extension lines, with a break for the dimension number.

Figure 2 Typical Dimensions on a Working Drawing

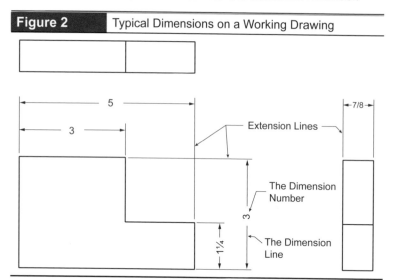

In all sketching, first draw the most important lines which are the ones which establish the main proportions of the sketch and enable this proportioning to be done in a most simple and direct manner. The practical application of this fundamental principle in sketching will be illustrated by the different examples of sketching to follow.

OBJECTIVE 2

Recognize standard views of an object.

STANDARD OBJECT VIEWS

Sketches Requiring One View Only

The sketch in Figure 3(a) shows an American Standard flat-head cap-screw and in Figure 3(b), an American Standard button head machine bolt. The dimensions are provided in SI units.

One view of such simple parts is sufficient. An end view to show that the head is round is unnecessary.

Figure 3	Examples of Sketches Requiring One View Only

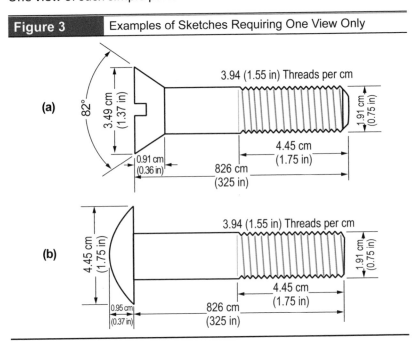

Sketches Requiring Two or More Views

The bracket shown by the sketch in Figure 4 requires three views to represent its shape. The top (or plan) view shows the circular form of the pad (or raised part) on the top of the bracket while the end view at the right shows the shape of the back plate, the width and shape of the central stiffening rib, and the exact locations of the bolt holes. The front view shows the slope of the stiffening rib and the thickness of the raised pad. If any one of the three views is removed, the sketch is incomplete since there is insufficient information to construct the bracket as required.

Figure 4	Sketch of a Bracket Requiring Three Views to Show Its Form

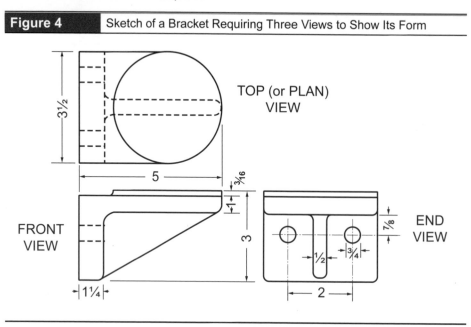

Standard Views

Figure 5 serves to illustrate the standard views used in engineering drawing practice. Six views are shown but there are rarely more than three used. The most commonly used three include:

- Front Elevation
- Plan (or top view)
- One Side Elevation

Figure 5	Six Views of a House

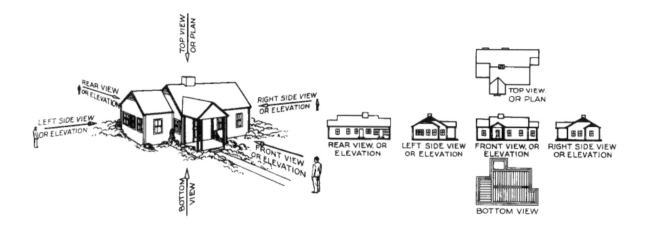

Figure 6 gives further illustration of the six standard views. Note that the front elevation is usually used as the key view. The remaining views are projected from this one.

Figure 6	Six Views

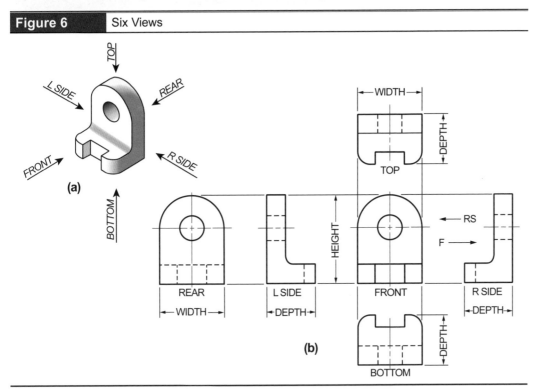

In each case, the view named shows the object as it appears when viewed from the stated direction. For example, the Right Side View shows the appearance of the object when viewed from the right side and so on.

OBJECTIVE 3

Apply simple techniques for drawing circles, ellipses and parallel lines.

BASIC SKETCHING TECHNIQUES

A few simple techniques that can be used to make sketching easier and to improve the quality of your drawings will be discussed in the following sections.

Dividing a Line or a Space into Equal Parts

Lay a scale or ruler across the space so that the required number of divisions can be counted on the scale between the boundary lines. In the example shown in Figure 7, there are 10 - 1/4 cm divisions. Mark these divisions on the paper and draw horizontal lines through these points. This space is then divided into 10 equal parts.

Figure 7	Dividing a Space into Equal Parts

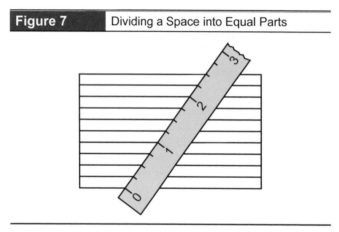

A similar method may be used to divide a line into equal parts when drawing gear teeth as shown in Figure 8.

Figure 8	Dividing a Line into Equal Parts

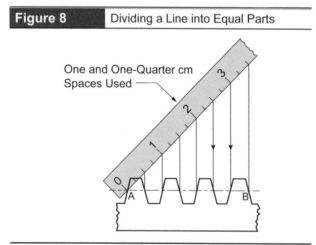

One and One-Quarter cm Spaces Used

Sketching Circles

Small circles and arcs can easily be sketched in one or two strokes; without any preliminary blocking in.

One method of sketching a larger circle, Figure 9(a), is to first sketch lightly the enclosing square and mark the mid-points of the sides, then draw light arcs tangent to the sides of the square; finally darken in the circle.

Another method, Figure 9(b), is to sketch the two centre lines, add 45° radial lines, then draw light arcs across the lines at the estimated radius distance from the centre; finally, sketch the required circle heavily.

Figure 9	Sketching Small Circles

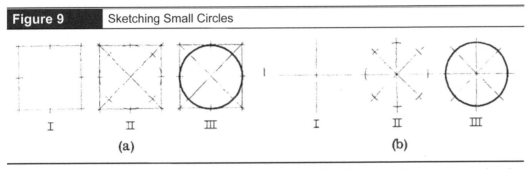

I   II   III   I   II   III

(a)   (b)

Another method, particularly for large circles, Figure 10(a), is to mark the estimated radius on the edge of a card or scrap of paper, set off from the centre as many points as desired, and then sketch the final heavy circle through these points.

Figure 10(b), 10(c) and 10(d) show further suggested methods of sketching circles without the use of drawing instruments.

Figure 10	Sketching Large Circles

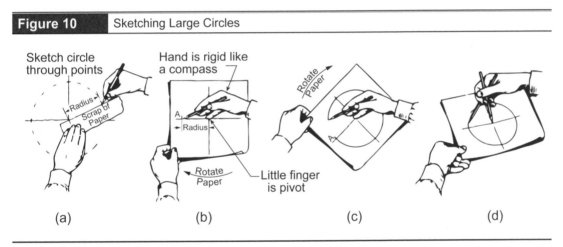

(a)   (b)   (c)   (d)

Sketching Ellipses

If a circle is viewed obliquely, it appears as an ellipse. With a little practice, the student can learn to sketch small ellipses with a free arm movement, as shown in Figure 11(a). Hold the pencil naturally, rest the weight on the upper part of the forearm, and move the pencil rapidly above the paper in the elliptical path desired; then lower the pencil so as to describe the several light ellipses.

Referring to Figure 11(b) - I, another method is to sketch lightly the enclosing rectangle, mark the midpoints of the sides and sketch light tangent arcs, as shown. Then, as seen in II, complete the ellipse lightly.

Figure 11	Sketching an Ellipse

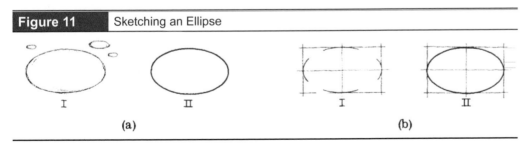

I   II   I   II

(a)   (b)

Finally, the method shown in Figure 12 is a practical approach using a pencil and string.

Figure 12	Ellipse Using Pencil

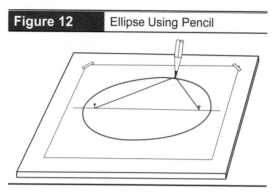

Measuring Angles

In the construction of many figures, diagrams or illustrations of machinery parts, it becomes necessary to measure the angle between two intersecting lines. Figure 13 illustrates the generation of an angle by a rotating arm. Imagine a folding ruler hinged as shown; if one section is held horizontally and the other rotated in a counterclockwise direction, a circle will be traced out by the outer end of the rotating section, the hinge being at the centre of the circle.

When the folding ruler is closed, the angle between the two parts is zero. As the ruler is opened, the angle between the two parts increases. One complete rotation measures out 360° or 90° in each of four quarter turns.

Figure 13	Angular Parts of a Circle

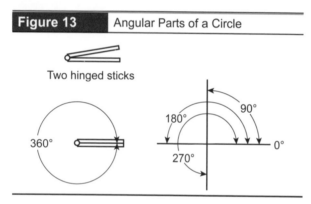

Two hinged sticks

Typical Angle Measurements

Figure 14 illustrates typical angle measurements and Figure 15 shows the instrument, the protractor used to measure angles and the method used to measure an angle of 75°.

Figure 14	Typical Angle Measurements

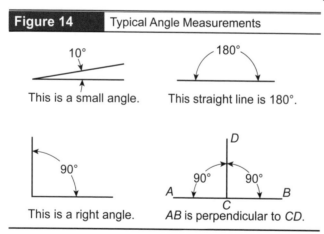

10°
This is a small angle.

180°
This straight line is 180°.

90°
This is a right angle.

90° 90°
AB is perpendicular to CD.

A protractor is used for measuring and laying out angles. To measure an angle with a protractor, set the centre on the vertex of the two lines forming the angle and measure off as shown in Figure 15. The vertex is the point of intersection of two lines.

Figure 15	A Protractor

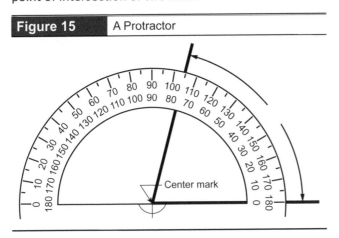

Center mark

Use of Triangles

Triangles may be used to draw lines set at certain angles to each other. The two triangles in use include:

- 45°, 45°, 90°
- 30°, 60°, 90°

Figure 16 shows these triangles set upon a horizontal line (which may be drawn by a T-square) and the angles which they make with that line.

Figure 16	Angles Drawn Using Triangles

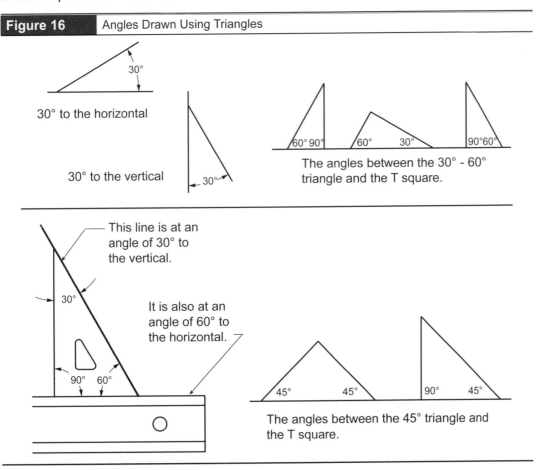

30° to the horizontal

30° to the vertical

The angles between the 30° - 60° triangle and the T square.

This line is at an angle of 30° to the vertical.

It is also at an angle of 60° to the horizontal.

The angles between the 45° triangle and the T square.

Drawing Parallel Lines

One of the main uses of triangles is in the drawing of lines parallel to, or at right angles, to each other. Assuming the triangles are held by the fingers of the left hand, in the position shown in Figure 17 and a horizontal line AB is drawn along the top edge of the upper triangle, then, by holding the lower triangle firmly in the same position and sliding the other triangle upward or downward, lines may be drawn perpendicular to or at right angles to AB. Thus, by sliding the upper triangle to the position shown by the dotted lines in the sketch, CD may be drawn parallel to AB and line DE at right angles to AB.

Figure 17	Drawing Parallel Lines

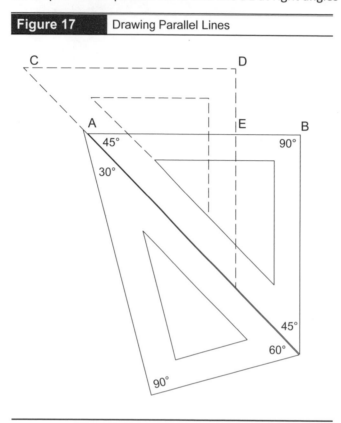

OBJECTIVE 4

Apply and recognize cross hatching methods in sectional drawings.

SECTIONING

In order to show all the necessary details on a sketch, the object is often shown in section, or as it would appear if cut in halves through the centre line and the half next to the observer removed. When this is done, all the parts that are cut through are cross hatched or section lined. Different materials of construction can be indicated by the design of cross hatching used.

Figure18 illustrates the method of section lining parts that are adjacent to each other. Section lines generally should be drawn at an angle of 45°. Two adjacent parts should be sectioned in opposite directions. A third part, adjacent to both, should be sectioned at 30° or 60°.

Figure 18	Section Lining

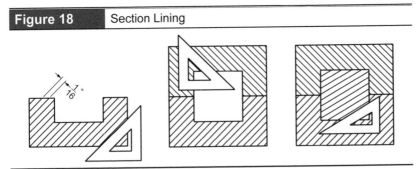

Figure 19 shows the American Standard symbols for sectioning to indicate various materials.

Figure 19	American Standard Symbols

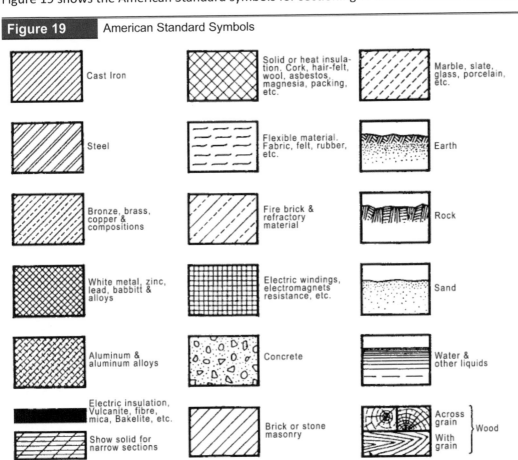

Figure 20 shows a sectioned sketch of a gate valve. Note that the internal details of the valve are illustrated by correct sectioning and the cross hatching used indicates that the material is brass

| Figure 20 | Section Lining in a Valve |

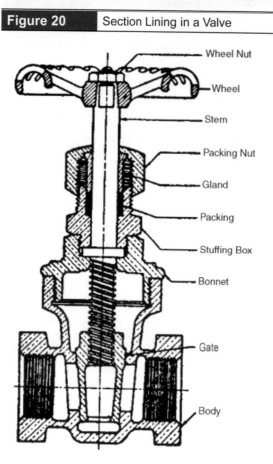

- Wheel Nut
- Wheel
- Stem
- Packing Nut
- Gland
- Packing
- Stuffing Box
- Bonnet
- Gate
- Body

Figure 21 shows the conventional method of indicating breaks in a long rod, tube or shaft where it is inconvenient to draw the whole length, or where it is required to indicate the shape to be used.

| Figure 21 | Indicating Breaks |

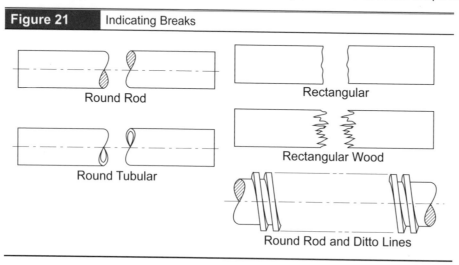

Round Rod

Rectangular

Round Tubular

Rectangular Wood

Round Rod and Ditto Lines

CHAPTER 21 - QUESTIONS

1. Foundation or centre lines of a sketch should be
   a) very bold and extended.
   b) made at the very beginning of the sketch.
   c) made for one view and not extended to other views.
   d) broken lines, not continuous.

2. In order to show all sides of an object being sketched the number of views required is
   a) three.
   b) eight.
   c) four.
   d) six.

3. A drawing instrument commonly used to draw parallel lines is the
   a) ruler.
   b) protractor.
   c) triangle.
   d) compass.

4. Section lines used to indicate specific construction material should generally be drawn at an angle of _____ degrees.
   a) 30
   b) 45
   c) 60
   d) 15

5. The view in an engineering drawing that is usually used as the key view is
   a) front elevation.
   b) side elevation.
   c) plan.
   d) top.

CHAPTER 21 - ANSWERS

1. (b)

2. (d)

3. (c)

4. (b)

5. (a)

Writing Fundamentals I - Sentences

LEARNING OUTCOME

When you complete this chapter you should be able to:

Identify correct and effective sentence structures and revise poorly worded sentences for clarity, conciseness, and correctness.

LEARNING OBJECTIVES

Here is what you should be able to do when you complete each objective:

1. Discuss how clarity, concrete language, conciseness and correctness assist with the creation of good writing skills.

2. Identify and correct errors in the punctuation of sentences.

INTRODUCTION

The typical technologist or engineer spends more time than ever writing. Writing is so important that in most cases the person who advances within any company is the person who not only has knowledge of a technical field, but also can communicate that knowledge to others in a simple, straightforward manner. Most often, communication means putting the information in writing. Therefore, not only does the novelist or journalist need writing skills, but so does any person who has to convey specialized knowledge to others.

This chapter concentrates on three general principles common to all forms of writing. Good writing is always **CLEAR, CONCISE** and **CORRECT**. This chapter will show how these characteristics are reinforced by certain rules of grammar, style, spelling and punctuation.

OBJECTIVE 1

Discuss how clarity, concrete language, conciseness and correctness assist with the creation of good writing skills.

CLARITY

Clarity refers to the quality of being easy to understand at a first reading. Most difficult technical material can be made intelligible by writing clear and complete sentences. Clear writing is vital to effective communication and is achieved by saying exactly what you mean and giving the reader the necessary details using concrete words and phrases.

Clarity can be achieved by observing the following grammatical rules regarding:

- Sentences and sentence fragments
- Run-on sentences
- Agreement
- Active/passive voice verbs

Sentences and Sentence Fragments

The first rule, is that ideas are expressed in sentences. A sentence is simply an idea consisting of a subject, what we are writing about, and a predicate, what we are saying about the subject. A sentence is always a complete thought and should make sense. For example, "Scientists calculate." is a sentence although it consists of only two words. It contains a subject, Scientists, and a predicate, calculate, and it does make some kind of sense.

The single word, "Hurry!", can also be a complete sentence. The subject, "you", is understood but not expressed. On the other hand, the 13 words in the example below are not a sentence because they do not express a complete thought:

Although scientists can solve complicated mathematical problems and put people on the moon

Such sentence fragments are to be avoided. The sentence must express a complete thought:

Although scientists can solve complicated mathematical problems and put people on the moon, poverty in Canada seems to be increasing every year.

Run-on Sentences

The opposite problem would be run-on or fused sentences where two or more complete thoughts are punctuated as one sentence. Two complete thoughts cannot be punctuated as one sentence.

The baby cried, she needed changing. (run-on sentence)

The baby cried she needed changing. (fused sentence)

The sentence can be corrected in several ways:

- Change the comma to a semi-colon or a period.

    The baby cried; she needed changing.

    The baby cried. She needed changing.

- Omit the comma and add a word such as: since or because.

    The baby cried because she needed changing.

Using a run-on or a fused sentence is a drawback to clarity in writing because the readers will tend to treat the two thoughts as one. Thus, they might miss important ideas in your message.

Agreement

Another hindrance to clarity is lack of agreement. Usually, this lack of agreement means that the subject of the sentence is singular while the verb in the sentence is plural or vice-versa. A singular subject always takes a singular verb; whereas, a plural subject always takes a plural verb.

> Incorrect: Every one of the letters were incorrect.
>> Several bottles in the crate seems to be missing.
> Corrected: Every one of the letters was correct.
>> Several bottles in the crate seem to be missing.

A pronoun must also agree with the noun (sometimes called its antecedent). The pronoun must agree with its antecedent in:

- Number
- Gender
- Person

Number

Number refers to singular or plural.

Gender

Gender refers to whether the noun is masculine, feminine, or neuter. In other languages, inanimate objects are masculine or feminine. *Crayon*, the French word for *pencil*, is masculine, while, *mädchen*, the German word for *girl*, is neuter.

Person

Person means either first person **I**, second person **you**, or third person **they**.

Table 1 lists the common personal pronouns by number, gender, and person.

Table 1	Common Personal Pronouns	
Person	**Singular**	**Plural**
1st person	I, me, my, mine	we, us , our, ours
2nd person	you, your, yours	you, your, yours
3rd person		
masculine	he, him, his	
feminine	she, her, hers	they, them, their, theirs
neuter	it, its	

The following additional examples further indicate how the pronouns in the table are used to make the subject agree with its verb.

> Scientists calculate every day. They calculate every day.

The noun **scientists** is plural in number and therefore requires the plural number of the verb, which is **calculated**. If the subject had been **scientist**, the correct form **calculates** would have been used.

> The scientist calculates every day. He calculates every day.

Also, a possessive adjective must agree in gender with the noun it describes.

> The cow had her calf.

The possessive adjective **her** agrees with **cow** in gender and in number.

In the sentence,

> "A group of students was talking."

The singular subject **group** requires the singular verb **was talking**.

Finally, in the sentence,

> "Bruce tried hard; eventually he succeeded."

The pronoun **he** is third person to agree with **Bruce**. The pronoun is also singular and masculine to agree with Bruce, its antecedent. An antecedent is the word that the pronoun **he** takes the place of or refers to. The antecedent of **he** is **Bruce**; the antecedent of **her** is **cow**.

Often, additional problems in agreement arise with pronouns in the following key areas:

- Antecedents
- Collective nouns
- Compound or multiple subjects
- Quantities
- Fractions

Antecedents

Antecedents, such as **each, everyone** and **everybody**, are always singular. Thus, this somewhat clumsy sentence is grammatically correct:

Everyone should go to his or her locker.

Everyone is singular and needs the singular **his** or **her** to agree with the antecedent **everyone**. A less awkward way of saying the same thing would be to make the whole sentence plural.

All students should go to their lockers.

Collective Nouns

Collective nouns, such as **team** and **group**, are usually singular when thought of as a unit, but plural when thought of as individuals within the unit.

Our team is winning this year.

The team is thought of as a single unit. However, if the team is thought of as individuals within the unit, use the plural pronoun.

Our team is getting into their uniforms.

Compound or Multiple Subjects

Compound or multiple subjects joined by **or** or **nor** such as **either . . . or** and **neither . . . nor** agree in number with the closer part of the subject.

Either the president or the two vice-presidents are going to attend.

Either the two vice-presidents or the president is going to attend.

Quantities

Quantities are always singular.

Nineteen dollars is a low price.

Fractions

Fractions of singular things are always singular.

Two thirds of the population is under 20.

Additional problems arise with pronouns when the antecedent for the pronoun is not made clear. The worst disaster in aviation history happened because the pilot mistakenly assumed that the control tower was referring to the fourth **cleared** runway rather than the fourth runway. In other words, the antecedent for the **fourth one** referred to in the transcript of the tape was the actual fifth runway for the pilot, but the actual fourth one for the control tower. Most of us are familiar with other less horrendous pronoun problem situations.

A pronoun must clearly refer to its antecedent. The pronoun reference in these two sentences is unclear:

This nail is proving difficult. Here's the hammer. When I nod my head, you hit it.

Richard smashed his car against the side of his house which was not insured.

In both sentences, the student needs to make clear which nouns the pronouns **it** and **which** refer to.

To avoid such problems, do not use a pronoun unless it has a clear antecedent. If there is any doubt about the antecedent, repeat the noun. Rather than say

> "Justin and I went to Joshua's place because he was lonely.",

say

> "Justin and I went to Joshua's house because Justin (or Joshua) was lonely."

In summary, make sure the pronoun or verb agrees with its antecedent or subject in number, gender and person.

Active/Passive Voice

Active voice sentences improve clarity as they generally have more impact than passive voice sentences. Active voice means the subject of the sentence performs the action of the verb. It has nothing to do with past tense. Active voice verbs can be past or present tense.

> He took a reading.

The subject **He** performs the action of the verb **took** and the verb **took** is therefore, said to be in the active voice. The opposite of active voice is passive voice which means the subject has the action of the verb performed on it.

> The reading was taken.

Since the subject **reading** has the action performed on it, it is said to be passive. Active voice is usually more forceful and concise than passive voice. In the example given, the passive voice usage is only the same length as the active sentence because some information, such as who actually did the reading, is omitted. Passive voice often needs to include a prepositional phrase to indicate the performer of the action.

> The car was driven by John.

The prepositional phrase **by John** is needed to show who drove the car. The active sentence would read,

> John drove the car.

Not only is the sentence shorter, but it is known quickly and clearly who drove the car.

In technical writing, the active voice is preferred with two exceptions:

1. Use the passive voice to avoid blaming a particular person or to be tactful or diplomatic.

   Passive: An error was made in the accounting office.

   Active: The accounting office made an error.

   Using the active voice might be seen as blaming a particular person.

2. Use the passive voice when the person who performs the action is not important.

   Passive: The show was seen by millions.

   Active: Millions saw the show.

In addition, the passive voice always uses a helping verb such as: **is, am, are, was, were or has been** along with the past participle of the verb.

> Passive: Katrina was given a job in personnel.

Given is the past participle of the verb **to give** and **was,** is the helping or auxiliary verb. The active sentence would be written,

> Syncrude gave Katrina a job in personnel.

CONCRETE LANGUAGE

Concrete and specific words, stand in opposition to abstract and general words. Concrete words refer to physical objects, concepts and generalizations; concrete ideas can be measured or verified. Abstract language, on the other hand, is often non-specific and subject to many interpretations. Technical writing is usually characterized by the use of specific, concrete writing, expressing a single message clearly. Table 2 shows similar ideas expressed in abstract and concrete terms.

Table 2	Abstract and Concrete Terms
Abstract or Vague	**Concrete or Specific**
Vehicle	1991 Eagle Vista
Very Hot	35 degrees Celsius
Soon	by January 20
Heavy	85 kilograms
Communications	letter

In technical reports, the student must constantly strive to be as concrete and specific, as possible. Table 3 shows how the sentences on the left can be improved to make them clear.

Table 3	Abstract and Concrete Sentences
Abstract or Vague	**Concrete or Specific**
The oil should be changed at frequent intervals.	Change the oil every 12 days.
Recently it was indicated that a large percentage of people contacted has some knowledge of the chemical.	A Globe and Mail survey in November indicated that 70% of employees knew the dangers of sodium chloride.
A large majority of those voting supported Ralph.	59% voted for Ralph
The deficit has been very substantially reduced in the last 12 months.	Since last year, the deficit has been reduced from $8 million to $2 million.

CONCISENESS

Conciseness means using the minimum number of words to express oneself clearly and correctly. Most experts in writing suggest that sentences should be short and specific. By short, the same experts mean that the ideal sentence is between 15 and 20 words long. Not every sentence should be within those narrow limits, but very few sentences should be over 25 words. Often, in writing, the student may use phrases that can be shortened without losing any meaning. These redundant or long-winded phrases can be changed as in Table 4.

Table 4	Wordy and Weak Phrases
Wordy & Weak Phrases	**Concise Version**
with the result that	therefore
in the event that	if
at this point in time	now
failed to negotiate	missed
as a result	so
in order to	to
in the area of	about, approximately
first of all	firstly
for this reason	because
small in size and stature	short
large in size	large
basic fundamentals	fundamentals
exactly identical	identical

CORRECTNESS

Correctness means the information is accurate and mechanically correct. Clear writing must also be correct. In order for writing to be taken seriously in business and industry, it must be mechanically correct. Incorrect writing or careless proofreading can create doubt of your ability to document evidence accurately or correctly in the minds of readers. The students' writing presents an image of their company and, as such, presents a more professional image by avoiding faulty grammar, careless spelling and word usage, and by punctuating sentences to make their writing easier to understand.

Spelling and Word Usage

Many people have remarked on the difficulties of English spelling in general. Some of these difficulties can be eliminated by the use of spell check on a computer program. Although spell check will spot a number of misspellings, every document must still be proofread carefully to spot words that are spelled correctly but are used incorrectly. Other spelling errors can be eliminated by mastering the following simple spelling rules:

- I before E
- Its and it's
- Their, there, they're
- Who's, whose
- You're, your
- Choose, chose

- Loose, lose
- Personal, personnel
- Principal, principle
- Were, where
- Weather, whether

I before E

In words containing the ie or ei combination, follow the rule learned in grade school:

Use "I before E except after C".

Unfortunately, not all of us learned the next part of the rule which states:

or when pronounced "a" as in "neighbour" and "weigh".

This simple rule enables us to spell correctly words such as:

- Believe
- Receive
- Eighty

The above examples illustrate all **three** parts of the rule. Several exceptions, however, are illustrated in the following two sentences:

Neither leisured foreigner seized weird heights.

A species of sheik uses caffeine, codeine and protein.

The main purpose of this section is not to review spelling, but to give a few hints on using commonly confused words. These words, which a computer spell check cannot correct, are homonyms or homophones—words which sound similar, but have different spelling and meaning.

Its and It's

Some of us may have learned that **the apostrophe indicates possession**. This statement is at most a half-truth since the apostrophe also indicates a contraction or the omission of a letter or letters and only indicates possession with nouns, not with pronouns. The following examples illustrate the apostrophe used to show possession or indicate a contraction:

It's late and past the boy's bedtime.

The first apostrophe indicates the letter **i** has been omitted; the second indicates that boys is possessive.

We'll win although it's still anybody's game.

Only the last apostrophe is an indication of the possessive; the first two both indicate missing letters.

It's his dog that is chasing its tail.

The first example of **it's** is the contraction and the second example of **its** is the possessive. Pronouns such as **its, hers, his and theirs** are already possessive in form and do not need the apostrophe.

An easy way to distinguish between the two words is that **it's** is always a contraction of **it is** and **its** is always possessive.

Their, There, They're

Another set of troublesome words are **their, there** and **they're. Their** is possessive; **there** is an adverb which indicates place or direction; **they're** is a contraction of **they are**.

> They're picking up their books which are over there.

Who's, Whose

Who's is a contraction of **who is** while **whose** is an adjective or a pronoun.

> Who's asking about whose books these are?

You're, Your

You're is a contraction of **you are** while **your** is a possessive.

> You're lucky your marks are so high.

Choose, Chose

Choose is the present tense; **chose** is the past tense of the verb meaning to select.

> Will you choose an easy topic?

> When I was asked to pick a topic, I chose an easy one.

Loose, Lose

Loose usually means not fastened while **lose** means to misplace or suffer a defeat.

> If you keep your money loose, you may lose it.

Personal, Personnel

Personal means private while **personnel** usually refers to the department of a business organization that looks after employee information.

> Don't divulge personal information.

> She works in the personnel department.

Principal, Principle

Principal can mean the head of a school or a major player in a company or action. In both cases, it has the meaning of chief or main person. In addition, **principal** can be an adjective meaning chief or main.

> Farming used to be Alberta's principal occupation.

Also, when we make a mortgage payment, it is usually divided into **principal** and **interest**.

Principle, on the other hand, is always a noun meaning rule or law.

> It's not the money but the **principle** of the matter that concerns me.

Were, Where

Were is the past tense of the verb **to be; where** usually indicates direction.

> We were going to Edmonton where we hoped to have a good time.

Weather, Whether

Weather is a noun referring to climate while **whether** introduces a direct or indirect question.

> The weather will determine whether we can ski or not.

OBJECTIVE 2

Identify and correct errors in the punctuation of sentences.

PUNCTUATION

Knowledge of punctuation is essential for correctness and for clarity. In a speaking situation, the student can use different types of non-verbal information to help the listener understand the message. However, in writing, with the absence of these non-verbal cues, punctuation must be used to help clarity and ease of reading. The following are some of the most common punctuation marks to aid in achieving clarity:

- Comma
- Semi-colon
- Colon
- Apostrophe

Comma

The **comma** is mainly used for separation. Use the comma to separate two main clauses joined by **but, for, nor** and **or**.

> The report was mailed last week, but I did not receive a copy until today.

Use the comma to separate an introductory word, phrase or clause from the rest of the sentence.

> Finally, I completed the course.

> Because my car would not start, I was late for the meeting.

Use a comma to separate words or phrases in a series.

> I have worked in Ontario, British Columbia and Alberta.

Use the comma to separate interrupters and/or non-essential information from the rest of the sentence.

> John, however, was not present.

> The house, which was built in 1912, is a terrible eyesore.

Make sure you distinguish between the previous sentence and a sentence such as:

> The house which is solidly built will last for years.

The clause **which is solidly built** is essential to the sentence and indicates that only that type will last for years. Because it is essential to the meaning of the sentence, no commas are required.

Use commas to separate the different parts of dates and addresses.

> What were you doing on January 25, 1993?

> He lives at 212 Dunvegan Road, Toronto.

Semi-Colon

The **semi-colon** can be regarded as a weak period. It often separates two closely connected ideas.

> The baby walked softly; he couldn't walk heavily.

The semi-colon, rather than the comma, has to be used since both parts of the sentence are complete thoughts. A period could be used after **softly** in place of the semi-colon. Semi-colons are also used when those two closely related ideas are separated by a word or a phrase such as: **however, accordingly, nevertheless, thus** or **for example**. These words or phrases can be classified as transitional expressions and show the relationship between the two clauses. Usually, the transitional expression is preceded by a semi-colon and followed by a comma. Again, such sentences could also be punctuated by using a period at the end of the first idea and beginning a new sentence with the transitional expression.

The following is a list of the more common transitional expressions:

accordingly	however
also	In conclusion
besides	in fact
consequently	moreover
finally	namely
for example	namely
for instance	therefore
furthermore	thus

Here are some examples of sentences using these transitions.

> Jim is very thrifty; for example, he bought all his stamps on December 3—just before the price went up.

> No scientist can produce a temperature of absolute zero; however, Calgary's winter temperature sometimes comes close.

Semi-colons should also be used to separate items in a series when one or more of the items already have internal punctuation.

> On their honeymoon, they visited Trail, British Columbia; Pincher Creek, Alberta; and Moose Jaw, Saskatchewan.

Compare with

> On their honeymoon, they visited Trail, Pincher Creek and Moose Jaw.

To sum up, use a semi-colon or a period to separate two complete thoughts. Use a semi-colon before and a comma after a transitional expression that links the complete thoughts. Finally, use semi-colons to separate a series of items if the items themselves contain internal punctuation.

Colon

In technical writing, the **colon** is probably used more often than the semi-colon.

- The colon is used to introduce formal lists frequently used in reports.
- The colon is used to introduce explanations.
- The colon alerts the reader to special information.

When introducing a list with a colon, ensure that the information before the colon is a complete thought.

I can't stand three things: peanut butter, pollution and politicians.

I can't stand peanut butter, pollution and politicians.

A colon after **stand** in the second example would be incorrect since the statement up to the word **stand** is incomplete. To give another example, do not use a colon to introduce an informal series.

We visited Edinburgh, Scotland; London, England and Oslo, Norway.

But use a colon following the complete thought in introducing the list as in this sentence:

We visited three cities: Edinburgh, Scotland; London, England and Oslo, Norway.

A colon tells the reader that an explanation follows.

Today's student needs one skill above all others: computer literacy.

A colon is also used to introduce a quotation if the introduction to the quotation is a complete thought.

Oscar Wilde had a flair for rewriting popular sayings: "Work is the curse of the drinking classes."

The colon is also used in expressions such as 7:30a.m. and in the salutation or attention and subject line of a letter.

Dear Mary Hart:

Attention: Occupational Health and Safety

Subject: RECOMMENDATION TO RENOVATE THE COMPUTER ROOM to sum up, a colon is a punctuation mark which alerts the reader to some special feature such as: a list, an explanation or a quotation.

Apostrophe

The **apostrophe** performs two main functions:

1. It indicates that a letter or letters have been omitted. In fact, the apostrophe is an indicator of where the missing letter(s) should be inserted.

   You'll see that they're on time, won't you?

In technical writing, avoid the use of too many contractions.

2. With nouns, it shows possession. Using the following rules for forming the possessive for nouns:

- If the noun ends in **any letter except s**, add **'s**.
- If the noun ends in **s**, add **'**.

Some writers prefer to add 's if the word ending in s has only one syllable, as in **the boss's decision** and **Burns's poems**. Also, distinguish words such as **company's, companies'** and **companies**.

My company's retirement policy is progressive.

Many companies' policies are similar.

Some companies do not have any policy.

The word **policies** in the second sentence and **companies** in the third sentence are plural and since they are not possessive, they don't require the apostrophe.

CHAPTER 22 - QUESTIONS

1. If the subject of a sentence is singular and the verb is plural, we have what is known as
   a) a run-on sentence.
   b) a lack of agreement.
   c) a passive voice.
   d) an active voice.

2. A more forceful and concise voice term is the _____ voice.
   a) active voice
   b) passive voice

3. An ideal sentence should be between _____ and _____ words long.
   a) 5, 10
   b) 20, 25
   c) 15, 20
   d) 10, 15

4. Unlike nouns, the possessive form of pronouns does NOT use a/an:
   a) colon.
   b) semi-colon.
   c) comma.
   d) apostrophe.

5. When introducing formal lists in a report, we normally use a
   a) comma.
   b) semi-colon.
   c) period.
   d) colon.

6. An apostrophe is used to:
   a) separate sentences that mean the same thing.
   b) join two unrelated ideas.
   c) show possession.
   d) separate interrupters.

CHAPTER 22 - ANSWERS

1. (b)

2. (a)

3. (c)

4. (d)

5. (d)

6. (c)

Writing Fundamentals II - Paragraphs

LEARNING OUTCOME

When you complete this chapter you should be able to:

Write a unified, coherent paragraph using a clear topic sentence, technical terminology and specific support, given a technical topic.

LEARNING OBJECTIVES

Here is what you should be able to do when you complete each objective:

1. *Discuss the structure, unity and coherence of a paragraph.*

2. *Identify the common patterns of paragraph development and summarize the rules for effective paragraphs.*

INTRODUCTION

Some of the same characteristics that make sentences effective apply equally to paragraphs. Like sentences, paragraphs must be structured to posses unity in that they are limited to one key idea. Also, like sentences, paragraphs should be clear and concise. In addition, an effective paragraph should be coherent in that the sentences are arranged in a logical sequence. Finally, a paragraph should have adequate development of a central or key idea. A well-structured paragraph has these three qualities: **unity, coherence** and **adequate development.**

Experienced writers use tone and emphasis to suit the topic. They also adjust the lengths of the different paragraphs they use so that a certain sense of variety, in addition to the other qualities mentioned, is achieved.

OBJECTIVE 1

Discuss the structure, unity and coherence of a paragraph.

PARAGRAPH STRUCTURE

Paragraphs serve as groupings of related sentences about discussing one idea. Often, a paragraph focuses thought and structures ideas in bite-size chunks that can be absorbed by the reader easily in a single reading. There is no one correct paragraph length.

- In typical academic essays, paragraphs may be ten sentences long and may consist of two hundred words.

- In a newspaper article, most paragraphs tend to be two or three sentences long and are seldom more than fifty words.

- In technical writing, most paragraphs tend to be four to seven sentences long and around one hundred words.

The key idea in each paragraph should be fully developed without any repetition. If the idea is very complex, each of its aspects should be dealt with in a separate paragraph. A detailed, fully developed explanation is more likely to convince your reader than a superficial overview in an extremely short paragraph.

An essential element in any paragraph is the **topic sentence**. In junior high, the student learned that the topic sentence is the key sentence in the paragraph and comes at the beginning. Later, it was learned that, in fact, the topic sentence can come anywhere in the paragraph. Later still, we learned that some paragraphs do not have a topic sentence since a professional writer can often carry the idea along without explicit signposts represented by the topic sentence. In technical writing, however, eighty percent of the time the topic sentence **should** come at the beginning of the paragraph.

There are several reasons why it is more effective to have the topic sentence at the opening:

- Since the topic sentence, sometimes called the control sentence, is the key or main sentence, it helps the reader when this key information is presented at the opening. The reader is then able to focus on the supporting sentences which back up this key information in the rest of the paragraph.

- The reader can read more efficiently when this key information is presented at the opening of the paragraph. If the reader is in a hurry, he or she can read only the opening sentence in each paragraph and still get the gist of the total information.

- Writers are more able to focus their thoughts so that the rest of the paragraph follows a logical pattern. They are then better able to develop the supporting evidence using the opening sentence as a focal point.

In addition to the topic sentence, many paragraphs end with a **summary**, or **clincher sentence**, which reinforces the key idea stated at the opening. This type of paragraph is more common in essays than in other types of writing. Occasionally, this type of paragraph is also found in more formal types of technical writing.

The following paragraph illustrates some of the above points:

> **The cellular telephone is a portable communication device with an integral transmitter-receiver and a whip antenna**. It communicates with a transmitter-receiver located within a city and its surrounding area. Each transmitter has a range of up to 12 kilometres. The area covered is called a cell, from which the name cellular has evolved. If a caller drives from one cell to another, the calls are transferred automatically from one cell to another.

(Adapted from R. Blicq. *Technically Write*)

This paragraph consists of five sentences with the topic sentence at the opening. The topic sentence suggests the paragraph will give information about the cellular telephone and the remaining four sentences do that. Because it is a comparatively brief paragraph, there is no need for a clincher sentence at the end.

Here is another example:

> **Laptop computers have become increasingly popular.** They can weigh as little as two kilograms and can easily be fitted into a briefcase. They are also inexpensive and can be purchased for under $700. However, they normally do not have a printer. They also have a much smaller memory than a PC and limited capability. **For many, however, these disadvantages are outweighed by the advantages.**

(Adapted from R. Blicq. *Technically Write*)

Again, this example has the topic sentence at the opening, but also has a clincher sentence at the end. The first paragraph simply expanded on the characteristics of the cellular telephone; whereas, the second example gave both advantages and disadvantages of the laptop computer. Because of this differentiation, the writer felt it necessary to tie both of these elements together in the sixth sentence which summarizes and links up with the opening topic sentence.

If the student were to illustrate those two paragraph development patterns, the first would resemble a triangle like the one shown in Figure 1.

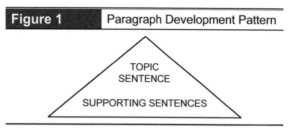

Figure 1   Paragraph Development Pattern

The second would resemble a diamond, as shown in Figure 2.

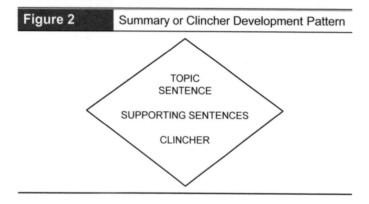

Figure 2   Summary or Clincher Development Pattern

PARAGRAPH UNITY

Despite their slightly different development patterns, both these paragraphs illustrate the principle of unity. In each of them, all the sentences relate to the same key idea. Look at the following example where this isn't the case. (The sentences are numbered for ease of reference.)

1. In the last few years, thousands of people have left the oil and gas industry entirely or have gone overseas to make a living.

2. Some experts estimate that when the rig count reaches 275, Alberta is in a crisis situation.

3. In 1985, there were 80 drilling contractors open for business in Canada.

4. Last week, there were 260 rigs operating which means the problem will be even greater in January and February.

(Adapted from *Calgary Herald*)

The four sentences all relate to problems in the oil and gas industry, as indicated by the opening topic sentence, but sentence (3) appears to deal with the situation of drilling contractors in 1985; whereas, sentences (2) and (4) relate to the present number of rigs. In other words, including sentence (3) in the paragraph violates the principles of unity.

Here is another example:

My roommate Randy is probably the brightest student at College. His IQ is so high that the last time he was tested it went off the scale. He has A's in every course he is taking this semester—all twelve of them. The mathematics teacher often asks him for help with the more difficult problems. Doctor Polyani, a Nobel prize winner in chemistry, often chats with him on the phone about their latest research. There are two other really bright people in my class this year also. Randy served on the budget committee and this year the deficit has been reduced by six million dollars. People as bright as Randy only come along once in a generation.

Sentence six beginning, **There are two other**, does not really belong in the paragraph. All the other sentences relate to the intelligence of Randy, but sentence six introduces a new idea. To sum up, every sentence in a paragraph should relate to a central idea normally announced in the topic sentence. Although the topic sentence can come anywhere in the paragraph, it is often more effective when placed at the opening.

COHERENCE

Coherence in sentences and paragraphs refers to the arrangement of ideas in a logical, orderly sequence. A coherent paragraph moves smoothly from one aspect of the central idea to the next, in an orderly fashion with no confusing gaps between statements.

Ensuring coherence often is part of the revision process, where the first draft is revised to ensure that each sentence relates to the previous and the subsequent sentence in grammar and structure. Of the many ways to achieve coherence, the following list indicates some of the most common:

- Transitional expressions
- Pronouns
- Repetition of words and ideas
- Parallel structure

Transitional Expressions

Transitional expressions are words and phrases that connect ideas expressed in a paragraph or in sentences. Transition means going across or linking.

Look at the following example:

> There are three reasons why many people believe an institution that concentrates on teaching specific skills in a narrow area is short-changing its students. **Firstly**, the workplace changes so rapidly that what may be relevant one year may be redundant the next. **Secondly**, students will have to constantly upgrade and develop their skills to cope with a rapidly evolving world economy, whether they take this upgrading in a formal setting or not. **Thirdly**, most students must learn broad humanizing skills to enable them to be better world citizens. Since learning is life-long, teaching students how to study and acquire new skills should be the function of every educational institute.

The three words in bold, **Firstly, Secondly** and **Thirdly**, are examples of transition words aimed at improving the coherence of the paragraph.

Table 1 indicates other specific transition words or phrases used to achieve coherence:

Table 1	Transitional Expressions
Types	**Transitional Words and Phrases**
Addition	Also, in addition, and, next, then, finally
Comparison	Similarly, in the same way, in comparison
Contrast	But, however, nevertheless, on the contrary
Example	Thus, namely, for example, for instance
Place	In the front, adjacent to, in the distance, near
Result	Therefore, consequently, with the result that, thus, so, so that
Sequence	First, second, third, firstly, secondly, thirdly, then, eventually, finally, afterwards, meanwhile, subsequently
Summary	In summary, to sum up, in conclusion, finally

If a paragraph length in a report extends beyond eight or ten lines, the paragraph can also be divided into numbered subparagraphs as illustrated below:

There are three reasons why many people believe that an institution that concentrates on teaching specific skills in a narrow area is short changing its students.

1. The workplace changes so rapidly that what may be relevant one year may be redundant the next year.

2. Students will have to constantly upgrade and change their skills to cope with a rapidly evolving world economy whether they take this upgrading in a formal educational setting or not.

3. Most students have to learn broad humanizing skills to enable them to be better world citizens.

Since learning is life-long, teaching students how to study and acquire new skills should be the function of every educational institute.

The numbers are used to improve the appearance of long paragraphs, but they can also take the place of transition words. The paragraph is still coherent in that the ideas in it are connected to the topic sentence.

Pronouns

Pronouns referring clearly to nouns or other pronouns can also help to connect ideas in a paragraph. For example, in the previous paragraph about Randy, the words, **He, his** and **him**, are **pronouns** referring to Randy which maintain the coherence of the paragraph. In the paragraph about laptop computers, the words, **they** and **these**, similarly help to maintain the coherence of the paragraph.

Repetition

Repetition is a third method used to achieve coherence in a paragraph. A key word used to express an idea in the topic sentence is repeated in a supporting sentence to link the idea expressed in the paragraph.

Here is a paragraph that achieves its coherence by the third method, repetition:

> The standard **textbooks** on technical communication give speaking very short shrift. Many otherwise excellent **texts** deal solely with the writing aspect and exclude by their very title all other aspects. Most of the remaining technical **textbooks** give little space to oral communications; the majority devotes fewer than four pages to it. **Textbooks** that give more extensive space to the topic usually incorporate the information in a single chapter, which is also devoted to listening.

The word **text** or **textbook** is repeated three times after its use in the first sentence.

Parallel Structure

Parallel structure, the most complex of the four methods used to achieve coherence, uses the same sentence or phrase pattern several times in a paragraph to achieve a rhythm that unifies the paragraph. Parallel structure is often used in technical writing to reinforce connection among ideas, but this structure has to be introduced in a deliberate and concise way. It uses a more complex form of repetition of structure in sentences or phrases rather than of single words. Here is a non-technical paragraph that achieves coherence by use of parallel structure:

The Beatles were already famous when they were "discovered" by Ed Sullivan in February, 1964. In Britain, **they had three consecutive chart toppers, they had appeared before the Queen at the Royal Command Performance and they had been voted the number one group of 1963.** In addition, they had toured Europe successfully several times and had top hits in Europe, in Hong Kong and in Australia. They also had their own radio show and were preparing to make their first movie. Only in North America were the Beatles unknown.

The parallelism of the three clauses in sentence two and the three phrases in sentence three reinforce the coherence of the paragraph. The paragraph also makes use of other methods of achieving coherence:

- The transitional phrase **In addition** is used in sentence three and the transitional word **also** in sentence four.
- The pronoun **they** is used several times throughout the paragraph.
- The past perfect tense of verbs characterized by the use of the word **had** is used several times.

This particular example illustrates that often a combination of techniques is used to achieve coherence.

OBJECTIVE 2

Identify the common patterns of paragraph development and summarize the rules for effective paragraphs.

PARAGRAPH DEVELOPMENT

Although there are over a dozen different patterns of paragraph the student should first examine the introductory and concluding paragraphs of a business document.

Introductory and Concluding Paragraphs

A short memo may, in fact, contain one single paragraph, but the introductory paragraph always lays the foundation for the remainder of the information in a report. A good introductory paragraph answers the journalistic questions: who, what, where, when, why and how; and like the news article, much of the key information is stated in the opening paragraph of a letter, memo or report. However, unlike a news article, the key information is often restated in specific terms in the conclusion of the report. The news article trails off into less significant details because the writer knows the editor may trim off the ending of it. On the other hand, the technical writer is deliberately repetitive and may state the key information three times:

- In general terms at the opening

- In specific details in the body

- In terms of future implications at the conclusion

The typical introductory paragraph in technical writing covers the origin, purpose and scope of the topic. It does not attempt to give all the information, but just enough so that the reader can decide whether the information is relevant or should be passed on to someone else who will be better able to act on it. Unlike the essayist who may anticipate the reader is going to read the whole essay, the technical report writer has to cater to a variety of different readers, only some of whom will read the whole document. Table 2 contrasts the difference between typical methods used in the introduction of the technical report and the essay.

Table 2	Typical Methods
Technical Report Opening	**Essay Opening**
Statistics	Anecdote
Definition of terms	Quotation
Identification of situation	Specific example
Background Information	Analogy
Purpose and scope of report	Thesis Statement

The concluding paragraph of any report should bring the discussion to a logical end. It should neither be too abrupt nor a mere restatement of previous ideas. It should leave the reader with a sense of completeness and a clear indication of what the next step should be. New material should not be introduced and no minor points from the body of the report should be recalled. Some possible devices for writing concluding paragraphs include the following:

- Summarizing key points

- Indicating future action

- Suggesting a change(s)

Patterns of Paragraph Development

All paragraphs must make use of sufficient detail to ensure that the paragraph has developed the topic fully enough to convey the writer's purpose to the reader. **RENNS** is a useful acronym to help remember some of the main methods of developing the details in a paragraph (Adapted from Simon & Schuster. *Handbook for Writers.* 2nd ed.). RENNS stands for:

- **R**easons
- **E**xamples
- **N**ames
- **N**umbers
- **S**enses (sight, smell, sound, taste and touch)

This device does not mean that every paragraph uses all categories, nor that the details of the development take place in any particular order. Read the following paragraph and see how many RENNS you can locate:

> The Canadian Association of Oilwell Drilling Contractors (CAODC) forecasts that 5200 wells will be drilled in Canada during 1993, compared to 4800 wells this year. CAODC also predicts that an average of 143 drilling rigs will work throughout 1993 compared to 124 rigs in 1992. With only 414 rigs expected to be available in 1993 compared to 436 in 1992, this prediction means a 35% utilization rate compared to 1992's rate of 28%. Art Hibbarb, president of the association, believes that 1992 will prove to be "the worst of the worst."

> (Adapted from *Calgary Herald*)

The paragraph contains the first four of the five types of RENNS. The student might also have noticed that the topic sentence is the last rather than the first as the key idea is that the oil and gas industry has turned the corner. Overall, RENNS is useful in showing methods of making any of our generalizations specific.

In any piece of writing, the paragraphs have to be developed by a logical pattern appropriate for the subject matter. Whatever the pattern of development used in a paragraph, the information has to be carefully selected. If necessary, tell the reader beforehand the basis of that selection. Often, the writer will indicate the pattern of development in the introductory section or in the topic sentence. Various patterns of paragraph development include:

- Chronological
- Spatial
- Comparison and contrast
- Reason and examples
- Process

Chronological

The chronological pattern of paragraph development presents the information in the order in which it happened. In technical writing, the chronological approach is often used for progress reports covering a short period, historical events, instructions and explanation of a process or procedure. The example is a paragraph using the chronological pattern of development:

> On February 13, 1947, the discovery of oil at Leduc ushered in a new era in Alberta. Further discoveries were made in the Leduc-Woodbend area so that by 1948 there were 131 productive wells. By 1949, there were over 350 and by 1951, over 800. Additional discoveries made at Pembina in 1953 and Swan Hills in 1957 ensured that by 1971, petroleum and its related products had superseded agriculture as the mainstay of the Alberta economy.

Here is another example of an introductory paragraph serving as a preview of the succeeding paragraphs:

> Scotland's greatest poet was born in the hamlet of Alloway in Southern Scotland on January 25, 1759. His early years were spent tending to the chores on the family farm. After several unhappy love affairs, he was contemplating emigrating to the West Indies when he learned of the success of his first publication, a book of Scots poetry. Later he married and moved to Dumfries where he died in 1796. His name was Robert Burns and his poetry has become famous the world over.

The following paragraph uses the chronological pattern of development to explain a completed procedure:

> First, a physical modelling method was used to confirm the initial mathematical models of windbox airflow. Then, a scale model of the windbox was built and water was pumped through it to simulate airflow. Next, tiny plastic shears of neutral buoyancy were introduced and their movement was observed. Finally, based on these observations, baffles were installed and the test was rerun.
>
> (Adapted from *Power Engineering*)

To sum up, use the chronological approach if the order of events is particularly important and if the events themselves are important enough to be of significance to the reader.

Spatial

Spatial order is occasionally referred to as location and usually involves the positioning of places or objects relative to each other. Usually, the topic sentence provides this central point of reference that orientates all the other places mentioned. Here is an example:

> As we entered the house, we were met by the stench of animals, both dogs and cats. The unheated front porch was subject to drafts as I could hear the constant whistle of the wind. Beyond, the minute living room was cramped with oversized furniture which impeded our progress. Off the living room, the kitchen retained the odor of the previous night's meal, liver and onions. Looking out the kitchen window, I could discern in the yard two dog runs and an abandoned Ford. The asking price of the house was $159 900.

Technical descriptions of mechanisms are also often arranged in spatial order. The description might begin with a general overall view of the mechanism followed by a specific description of the parts. The organization used in describing these parts is spatial which might be **from outside to inside, top to bottom, the order in which the parts work or are put together.**

When writing a paragraph organized according to the spatial pattern, ensure that you use adequate transitions to reinforce the sense of movement.

Comparison and Contrast

A comparison and contrast paragraph shows both similarities and differences between objects, people or ideas. The following paragraph compares and contrasts solar energy with more conventional energy sources:

> Solar energy makes use of the largely untapped and unlimited energy of the sun. Its rays are nonpolluting, renewable and not subject to manipulation by any multinational corporation. It is natural, creates no disposal problem and is clean and convenient. However, being natural, solar energy is subject to the vagaries of climate. It also requires expensive initial construction costs. In addition, some people find the sight of collectors on rooftops and the side of buildings to be a mere substitution of a new form of visual pollution for the old.

Here is another example, which compares and contrasts a memo and a business letter:

> Letters and memos have both similarities and differences. Both business letters and memos are written in a vocational context as part of our work duties. Both tend to be short and relatively informal. Both should be clear, concise, correct and enable the reader to focus on the key information immediately. However, the memo is an internal document that stays within the organization while the letter is an external document and goes to a reader outside the organization. Typically, we have a close working relationship with the reader of our memo while we may not ever have met the person who reads our letter. Finally, the formats of letters and memos are vastly different.

When writing comparison and contrast paragraphs, it is best to have at least three similarities and differences in the paragraphs. Fewer than that tends to leave the paragraph undeveloped and the reader unconvinced.

Reasons and Examples

The reasons and examples pattern of development is common in all types of writing, particularly technical writing. Usually, the opening topic sentence contains a generalization or a premise proved by the examples given in the remainder of the paragraph. This method is usually termed the deductive approach and goes from the general to the specific. The inductive approach, by contrast, presents the specific information in the opening sentences of the paragraph and ends with the generalization in the final topic sentence. The two methods can be illustrated in Table 3.

Table 3	Patterns of Organization
Deductive	**Inductive**
Generalization	Specific details (topic sentence)
Specific details	Generalization (topic sentence)

The deductive approach is used more often than the inductive approach since, when time is at a premium, most of us want the key information first before we look at the evidence. In laboratory reports, however, the inductive approach is used more often since the reader is interested in the details and in the evidence as well as the conclusion itself.

Here is an example of a reasons and examples paragraph which uses the deductive approach:

The Integrated Services Digital Network, which uses fibre optic cable rather than standard wire telephone lines, transmits information through a digital rather than an analog network. It offers the following significant advantages compared to a standard telephone system:

- Telephone conversations, pictures and computer messages can be sent simultaneously over the same line with enhanced clarity

- Computer messages can be transmitted instantaneously without the use of a modem

- Fax messages can be sent ten times as quickly compared to traditional systems

Note that in this paragraph, the first sentence gives necessary background information and the topic sentence is the second one. The advantages can be written in subparagraphs or points, all supporting the topic sentence.

Process

The process paragraph explains to the reader how to make or do something or how something works. Often, the opening sentence is a preview statement that establishes why the process is important and what major steps or stages are involved. In a technical report, the key information may be given in the form of a numbered list of steps, each beginning with an action verb in the imperative mood such as:

1 Press the **ENTER** key.

2. Enter new data. . . .

In paragraph form, the format may be different, but the information is also broken down into simple steps presented in chronological order. The amount of detail given depends both on the knowledge of the reader and the purpose of the writer. If the process is, for example, a description of how a volcano erupts, the paragraph would normally give the reader a general picture. If describing how to adjust the carburetor in a 1957 T-Bird, you would be better to be as detailed as possible.

Generally, if the author is giving the reader a set of specific instructions that need to be followed, the numbered steps would be used, as shown in the example below:

The following steps will help you prepare for the job interview:

1. Research the company and find out as much as possible about it and its product(s) or service(s).

2. Rehearse some responses to typical job interview questions.

3. Review the information on your resume and be prepared to elaborate on the information contained therein.

In order to improve your chances of success at the interview, make sure you are neat, presentable and punctual on the actual interview day.

Note the use of action verbs, **research, rehearse, review** and also the enumeration of the key steps. Again, the topic sentence is the opening one.

Here is another paragraph instructing students on how to prevent student burnout:

> Burnout is not only a problem affecting business executives; it can also affect you as a student. To control burnout, exercise moderation in all areas. It's not always possible to be an A student, be a star athlete, maintain a job and lead a busy social life. Avoid doing any single activity for extended periods of time. Try to get at least eight hours sleep every night and avoid alcohol, tobacco and caffeine. No one is immune to burnout, but moderation minimizes your chances of being a victim.

Make sure your process paragraph is written at the reader's level of understanding and communicates the basic steps in the process in a simple, straightforward fashion. Try to imagine yourself doing something for the first time by following the information in the paragraph.

SUMMARY OF RULES FOR EFFECTIVE PARAGRAPHS

1. Ensure that the paragraph deals with only one main idea.

2. Express the main idea in a topic sentence, usually at the beginning of the paragraph.

3. Ensure that the paragraph has unity by having all sentences support the main idea.

4. Ensure the paragraph flows smoothly by using appropriate coherence devices.

5. Ensure the paragraph is adequately developed using RENNS.

6. Use a variety of patterns of paragraph development including: chronological, spatial, comparison and contrast, reasons and examples and process.

7. Strive for variety in paragraph length. While most paragraphs should average four to seven sentences, occasional use of a short paragraph is often very effective. Avoid writing too many paragraphs that are over ten lines long.

CHAPTER 23 - QUESTIONS

1. Customarily, all good paragraphs have a _____ sentence.

    a) concluding
    b) key
    c) chronological
    d) spatial

2. When paragraph sentences all relate to the same key idea, the paragraph has

    a) unity.
    b) a sound structure.
    c) a parallel structure.
    d) coherence.

3. One difference between an essay and a technical report is

    a) very few readers will read the complete report.
    b) essays tend to have a greater variety of readers.
    c) authoring a report is easier than authoring an essay.
    d) the essay has much more specific detail.

4. _____ is not a means used to achieve coherence.

    a) Parallel structure
    b) Pronouns
    c) Transitional expressions
    d) Digression

5. When writing a paragraph on how to make or do something, the development is called

    a) parallel structure.
    b) spatial.
    c) coherence.
    d) process development.

6. When the topic sentence is composed of a generalization or premise that is supported by specific information that fol!ows, the paragraph development pattern is referred to as

    a) spatial.
    b) chronological.
    c) deductive approach.
    d) process.

CHAPTER 23 - ANSWERS

1. (b)

2. (a)

3. (a)

4. (d)

5. (d)

6. (c)

Writing Memos

LEARNING OUTCOME

When you complete this chapter you should be able to:

Plan, write, and edit routine and positive messages in memo format, given a work-related scenario.

LEARNING OBJECTIVES

Here is what you should be able to do when you complete each objective:

1. **Identify the parts of a memo and their functions.**

2. **Write effective subject lines and organize the contents of memos.**

3. **Describe effective format design.**

4. **Describe how to plan the writing task.**

INTRODUCTION

In industry, where time is money, the immediate transfer of information is important. One of the formats most commonly used is the inter-office memorandum.

The term "memorandum" means "a thing worth remembering". Today, the shortened form of memorandum, memo, is used to refer to any written correspondence within a business or an organization. Its purpose is to communicate rapidly and precisely whether the message is informal or formal, or printed electronically or on memo paper.

Letters are used for external communication; whereas, memos are used for internal communication. Memos may meet the goals of the organization, but they may also serve the personal needs of an employee. As part of every individual's job, memos are written for the following purposes:

- To record an action, policy or conversation

- To report incidents, events and announce changes within an organization

- To request information or assign a task

- To request approval for funds

- To persuade an employer or manager of a course of action to suit the needs of the company

The message of a memo may be contained in a few words, or pages. It may be one paragraph or a complete report. Nevertheless, the memo reflects an individual's ability to communicate effectively with managers and/or colleagues. Memos are organized for reader benefit; so the reader should know within seconds whether the memo is for the purpose of recording, informing or acting. Also, the memos should be concise, clear, complete and correct to meet the purpose of the message and the needs of the audience.

OBJECTIVE 1

Identify the parts of a memo and their functions.

THE PARTS OF A MEMO

Most memos follow a specific format, known as a standard memo, provided on company stationery. Most organizations provide a simple printed form for their employees. The standard memo must have headings that name the organization and identify the sender, receiver, subject and date.

An example of a simple memo announcing a change in leasing charges is shown below.

**MEMORANDUM
PEPPERCOMBE IMPORTS
345 Canyon Drive SE
Calgary, Alberta**

TO: Maria Jamison
Customer Service Department

FROM: Shane Ingraham   DATE: March 13, 20xx
Manager
Administration Department

SUBJECT: CHANGES IN OVERDUE LEASING CHARGES

The following charges on overdue leased equipment will be in effect as of March 18, 20xx:

overdue equipment	$10.00 per day
overdue videos	$3.00 per day

These charges will be levied to the maximum of one week. Furthermore, a customer's leasing privileges will be suspended until all penalties are paid in full.

The main parts of a standard memo are:

- Organization identification
- Receiver identification
- Sender identification
- Date
- Subject line
- Body or memo contents
- Signature
- Identification of other readers
- Pagination reference

Organization Identification

The name of the company or **organization** usually appears across the top of a memo. Some companies also show their company logo and address as part of this identification.

Receiver Identification

The name of the **receiver**, job title and department appear after the heading TO. A courtesy title such as Mr., Mrs. or Ms. may be omitted depending on the degree of informality in the organization and on how well the writer knows the receiver. The following example illustrates the format:

TO: Linda Spicer
Supervisor
Marketing Division

Sender Identification

Your name (the **sender**) appears after the heading FROM and is followed by your corporate title and department, if relevant. Use a format and margins consistent with what you used in the TO section of the memo:

FROM: Carl Lang
Project Supervisor
Inspections

Date

A date line can appear to the right of or below the TO and FROM sections. The date you send the memo follows the heading DATE, as shown here:

TO: Linda Spicer
Supervisor
Marketing Division   DATE: June 12, 20xx

FROM: Carl Lang
Project Supervisor
Inspections

Subject Line

The subject line is a phrase or title identifying the content and the purpose of the memo. Follow these guidelines in writing effective subject lines:

- Try to restrict the subject line to one line or no more than 10 words

- Use uppercase letters or underlining to highlight the title

Example:

SUBJECT: REQUEST TO ATTEND WRITING SEMINAR

RE: INTRODUCTION OF NEW TELEPHONE SERVICE

Note: Often, RE is used in place of SUBJECT as an abbreviation, meaning "in the matter of" or "in the case of".

Body or Memo Contents

The body of the memo is the most important component because it contains your message. It may be a brief reminder of a meeting or a full length in-house report.

Headings, used to clarify the contents of the memo, must be directly related to the content. Never use the words, "body" or "contents", as headings. They have virtually no meaning for the readers who already know they are reading the content. If the memo is particularly short (one or two paragraphs), you probably will not want to use content headings.

Write the memo contents in effective paragraphs, lists that follow a parallel construction or a combination of paragraphs and lists depending on which format most clearly transmits your message.

Avoid over-using abbreviations and symbols when writing; your message could get lost. Write in complete sentences and present the information logically, completely and clearly.

Always begin the memo with the main message followed by the details which support or explain it.

Signature

Since the memo is a relatively informal method of written communication, and your name already appears at the top of the memo, a formal signature is not really necessary. However, to ensure that you are, indeed, the writer and that you are willing to take responsibility for the validity or accuracy of the content, you should sign or initial the memo at the bottom.

Identification of Other Readers

If you want an individual other than the main reader(s) to be informed of your message, but not necessarily respond to the message, you would send them a copy of the memo. If more than one person is to receive a copy of the memo, their names appear below your signature following the copy notation "cc". Usually, their names are listed alphabetically or in the order of their position in the organization.

Example:

        cc: J. Danson
              W. Jones
              T. White

Pagination Reference

The first page of a memo is not numbered. However, if the memo exceeds one page, each additional page is numbered in sequence. The pagination reference appears in the left corner and includes the receiver's name, the date and the page number.

Example:

        V. Samson
        June 13, 20xx
        Page 2

The memo, unlike the letter, is not centred on the page. The message of the memo appears three lines below the subject line, just enough space to separate the memo headings from the memo content.

Left margins are usually lined up evenly below the TO and FROM headings. The body is typed, single-spaced, with double spacing between paragraphs. Divide the message under content headings if the memo is long. If you use content headings, leave three lines above the heading and two lines below the heading to separate the headings clearly from the text.

OBJECTIVE 2

Write effective subject lines and organize the contents of memos.

WRITING EFFECTIVE SUBJECT LINES

An effective subject line prepares the reader for the content of the memo; therefore, it must be specific but concise. It saves the reader time by specifically identifying the purpose and describing the content of the message.

General: COMPANY AIRCRAFT

Specific: CHANGES IN CHARGES FOR JOINT COMPANY AIRCRAFT OPERATIONS

The subject line should contain a precise, descriptive title indicating to the reader whether the memo is written to keep employees and customers informed of events or of changes made, or whether the memo requires action.

Information: INCREASE IN HEALTH CARE PREMIUMS

Action: REQUEST FOR TRAINING IN SAFETY PROCEDURES IMPLEMENTING CHANGES IN REPORTING EQUIPMENT FAILURE

The subject line serves the following functions:

- It identifies the purpose and content of the memo
- It indicates immediately whether the memo requires action or simply gives information
- Because the memo is often a short announcement or reminder, it often serves as an introduction to the memo
- It assists in filing and in retrieving the document

ORGANIZING THE CONTENT OF MEMOS

Because employees and managers receive numerous memos each day, the memo should:

- Get to the point quickly
- Be limited to one subject and purpose
- Include only the relevant information to support that purpose

Effective memos are organized for the reader's needs and must get to the main message quickly. They follow a clear beginning, middle and closing organization. Thus, most routine and positive messages will follow the direct organizational pattern:

- Main Message
- Supporting Details
- Explanation

The Subject Line

The subject line of a short memo introduces the topic and purpose of the message.

The Beginning

The beginning paragraph states the most important thing the reader needs to know to about the subject. It is similar to the first paragraph in a newspaper article answering the who, what, where, when and why questions.

The Middle

The middle paragraph(s) provides the reader with the details needed to support the main message. It often answers the how question.

The Closing

The closing may be omitted if the memo is written merely to record information or to announce changes. However, often the writer will close a memo by inviting questions about the content of the memo and by leaving a contact number.

An example of a short memo announcing a change in a meeting date is shown below.

MEMORANDUM
PEPPERCOMBE IMPORTS
67 Harris Avenue N
Saskatoon SK S0K 7T3

TO: Members of the Renovations Committee

FROM: Ted Smith, Chairperson   DATE: January 3, 20xx

SUBJECT: CHANGE IN MEETING DATE

Because James Danson, our architect, can attend Monday meetings only, the regularly scheduled January 17 meeting of the Renovations Committee is rescheduled for Monday, January 27 at 4:00 p.m. in the Penthouse Lounge.

Please call me at 7089 if you are unable to attend.

OBJECTIVE 3

Describe effective format design.

DESIGN AN EFFECTIVE FORMAT

Because memos are so numerous in the daily transaction of business, the page should be designed so the information can be read quickly. **Headings**, effective use of **white space** and **visual cues**, such as bolding and underlining, will make your message more visible to your audience.

Headings

A heading is a word or phrase that announces to a reader the main idea of the paragraph or section of writing to follow. In many ways, headings act as a topic sentence while eliminating the need for transitions that join one written section to the following or preceding written section.

Headings serve four main functions:

1. To act as attention-getting devices because they are easy to see and understand.

2. To act as transitions as they guide the reader from one section to another.

3. To access the information in a memo because they break down and organize large, diverse sections of material into smaller, more readable parts.

4. To break up a page of text uninterrupted by white space.

Since headings clarify the content of the memo, they must describe the content of the section. INTRODUCTION, CONCLUSION, RECOMMENDATION, FORECAST or even REQUEST FOR ACTION may be used as headings, but never use the words, BODY, TEXT, THEORY or DETAILS, as headings because they are too vague. They have virtually no meaning for the readers who already know they are reading the content. If the memo is short (one to three paragraphs), you probably will not want to use content headings.

White Space

White space refers to the empty space on a page of text. Using white space effectively makes a document easier to read as it separates important information from the text. An effectively designed page is more visually appealing and less intimidating than a page filled with text. Effective use of white space can be achieved in three ways:

- Lists using point form
- Short paragraphs
- Columns instead of complete sentences

Lists Using Point Form

Lists are often used to emphasize information. Using lists is also referred to as point form. If the points in the list are sequential, introduce them with numbers. If the list is fairly short and the sequence is not important, use a closed bullet (•) or an open bullet (o) to highlight the information. Follow these guidelines in using point form:

a) Use point form for all lists of similar items:

- Include only items of similar nature and importance in a single list
- Phrase all points in a list in similar ways using parallelism

Not parallel: Logical thinking is one of the things necessary for good writing. Good writers also have to organize their ideas coherently. And, finally, anyone who wants to write well must express his/her ideas clearly.

Parallel: Anyone who wishes to write well must learn to:

- Think logically

- Organize ideas coherently

- Express ideas clearly

Parallel structure also provides the means to use white space effectively. The sentence is rewritten into a compact, clear sentence. The bullets immediately draw the reader's eyes to the message.

b) Introduce all point form lists completely:

- Begin every list with a self-explanatory label or introduction

- Make each point in a list complete the introduction in some way

Example: Training should be developed in two areas:

- Communicating bad news to managers

- Giving and receiving criticism

c) Organize point form to help the reader understand and remember what you are saying:

- Break long lists into sub-categories

- Avoid using lists in inappropriate situations. Give the reader organized and complete points, not simply rough notes

- Avoid telegraphic tendencies by including all the articles a, an, the

Short Paragraphs

Short paragraphs are easier to read than long ones. If the paragraph is longer than eight to ten lines, look for ways of breaking it up perhaps into shorter paragraphs, bulleted sentences or listings. Limit paragraphs to one idea only. They can even consist of one sentence, particularly true in letters and memos.

If you have access to word processing packages, use a ragged right margin rather than justified margins that end evenly on the right side of the page. Many of the word processing programs are able to justify margins; however, they leave wide spaces between words. These "rivers of white" are distracting to readers. (This paragraph is an example of justified margins.)

The rest of this chapter is written using ragged margins. Research suggests that readers find it more difficult to skim read the block margins than the margins with varying line length.

Columns Rather than Sentences

Organization of space, text and headings is an important part of data presentation. Comprehensive test results show a reader's understanding and retention of written material are higher:

- when short units of information are surrounded by space so they stand out.

- when units of information are presented in columns rather than in wide sections stretched across a page in complete sentences.

When you find yourself repeating similar words and phrases, try converting the information into a short table with an introductory sentence instead of sets of sentences and paragraphs.

Study the following example of paragraphs taken from a report detailing the demographics of three areas in Calgary to see how the information can be converted to an informal table.

EDGEMONT - This community has the highest family incomes ($68 537) of the 16 communities receiving the "super mailbox" service. The population is 1245 residents in the 25 - 44 age group. Most of these residents live in apartments and condominiums. They are in the upper-middle class. The community shows a good interest in the Mailchek service.

RIVERBEND - This community has an average family income of $38 042. The population of this community is 1931 people, with a good population spread in the 25 to 44 age group. This is a single family home community which is continuing to grow. This middle class neighbourhood showed a fair interest in the services of Mailchek Security Inc.

VISTA HEIGHTS - This community has an average family income of $44 423. The population is continually growing due to the steady development of this NW community. The population is 2129 residents, with a strong representation in the 25 to 44 age group. This is a middle class community which showed a strong interest for the Mailchek service.

The paragraphs can easily be written as an informal table with an introductory sentence telling the reader what is to follow.

Table 1 compares the demographics in the 25 to 44 age group of three areas showing an interest in the Mailchek program:

Table 1	Sample Table		
	Edgemont	**Riverbend**	**Vista Heights**
Average Family Income	$68 537	$38 042	$44 423
Population (Age 25-44)	1245	1931	2129
Class	upper-middle	middle	middle
Interest	good	fair	strong

Visual Cues

A writer can use other visual cues such as UPPER CASE LETTERS, underlining and boldface type to highlight information. However, do not overuse these elements as the page quickly looks too busy and becomes distracting to the reader.

Similarly, if you have access to word processing packages with different fonts (style of type), generally, use no more than two fonts in one document.

OBJECTIVE 4

Describe how to plan the writing task.

PLANNING THE WRITING TASK

Written messages often do not communicate effectively because not enough time is taken to think about the interaction of the writer, the reader and the message. In order for messages to be effective, the author needs to spend time anticipating the response of the reader.

All writings should keep the needs of the reader in mind rather than the wishes of the writer. More effective messages can be created if time is taken to define the purpose of the message, the audience receiving the message and the content of the message to meet the needs of the purpose and audience.

The author should consider the following when creating written messages:

- Define the purpose
- Describe the audience
- Decide on the content of the message

Define the Purpose

The first step in any writing task, whether it is a memo, letter or report, is to analyze the situation and decide the main purpose of the writing task. The clearer you are about the purpose of the task, the more likely you are to communicate successfully with the intended audience.

To communicate effectively in a memo, the answer to these three questions will clarify the purpose of the memo:

1. Why do I need to write this memo?

2. What do I want my audience to know, think or do after reading my memo?

3. How will my memo be used?

Describe the Audience

Memos are written to be read. Thus, they are effective only if the intended audience understands the message. Therefore, you must adapt your message to the individual who needs to act on the content of the memo. For example, if you were requesting money from your department to support a training program, your message would be quite different from one requesting money from a friend. The tone of the message, the vocabulary used in the content and the length of the message will change for your audience.

The more you know about your audience, the easier it is to design a communication that fits. Visualize your audience. Ask yourself, "Who will read this memo?" The answer to this question will help you to determine how much detail is needed and at what language level the memo should be written.

In defining an audience, ask yourself these questions:

- Who will act on the message in this memo?
- Is my audience motivated to read my memo? What is the level of interest? How may the reader feel about receiving the memo? How much knowledge does the reader have of the topic or situation?
- What objections to my message can I expect my readers to have?

Decide on the Content of the Message

Memos are written to communicate specific information that someone else needs. Your purpose in writing the memo is to meet the needs/wants of the audience. The message will grow out of a clear definition of your purpose and audience.

Before writing the memo, brainstorm the contents by answering: **Who?, What?, Where?, When?, Why?** and **How?** Also, answer these questions to help to focus on the content of the memo:

- What is the most important thing to say to the audience?

- What information must the memo include to provide evidence for my position?

- What positive elements should be emphasized? What should be de-emphasized?

CHAPTER 24 - QUESTIONS

1. Memos are organized effectively for the benefit of the

   a) Alberta Boiler Safety Council.
   b) plant manager.
   c) creator of the memo.
   d) reader.

2. The most important part of a memo is the

   a) body.
   b) salutation.
   c) beginning.
   d) closing.

3. The subject line of a short memo introduces the

   a) topic.
   b) author.
   c) intended audience.
   d) beginning paragraph.

4. White space on a page of text refers to the

   a) size of the margins.
   b) middle section.
   c) size of the memo.
   d) empty space.

5. The points in a list should be phrased in a similar way using a method called

   a) indentation.
   b) sequential order.
   c) organized point form.
   d) parallelism.

6. Which of the following functions is not served by the subject line?

   a) Identification of the purpose and content of the memo
   b) Total number of pages in the memo
   c) Assists in filing and retrieving the document
   d) Indicates immediately whether the memo requires actions or gives information

CHAPTER 24 - ANSWERS

4th Class • Part A1

1. (d)

2. (a)

3. (a)

4. (d)

5. (d)

6. (b)

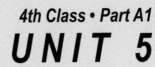

CODES & STANDARDS

Chapter 25	Industrial Legislation	25-1

CHAPTER 25

Industrial Legislation

LEARNING OUTCOME

When you complete this chapter you should be able to:

Discuss the purpose of codes and provincial acts and regulations with respect to boilers and pressure vessels.

LEARNING OBJECTIVES

Here is what you should be able to do when you complete each objective:

1. *State the purpose and function of the ASME Boiler and Pressure Vessel Committee.*

2. *Describe provincial acts and regulations.*

3. *Discuss typical regulations pertaining to design, construction and installation of boilers and pressure vessels.*

4. *Discuss the regulations pertaining to Power Engineers and pressure welders.*

OBJECTIVE 1

State the purpose and function of the ASME Boiler and Pressure Vessel Committee.

ASME BOILER & PRESSURE VESSEL COMMITTEE

The legislation acts, and codes used in the pressure vessel industry are frequently under revision. The student should be aware that all terminology (For example, Boilers and Pressure Vessels Act) may be replaced by alternative terms such as Safety Codes Act. However, the content of these government documents is consistent with the general information contained in this chapter.

Before the turn of the century and for a short time thereafter, boiler explosions were a frequent occurrence and were regarded by many as "acts of God". It was felt that little could be done to prevent these disasters, that they were an inevitable result of the growing industrialization of the country. However, responsible people soon began to realize that these disastrous accidents could be prevented by the proper design, construction, inspection and operation of boilers and pressure vessels. Accordingly, rules and regulations relating to these factors were formulated and adopted by the Canadian provinces and territories as well as by many of the states and cities in the United States.

At first, these rules differed greatly from province to province and from state to state and in many cases conflicted with one another. In an effort to achieve uniformity, the American Society of Mechanical Engineers (ASME) set up a committee in 1911 for the purpose of formulating standard rules for the construction of steam boilers and other pressure vessels. This committee is now known as the **Boiler and Pressure Vessel Committee.**

The function of this committee is to establish rules of safety governing the design, fabrication and inspection during construction of boilers and pressure vessels. The objective of the rules is to afford reasonably certain protection of life and property and provide a reasonably long, safe period of usefulness for boilers and pressure vessels.

These rules have been adopted in varying degrees by all the Canadian provinces and territories.

The ASME Boiler and Pressure Vessel Committee also provides suggested rules for the care of boilers and pressure vessels in service as an aid to owners, operators and inspectors.

National Board

Another body concerned with the promotion of safety and uniformity in the construction, installation and inspection of boilers and pressure vessels is the National Board of Boiler and Pressure Vessel Inspectors which was first organized in 1919. This body is composed of Chief Inspectors in states and municipalities in the United States and in the provinces in Canada that have adopted the ASME Boiler and Pressure Vessel Code. The Board's function is to uniformly administer and enforce the rules of the Code.

> In Canada, the ASME Code is complemented by Canadian Standards Association Code B51, the Boiler, Pressure Vessel and Pressure Piping Code. CSA B51 is recognized in legislation in the same way that the ASME Code is.

When looking at legislation and codes, there are, in Power Engineering, three basic levels of "Rules". There is an heirchy, or order in which to look at and read these rules. The first set to look at is the **act** of the jurisdiction in which you are working then the **regulations** made under that **act**. The second place to get information would be the CSA (Canadian Standards Association) Codes, referred to later in this chapter. The next would be the ASME (American Society of Mechanical Engineers) Codes for Boilers and Pressure Vessels. If you find conflicting information in any of these documents, use the above heirchy to discern which code or **rule** would take precedence.

OBJECTIVE 2

Describe provincial acts and regulations.

PROVINCIAL ACTS & REGULATIONS

All the Canadian provinces and territories have passed laws, rules and regulations relating to the installation, construction, inspection and operation of boilers and pressure vessels.

Many of these laws have been in existence since or before the turn of the century as Table 1 indicates.

Table 1	Provincial Acts

Province or Territory	Date of Passage of Law	Name of Legislation (2009)
Quebec	1867	Boiler & Pressure Vessel Act
Alberta	1898	Safety Codes Act
Saskatchewan	1898	Boiler & Pressure Vessel Act
British Columbia	1899	Safety Standards Act
Manitoba	1912	Steam & Pressure Plants Act
Ontario	1913	Technical Standards & Safety Act
Nova Scotia	1942	Steam Boiler & Pressure Plants Act
Prince Edward Island	1948	Boiler & Pressure Vessel Act
Newfoundland/Labrador	1949	Public Safety Act
Yukon Territory	1949	Boiler & Pressure Vessel Act
Northwest Territories	1951	Boiler & Pressure Vessel Act
New Brunswick	-	Boiler & Pressure Vessel Act
Nunavut	-	Boiler & Pressure Vessel Act

In some jurisdictions, these laws are called "The Boilers and Pressure Vessels Act" while in others, alternate titles may be used including "The Steam and Pressure Plants Act". However, no matter under what title they fall, these laws all have the same intent and objective - namely, to safeguard life and property.

In order to illustrate how these laws function to attain their objective, a general discussion is given in the following sections but it is not possible to discuss the laws of every jurisdiction in this chapter. It is the responsibility of the individual to become well-versed in the Acts and Regulations of the jurisdiction in which he or she resides or works.

An Act is a piece of legislation which becomes law when it is approved by the elected government. Each Act is administered by a regulatory agency which has the authority to enact and enforce Regulations relating to the Act's requirements and that provide more detailed rules. Depending on the local jurisdiction, the following sections may appear in either the Act itself or in the subordinate Regulations, but the content is typical of that found in all jurisdictions in Canada.

Definitions
The Act begins by defining various terms that are used throughout the Act itself and the Regulations under the Act.

Exceptions
Examples of Equipment to which the Act and the regulations do not apply are listed below:
- Boilers below a certain rating
- Pressure vessels of less than a certain internal diameter
- Pressure vessels operating below a specified pressure
- Refrigeration systems of less than a certain capacity

- Any boiler, pressure vessel or pressure piping system which does not constitute a sufficient hazard to require it to be subject to the Act

Design, Construction and Sale

This section deals with the approval and registration of designs of boilers and pressure vessels to be constructed within the jurisdiction or brought into the jurisdiction.

Fittings

All fittings constructed within the jurisdiction for use within the jurisdiction must be registered in accordance with the regulations. Registration of fittings brought into the jurisdiction and changes to fittings are dealt with along with unsafe or obsolete fittings.

Boiler and Pressure Vessel Identification

This section states that before an inspector issues the first certificate of inspection for any boiler or pressure vessel, he/she must make sure that the boiler or pressure vessel is stamped with the jurisdiction's identification number.

Construction, Installation & Sale of Boilers, Pressure Vessels & Fittings

This section covers the restrictions with regard to the construction, sale or disposal, and installation of boilers, pressure vessels, fittings and pressure piping systems.

Inspections

This section lists the rules regarding inspections, orders issued by the inspector, the powers of the inspector and responsibilities of the owner or person in charge of the equipment with regard to assisting the inspector. The certificate of inspection is described in this section as well as the responsibilities of the owner or person in charge with relation to retaining and displaying this certificate.

Operation and Supervision

The requirement of a certificate of competency for the Chief Power or Operating Engineer and for the Shift Engineers of a power plant is discussed and exceptions to this requirement are listed. It is also noted that if supervision of the plant by the holder of a certificate is not required, then the owner of the plant is responsible for the proper care and safe operation of the plant.

Accidents and Investigations

The procedure to be followed by the owner or person in charge in the event of an accident involving the boiler, pressure vessel or power plant is detailed here. It is also noted that such an accident may be investigated by the Chief Inspector (The Chief Inspector may be referred to as an Administrator) of the regulatory authority or by other persons directed by him to do so.

Certificates of Competency

The various Power Engineers' certificates of competency are listed and the duties that the holder of such a certificate is authorized to perform are detailed.

It is emphasized that a boiler, pressure vessel, piping system or fitting must not be welded by any persons unless they have the necessary pressure welder's certificate and authorization to do so.

Complaints, Investigations, Disciplinary Action

If the Chief Inspector receives a complaint against the holder of a certificate of competency stating that the certificate holder has acted incompetently, negligently, dangerously, improperly or that he is incapable of performing his duties, then the Chief Inspector will make a preliminary investigation into the complaint.

If this preliminary investigation justifies a further inquiry, a committee of inquiry will be established. After the completion of its inquiry, the committee must then prepare a written report on the matter.

If the committee finds that the certificate holder has acted incompetently, negligently, dangerously, or improperly, or if he or she is incapable of performing his or her duties, then the committee may either suspend or cancel the certificate of competency of the person investigated.

This suspension or cancellation may be appealed by the person involved to the Supreme Court of the jurisdiction.

OBJECTIVE 3

Discuss typical regulations pertaining to design, construction and installation of boilers and pressure vessels.

REGULATIONS & OFFENCES

This part of the Act states that the governing body of the jurisdiction may make regulations with regard to boilers, pressure vessels, power plants and fittings concerning the registration of design, construction, testing, installation, inspection, operation and repair.

Many other types of regulations the governing body may make are also listed in this section, including rules concerning certificates of competency.

Finally, this section states that contravening any provision of the Act is an offence; the penalty for so doing may be a fine or imprisonment.

DESIGN, CONSTRUCTION & INSTALLATION

Exemptions
The various types of equipment which are exempted from the provisions of the Act are listed.

Adoption of Codes
Codes and standards are not mandatory unless adopted. All codes and standards become law when they have been officially adopted as regulations. The codes which have been adopted as regulations are listed. The ones of particular interest to Power Engineers are:

1. Canadian Standards Association (CSA)

   CSA B51—Boiler, Pressure Vessel, and Pressure Piping Code

   CSA B52—Mechanical Refrigeration Code

2. American Society of Mechanical Engineers (ASME)

   ASME Section I   Power Boilers

   ASME Section II Materials – Part "A" Ferrous Material Specifications

   ASME Section II Materials – Part "B" Nonferrous Material Specifications

   ASME Section II Materials – Part "C" Specifications for Welding Rods, Electrodes and Filler Metals

   ASME Section II Materials – Part "D" – Properties (Metric)

   ASME Section II Materials – Part "D" – Properties (Customary)

   ASME Section III Rules for Construction of Nuclear Power Plant Components – Division I

   ASME Section III Rules for Construction of Nuclear Power Plant Components – Division II

   ASME Section IV Rules for Construction of Heating Boilers

   ASME Section V Nondestructive Examination

   ASME Section VI Recommended Rules for Care and Operation of Heating Boilers

   ASME Section VII Recommended Guidelines for the Care of Power Boilers

ASME Section VIII Rules for Construction of Pressure Vessels – Division I

ASME Section VIIIRules for Construction of Pressure Vessels – Division II – Alternative Rules

ASME Section VIII Rules for Construction of Pressure Vessels – Division III – Alternative Rules

ASME Section IX Welding and Brazing Qualifications

(Note: The following four codes were previously issued by ANSI, but are now under the jurisdiction of the ASME)

ASME B.31.1	Power Piping
ASME B.31.3	Process Piping
ASME B.31.5	Refrigeration Piping and Heat Transfer Components
ASME B.16.5	Pipe Flanges and Flanged Fittings

3. American National Standards Institute (ANSI)

   ANSI K.61.1   Safety Requirements for Storage and Handling of Anhydrous Ammonia

Registration and Approval of Designs and Welding Procedures

The details of the drawings and specifications required for acceptance of a design of a boiler or pressure vessel are listed. These must be submitted to the Chief Inspector in duplicate and must bear the signature of the owner of the design or the manufacturer of the boiler. A similar list is expected to fulfill for the requirements for the approval of a pressure piping system.

The method of approving and registering a design of boiler, pressure vessel or pressure piping system by an inspector is described. In order to obtain approval for changes to a design it is also necessary to submit drawings and specifications to the Chief Inspector.

Similarly, when a boiler, pressure vessel, fitting or pressure piping system is to be constructed, altered or repaired by welding, the welding procedure specifications and procedure qualification records must be submitted in triplicate for approval and registration.

Registration of Fittings

If a fitting is to be constructed in the jurisdiction for use in the jurisdiction, application must be made to the Chief Inspector for registration. The drawings, information and procedure necessary to obtain this registration are listed. Manufacturers of fittings are required to have a satisfactory quality control system in operation.

Boiler and Pressure Vessel Fees

The following fees for boilers, pressure vessels, pressure piping systems and heat exchangers are listed:

- Design registration
- Welding procedure
- Design survey
- Fitting registration
- Shop inspection
- Initial inspection
- Annual

Construction and Inspections

The requirements relating to the construction of a boiler or pressure vessel within the jurisdiction are discussed. These deal with submission of drawings and specifications, quality control programs during construction and manufacturers' data reports. Manufacturers of boilers, pressure vessels and pressure piping systems are required to have a satisfactory quality control system in operation.

Regulations regarding inspection openings in pressure vessels are given in this section as well as those regarding stamping on a boiler or pressure vessel.

Installation

The responsibility of the owner or person in charge with respect to use of registered fittings and pressure relief equipment is discussed, as well as rules regarding the repair, servicing and setting of safety valves, relief valves and safety relief valves. In addition, rules governing the anchoring of boilers, pressure vessels and pressure piping systems are given.

Other rules discussed in this section include those dealing with installation requirements to provide accessibility to boilers and pressure vessels and installation of check valves in blowdown lines when required.

Inspection

This section, dealing with inspection of boilers, pressure vessels and pressure piping systems, lists rules concerned with the following:

- Nondestructive examinations
- Report of damage to boilers and pressure vessels
- Notification to the inspector of commencement of repairs
- Submission to the inspector of a detailed work procedure
- Provision of low voltage (12 volts or less) portable lamps during internal inspections

Also detailed in this section are the procedures to be followed when the boiler or pressure vessel premises are locked and the rules regarding the availability of a boiler room key.

Safety precautions during inspection are then discussed covering such topics as: nonsparking hammers, explosive or toxic gases and personnel present during testing and initial start-up.

A number of rules regarding testing and inspection of cargo transport pressure vessels may be listed, as well as rules covering the garaging, repair and safe operation of this type of pressure vessel.

Inspection of pressure piping systems is discussed including observation of safety precautions, test procedures, hydrostatic tests, test liquid temperature and test data reports.

Miscellaneous rules may also be included regarding boilers and steam engines operated in a parade.

OBJECTIVE 4

Discuss the regulations pertaining to Power Engineers and pressure welders.

ENGINEERS' REGULATIONS

Engineers Regulations are of particular interest to the Power Engineer as they detail, among other things, how the Power Engineer can advance to obtain higher certificates of competency and what these certificates of competency qualify the holder to do.

Definitions
Herein are defined such terms as: Chief Engineer, Shift Engineer, Assistant Engineer, Assistant Shift Engineer and Fireman.

Requirements and Exemptions
Types of plants which are exempted from requiring continuous supervision are listed; however, it is pointed out that these plants do require general supervision by the holder of a certificate of competency. Heating plants are also specified as being required to be under the general supervision of the holder of a valid certificate of competency unless they are below a certain boiler kilowatt rating.

Certificates of Competency
Rules regarding the issuing of certificates of competency by the Chief Inspector are discussed, as well as the requirements regarding posting of these certificates on the premises of the power plant or heating plant. Also, circumstances where duplicate certificates may be issued are mentioned.

Some jurisdictions will establish certificate classes that are unique to them.

The following certificates of competency are discussed with regard to what they qualify the holder to do:

- First Class Power Engineer
- Second Class Power Engineer
- Third Class Power Engineer
- Fourth Class Power Engineer
- Fifth Class Power Engineer
- Certificates unique to the jurisdiction

For example, a First Class Engineer's Certificate of Competency qualifies the holder to:

1. Take charge of the general care and operation of any power plant as Chief Engineer, and to supervise the Power Engineers in that plant.

2. Take charge of a shift in any power plant as Shift Engineer.

The issuance of temporary certificates of competency is discussed in regard to conditions requiring a temporary certificate and how it is applied for; as well as the duration of such certificates.

Qualifications and Examinations

In order to obtain a certificate of competency, a person must pass an examination set by the jurisdiction issuing the certificate. In order to qualify to take this examination, the candidate must fulfill certain conditions, usually with regard to previous working experience and educational requirements. In addition, in some cases, the candidate must be the holder of a certificate of competency one grade lower than that for which he/she is applying.

For example, to qualify to take the examination for the First Class Engineer's Certificate of Competency, the candidate shall typically:

1. hold a Second Class Engineer's Certificate of Competency or equivalent and

2. furnish evidence of a period of employment satisfactory to the Chief Inspector such as: thirty months as Chief Engineer in a power plant of a certain capacity, or thirty months as Shift Engineer in a power plant of greater capacity, or forty-five months as Assistant Shift Engineer in a power plant of a large capacity.

Educational requirement are also listed, such as:

3. having at least a 50% standing in specified Physics, Mathematics and English courses at the high school level OR having passed the Part "A" of a First Class Course satisfactory to the Chief Inspector.

Similarly, the conditions for qualifying for all the other certificates of competency examinations are listed in this section, as well as descriptions of the examination format for each class of certificate.

The existence of a reference syllabus as established by the Chief Inspector for each class of examination is pointed out.

Other information given in this section deals with:

*   examination pass marks

*   credits which may be granted in lieu of operating experience

*   credits which may be granted to a holder of a Power Engineering Diploma issued by an educational institute, as well as credits for other technical courses

Another important part of this section deals with the issuing of equivalent certificates of competency to persons from other jurisdictions.

Application and Conduct of Examinations

The procedure for submitting applications for examinations is discussed, as well as the type of references required.

If a candidate who is unable to write, he/she may employ another person to write the candidate's answers or the Chief Inspector may authorize an oral examination. However, this ruling only applies to lower classes of certificate examinations as specified in this section.

The causes for disqualification of a candidate are listed, including: copying from another candidate or using unauthorized material during the examination. The full set of examination rules are available on the www.sopeec.org web site. By looking here you will also be able to see any changes that may affect you and your exam writing.

Miscellaneous

Among the miscellaneous items discussed here are:
*   calculation of boiler power

*   loss of a certificate of competency

*   maintenance of a log book to record matters relating to the operation of the power plant or heating plant

Examination and Certificate Fees

Fees payable for taking the various certificates of competency examinations are listed as well as those for re-marking examination papers. Other fees listed include those paid for specimen examinations and temporary and duplicate certificates.

PRESSURE WELDERS' REGULATIONS

These regulations begin by defining such terms as: performance qualification card, pressure welder and pressure welding.

Classification of Certificates

The various certificates of competency for pressure welders are listed as well as the duties that such certificates permit the holder to perform.

For example, a Grade A Pressure Welder's Certificate of Competency may permit the holder to:

1. engage in pressure welding of a type described on the performance qualification card held.

2. supervise other pressure welders employed on the construction, installation, or repair of boilers, pressure vessels and pressure piping systems.

Other certificates of competency listed in this section may include:

*   Grade B Pressure Welder's Certificate of Competency

*   Grade C Pressure Welder's Certificate of Competency

*   Machine Welding Operator's Certificate of Competency

Qualifications and Examinations

To obtain a pressure welder's certificate of competency, a person must pass an examination set by the jurisdiction issuing the certificate. In qualifying to take this examination, the candidate must fulfill certain conditions listed in this section, usually with regard to previous experience as a welder. Also covered in this section are details relating to application for examination and payment of the examination fee.

Conduct of Examinations

It is noted in this section that if an examination candidate is unable to write he/she may employ a person to write for him/her during a written examination. If this arrangement is not possible, then the candidate may be given an oral examination.

The use of code books and calculators during an examination is discussed together with the penalty for misconduct during an examination.

Performance Qualification Tests

In the initial performance qualification test, the candidate, under the supervision of an authorized inspector, performs the required welding of test coupons which may subsequently be tested for soundness by the inspector. Re-qualification of performance qualification tests are carried out by accredited organizations holding valid certificates of authorization.

The frequency of testing is discussed as well as the issuance of performance qualification cards by an inspector or an approved accredited organization.

The information required on a performance qualification card is listed. Conditions that may result in the suspension of a performance qualification card are discussed.

Miscellaneous

Among the things covered in this section are rules regarding identification of pressure welds and duplicate certificates of competency.

Fees

The fees payable for certificate of competency examinations are listed for both theory and performance qualification tests. Also listed are fees for:

*   duplicate certificates of competency

*   duplicate performance qualification cards

*   special examination fees

This page has intentionally been left blank.

CHAPTER 25 - QUESTIONS

1. A body formed in 1919 for the promotion of safety and uniformity in the construction, installation and inspection of boilers and pressure vessels was the

   a) American Society of Mechanical Engineers.
   b) National Board of Boiler and Pressure Vessels Inspectors.
   c) Canada Standards Association.
   d) American National Standards Institute.

2. The code that regulates mechanical refrigeration is

   a) American Society of Mechanical Engineers.
   b) CSA B-51.
   c) CSA B-52.
   d) Alberta Boiler Safety Association.

3. When a fitting is to be registered within a jurisdiction an application must be made to

   a) CSA B-51.
   b) CSA B-52.
   c) the National Board of Boiler and Pressure Vessels Inspectors.
   d) the Chief Inspector.

4. Before an inspector issues the first certificate of inspection for any boiler and/or pressure vessel, he must make sure the vessel is _____ with the jurisdiction's identification number.

   a) colour coded
   b) registered
   c) stamped
   d) tested

5. The ASME publication dealing with the care of heating boilers is

   a) section I.
   b) section IV.
   c) section IX.
   d) section VI.

6. Before a fitting is to be constructed in the jurisdiction for use in the jurisdiction, application must be made to the Chief Inspector for

   a) registration.
   b) nondestructive examination.
   c) pressure testing.
   d) a quality control procedure.

CHAPTER 25 - ANSWERS

1. (b)

2. (c)

3. (d)

4. (c)

5. (d)

6. (a)

WORKPLACE HAZARDOUS MATERIALS

WHMIS Part I - Classification of Controlled Products

LEARNING OUTCOME

When you complete this chapter you should be able to:

Explain the significance of the Workplace Hazardous Materials Information System (WHMIS) and its application to the worksite.

LEARNING OBJECTIVES

Here is what you should be able to do when you complete each objective:

1. Describe the classification system for "controlled products".

2. List the six WHMIS classes, their subdivisions and exempted materials.

3. Describe the criteria for classifications.

INTRODUCTION

This chapter is designed to help develop an understanding of the requirements of the Workplace Hazardous Materials Information System (WHMIS) and its application to the worksite.

It will provide an outline of the three basic components of the regulations:

1. Labeling

2. Material Safety Data Sheet (MSDS)

3. Employee training

WHMIS is a pan-Canadian law, meaning it applies equally in all federal, provincial and territorial jurisdictions.

Supplier labels and Material Safety Data Sheets (MSDS) are a condition of sale for importation of controlled products in Canada, meaning that every controlled product sold or imported into a Canadian workplace must have a supplier label on the package or container and an MSDS must be provided to the employer. The employer must make sure that such MSDS are made available to the workers using such products.

Worksite labels and worker training are responsibilities equally shared between employers and employees.

OBJECTIVE 1

Describe the classification system for "controlled products".

LEGISLATION

The primary vehicle governing the application of WHMIS is the federal model Controlled Products Regulation (SOR/88-66 am. SOR/88-555). Most jurisdictions have enacted companion regulations to adopt the model laws as shown in Table 1.

Table 1	WHMIS Legislation
British Columbia	Workers' Compensation Act Occupational Health and Safety Regulation, Part 5
Alberta	Occupational Health and Safety Act Occupational Health and Safety (OHS) Code, Part 29
Saskatchewan	Occupational Health and Safety Act Occupational Health and Safety Regulations, Part XXII
Manitoba	The Workplace Safety and Health Act Workplace Hazardous Materials Information System Regulation
Ontario	Occupational Health and Safety Act Workplace Hazardous Materials Information System (WHMIS) Regulation
Quebec	Act Respecting Occupational Health and Safety Regulation Respecting Information on Controlled Products
New Brunswick	Occupational Health and Safety Act Workplace Hazardous Materials Information System Regulation
Nova Scotia	Occupational Health and Safety Act Workplace Hazardous Materials Information System (WHMIS) Regulations
Prince Edward Island	Occupational Health and Safety Act Workplace Hazardous Materials Information System Regulations
Newfoundland	Occupational Health and Safety Act Workplace Hazardous Materials Information System (WHMIS) Regulations
Yukon Territory	Occupational Health and Safety Act Workplace Hazardous Materials Information System Regulations
Northwest Territories & Nunavut	Safety Act Work Site Hazardous Materials Information System Regulations

CLASSIFICATION SYSTEM

The Workplace Hazardous Materials Information System (WHMIS) deals with the identification of controlled products and their hazards and the delivery of that information to the Canadian workplace. This system is a condition of sale or importation.

Essentially "worker's right to know" legislation, WHMIS provides specific hazard information to every workplace where controlled products are in use. It also deals with the training needs of workers handling such products as part of their job.

The classification system has the following basic components:

- Supplier and workplace labels
- Material Safety Data Sheets (MSDS)
- Employee training

Supplier and Workplace Labels

Supplier and workplace labels identify controlled products by requiring labels with specific content. This is the primary step creating an immediate awareness of the inherent hazards of such products.

The labeling system not only includes marking requirements for packages and containers, but also extends to identification of piping and vessels and similar process equipment. Labeling may be in the form of color coding or similar types of visual identification.

An important part of the supplier label is the requirement to display the appropriate WHMIS hazard symbol(s). WHMIS includes eight specific hazard symbols.

The workplace label extends the controlled product identification to products decanted at the workplace. Almost every time a controlled product is moved from its original container into another container at the workplace, some form of labeling is required. There are only a few exceptions to this rule, such as "for immediate use" or for certain types of "consumer products". The use of Supplier and Workplace Labels are covered in the other WHMIS Part II.

Material Safety Data Sheets (MSDS)

Because the labeling system includes only limited hazard information, the MSDS provides additional data about a specific product. An MSDS for every controlled product must be provided by the product supplier.

This added information, addressing nine specific areas, must be available at every workplace to workers actually working with the product. It contains information on the physical and toxicological properties of the product and on how to store, use, handle and dispose of it. Material Safety Data Sheets are covered are covered in the other WHMIS Part III.

Employee Training

The final component of WHMIS is employee training. It requires that employers establish a training system that ensures that every employee fully understands the hazards of controlled products with which they are working.

Placing all three components together effectively (Fig. 1) will result in a safer and healthier workplace for all workers.

Figure 1	WHMIS Components

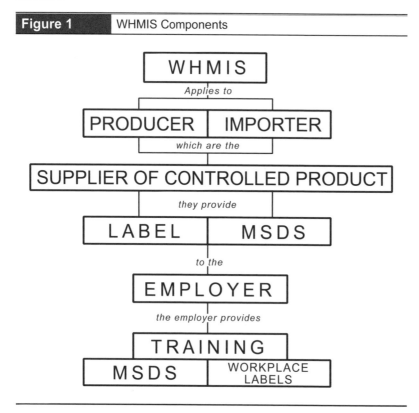

OBJECTIVE 2

List the six WHMIS classes, their subdivisions and exempted materials.

WHMIS CLASSES

The model Controlled Products Regulation applies only to those products that meet one or more of the criteria as defined in Sections 34–66 of the regulation (SOR/88-66).

The system includes six classes of controlled products:

1. Class A: Compressed Gases
2. Class B: Flammable and Combustible Material
3. Class C: Oxidizing Material
4. Class D: Poisonous and Infectious Material
5. Class E: Corrosive Material
6. Class F: Dangerously Reactive Material

To accommodate different hazards within the same group of material, some classes are subdivided. An example would be the difference in flammability between gasoline and diesel fuel. Even though they are both "flammable" in common terms, gasoline is certainly much more hazardous because of its extremely low flash point. Some gasolines readily ignite at temperatures as low as -45°C, whereas diesel fuels ignite usually only if heated above 55°C.

Divisions

Class A: Compressed Gas

Class B: Flammable and Combustible Material

    Division 1: Flammable Gas

    Division 2: Flammable Liquid

    Division 3: Combustible Liquid

    Division 4: Flammable Solid

    Division 5: Flammable Aerosol

    Division 6: Reactive Flammable Material

Class C: Oxidizing Material

Class D: Poisonous and Infectious Material

    Division 1: Materials causing Immediate and Serious Toxic Effects

        Subdivision a: Very toxic material

        Subdivision b: Toxic material

    Division 2: Materials causing Chronic Toxic Effects

        Subdivision a: Very toxic material

        Subdivision b: Toxic material

    Division 3: Biohazardous Infectious Materials

Class E: Corrosive Material

Class F: Dangerously Reactive Material

Subdivisions

Two of the divisions in Class D are further subdivided to distinguish between different degrees of toxicity. Because some materials are very poisonous while others are less so, the terms "very toxic" and "toxic" are used to describe that difference.

Exempted Materials

Even though they appear to be controlled products, some groups of materials are currently fully or partially exempt from the Controlled Products Regulation.

Fully exempted materials are:

- manufactured articles.

- tobacco and products made of tobacco.

- wood products or products made of wood.

The following are materials exempt from supplier labels and MSDS:

- Consumer products (as per Hazardous Products Act - Schedule I, Part II)

- Explosives regulated under the Explosives Act

- Foods, drugs and cosmetics under the Food and Drug Act

- Materials regulated under the Pest Control Products Act

- Radioactive substances regulated under the Atomic Energy Control Act

Special materials include:

- hazardous waste for which safe handling and storage at the workplace must be ensured. Any combination of identification, marking and worker education that achieves the minimum requirements is acceptable.

- special shape controlled products which cannot endanger worker health because of their size and shape, such as sand containing crystalline silica. These require labeling, MSDS and employee training.

OBJECTIVE 3

Describe the criteria for classifications.

CRITERIA FOR CLASSIFICATIONS

Class A – Compressed Gas

Figure 2	Class A Symbol – Compressed Gas

Class A (Fig. 2) includes any product, material or substance contained under pressure, including compressed gas, dissolved gas or gas liquefied by compression or refrigeration that matches any of the following:

- Has a critical temperature of less than 50°C

- Has an absolute vapor pressure greater than 294 kPa at 50°C

- Has an absolute pressure in the vessel in which it is contained, exceeding 275 kPa (±1 kPa) at 21.1°C, or 717 kPa (±2kPa) at 50°C

- Has an absolute Reid Vapor Pressure (ASTM D-323-82) greater than 275 kPa at 37.8°C

Summarizing the above, any product that is normally a gas below 50°C, or is contained under pressure greater than 294 kPa, at 21.1°C, or has an RVP greater than 275 kPa, at 37.8°C, is in Class A.

Example 1:

Propane has a boiling point of -42.1°C at atmospheric pressure. This means that it is a vapour at any temperature higher than that. The only way a liquid can be contained above its boiling point is to confine it under pressure.

At room temperature, that pressure equals about 830 kPa. The warmer it gets, the higher the pressure will be in the container. On a hot summer day, the pressure in a propane cylinder can increase to more than 1380 kPa, often resulting in gas venting through the safety valve.

Class B – Flammable and Combustible Materials

Figure 3	Class B Symbol – Flammable and Combustible Materials

Division 1: Flammable Gas

Any compressed gas (such as: acetylene, hydrogen or propane) included in Class A that at normal atmospheric pressure forms a flammable mixture with air when in concentration of 13% or less by volume, or over a concentration range of at least 12% by volume.

Division 2: Flammable Liquid

Any liquid (such as: gasoline, methanol or acetone) that has a flash point of less than 37.8°C.

Division 3: Combustible Liquid

Any liquid (such as: diesel fuel or Varsol) that has a flash point between 37.8°C and 93.3°C.

Division 4: Flammable Solid

Any solid (such as: matches or molten sulphur) that causes fire through friction or retained heat from manufacturing or processing.

Any solid (such as flares or charcoal starter cubes) that can be readily ignited and burns so persistently and vigorously as to create a special hazard.

Any solid material that ignites readily and burns with a self-sustaining flame at a rate of more than 0.254 cm per second along its major axis.

Division 5: Flammable Aerosols

Any product that is packaged as an aerosol and, when tested, yields a flame projection at full valve opening or a flash back at any amount of valve opening.

Division 6: Reactive Flammable Materials

Any product (such as: red phosphorus, sodium or calcium carbide) liable to spontaneous combustion or ignition when in contact with air, or liable to emit a flammable gas or become spontaneously combustible when in contact with water or steam.

Class C – Oxidizing Materials

Figure 4	Class C Symbol – Oxidizing Materials

Class C (Fig. 4) includes any material that causes or contributes to the combustion of another product by yielding oxygen or any other oxidizing substance, whether or not the material is itself combustible. Examples are ammonium nitrate and potassium permanganate).

Class C also includes any organic peroxide (such as: dibenzoyl peroxide or butyl hydroperoxide) that contains the covalent O-O structure.

Class D – Poisonous and Infectious Material

Figure 5	Class D Symbol – Poisonous and Infectious Material

Division 1: Immediate and Serious Toxic Effects

This division includes any product or material that has immediate toxic effects causing serious illness or death in a short period of time.

Subdivision A, Very Toxic

Any product (such as: sodium cyanide, arsenic, nitric oxide or phosgene) that results in death if very small amounts are ingested or inhaled. This also includes any poisonous gas in Class 2.3 and any liquid or solid poison listed in Class 6.1, Packing Group I & II of TDG.

- Oral LD_{50} not exceeding 50 mg/kg of body weight
- Dermal LD_{50} not exceeding 200 mg/kg of body weight
- Inhalation LC_{50} not exceeding 2500 ppm (parts per million) by volume of gas for 4 hours
- Inhalation LC_{50} not exceeding 1500 ppm by volume of vapour for 4 hours
- Inhalation LC_{50} not exceeding 0.5 mg/l of dust, mist or fumes for 4 hours

Note: "LD" is the acronym for Lethal Dose. LD_{50} is the amount of a material, given all at once, that causes the death of 50% of a group of test animals.

LD_{50} **is a** means to measure the short-term poisoning potential (acute toxicity) of a material.

"LC" is the acronym for Lethal Concentration. LC values are the concentration of a chemical in air, but, it can also indicate the concentration of a chemical in water. For inhalation experiments, the LD_{50} value is the concentration of the chemical in air that kills 50% of the test animals in a given time (four hours).

Subdivision B, Toxic

Any product (such as: hydrazine or Benzedrine) that results in death if moderate amounts are ingested, absorbed or inhaled. This includes any solid or liquid poison listed in Class 6.1, Packing Group III of TDG.

Oral	LD_{50}, more than 50 mg/kg but not exceeding 500 mg/kg of body weight
Dermal	LD_{50}, more than 200 mg/kg but not exceeding 1000 mg/kg of body weight
Inhalation	LC_{50}, more than 1500 ppm but not exceeding 2500 ppm by volume of vapour for 4 hours
Inhalation	LC_{50}, more than 0.5 mg/l but not exceeding 2.5 mg/l of dust, mist or fumes for 4 hours

Division 2: Materials Causing Other Toxic Effects (Chronic Toxicity)

	Class D, Division 2 Symbol – Materials Causing Other Toxic Effects (Chronic Toxicity)

Subdivision A, Very Toxic:

Any material that if ingested, absorbed or inhaled in small amounts, results in sufficient severity to threaten life or causes serious permanent impairment.

Subchronic oral , not exceeding 10 mg/kg of body weight per day

Subchronic dermal , not exceeding 20 mg/kg per day

Inhalation , not exceeding 25 ppm by volume of gas or vapour

Inhalation , not exceeding 10 µg/L of dust, mist or fumes

Any material that causes injury (teratogenicity or embryotoxicity) to the embryo or fetus in a concentration that has no effect on the pregnant female.

Any material known to cause cancer (carcinogenicity in humans or animals).

Any material that causes sterility or has adverse effects on reproductive capability (reproductive toxicity) in humans or animals.

Any material that shows evidence of heritable genetic effects or mutagenicity in vivo testing, or evidence of mutations transmitted to offspring, chemical interaction with genetic material, gene mutation or chromosomal aberration.

Subdivision B, Toxic

Any material that if ingested, absorbed or inhaled in small amounts, results in sufficient severity to threaten life or causes serious permanent impairment.

Any material proven to cause an effect graded at a mean of two or more for erythema formation, edema formation, corneal damage, one or more for iris damage, or 2.5 or more for conjunctival swelling or redness. (Skin or eye sensitization)

Any material that produces a response in 30% or more of the test animals when using an adjuvant, or 15% or more, when not using an adjuvant, or where evidence shows that it causes skin sensitization in persons following exposure in a workplace.

Any material that shows evidence of mutagenicity in mammalian somatic cells in vivo in a test to assess either gene mutation or chromosomal aberration.

The Class D, Division 2 hazard symbol (Fig. 6) represents chronic toxicity, which is poisoning over long periods of time. It is never used in conjunction with the acute poison hazard symbol!

Figure 7	Class D, Division 2 Symbol – Materials Causing Other Toxic Effects (Chronic Toxicity)

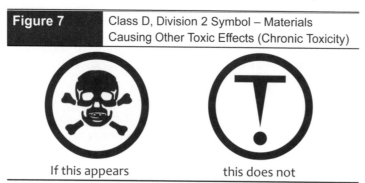

If this appears   this does not

Division 3: Biohazardous Infectious Materials

Figure 8	Division 3 Symbol – Biohazardous Infectious Materials

Division 3 (Fig.8) of Class D includes very special materials:

- Organisms known or suspected to cause serious illness or death in humans or animals.
- the toxins of such organisms.

Organisms referred to above may be bacterial, viral, fungal, protozoal, rickettsial or helminthic.

Examples of materials falling into Division 3 would be:

- cultures of such organisms.
- specimens such as blood, urine, sputum, feces or tissue samples for diagnostic purposes.
- vaccines containing such organisms.

Organisms are assigned to one of four risk groups, using the World Health Organization's classification system:

Risk Group I (low risk):

Organisms (such as escherichia coli) that are unlikely to cause serious human disease.

Risk Group II (moderate risk):

Pathogens (such as salmonella) that can cause severe human disease, but present only moderate risks to the community. Effective treatment is usually available.

Risk Group III (high risk):

Pathogens (such as AIDS viruses) that produce serious human diseases but are not spread by casual contact.

Risk Group IV (very high risk):

Pathogens (such as marburg virus) that usually produce very serious human disease often resulting in death. They are highly infectious and often untreatable.

Class E – Corrosives

Figure 9	Class E Symbol - Corrosives

Class E (Fig. 9) contains any acid or caustic substance that meets one or more of the following criteria:

- Corrosion of steel (SAE 1020) or non-clad aluminum (SAE 7075T6) at a rate exceeding 6.25 mm per year when tested in accordance with NACE (National Association of Corrosion Engineers) standard test TM-01-69

- Corrosive to skin when tested by the appropriate OECD standard test No.404

- Cause visible necrosis (death) of human skin tissue

The common expression for corrosiveness is the pH value which expresses the concentration of hydrogen ions (by way of its negative logarithm) on a scale of 0 to 14. The middle of that scale, 7, is considered to be neutral. Numbers below 7 indicate an acidic solution, whereas those above 7 indicate bases (caustics). The closer the pH value is to 0, the stronger the acid and the closer to 14, the stronger the base.

Sulphuric acid, such as found in a car battery, is a strong acid with a pH of very near 0. Powdered or granular drain cleaners, such as "Drano", are strong caustics. When mixed with water, they will have a pH very close to 14.

Class F – Dangerously Reactive Materials

Figure 10	Class F Symbol – Dangerously Reactive Materials

Class F (Fig.10) contains controlled products which meet one or more of the following criteria:

- Products that can undergo vigorous polymerization, decomposition or condensation (liquefied acetylene, unless stabilized, can explosively decompose).

- Products that become self-reactive under conditions of pressure or shock (such as ammonium azide or cyanuric triazide).

- Products that, on contact with water, react by releasing a poisonous gas with an LC_{50} not exceeding 2500 ppm (alkali metal cyanides can release the highly toxic gas hydrogen cyanide on contact with water).

Class F is often confused with incompatibility of products. Many chemicals, or controlled products, are incompatible with other chemicals or whole families of other chemicals. Examples of such incompatibility are acids and caustics or oxidizers and flammable substances.

Mixing ammonium nitrate with diesel fuel produces a substance like dynamite, while oiling the pressure regulator used on a compressed oxygen cylinder can result in a violent explosion.

Class F does not deal with incompatibility hazards. The only criterion found in this class which involves incompatibility is that between a product and water. All other incompatibilities are normally addressed on the material safety data sheet under the section of "Reactivity Data".

Subject to TDG Regulations

While controlled products are subject to the Transportation of Dangerous Goods Regulations, none of the WHMIS requirements apply. Many controlled products are equally identified as regulated "Dangerous Goods".

Example 2:

A company manufactures a windshield washer fluid. Upon classifying the finished product, using WHMIS criteria, it is found that the fluid has a flash point of 32°C and an LD_{50} of 480 mg/kg. LD_{50} means a lethal dose that results in the death of 50% of the tested population. This puts the material into Class B, Division 2 and Class D, Division 1, Subdivision B. Because of its flash point, the fluid also matches the classification criteria for a Class 3.3 Flammable liquid under TDGR.

In order to offer the fluid for transport, handle it for transport or transport it, the consignor must comply with the TDG Act and Regulations. When the manufacturer ships the fluid, WHMIS does not apply to anyone involved in the transporting of the product.

In order to comply with both regulations, the package would reflect two systems and look similar to the TDGR package in Figure 11.

Figure 11	Typical TDGR Package

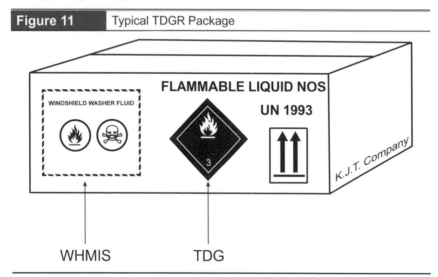

WHMIS   TDG

CONSUMER PRODUCTS

Consumer products exemptions occur for commodities that are:

- included in Part II of Schedule I of the Hazardous Products Act.
- packaged as "consumer products".

To qualify, the product has to meet the following criteria:

- Must be packaged for the consumer in a size that is primarily intended to be sold to the public for personal use and consumption
- Available to the public through retail outlets
- The labeling and packaging complies with the Consumer Chemicals and Container Regulations and the Consumer Packaging and Labeling Act and Regulations

Examples of such products are household cleaners readily available at retail outlets such as: certain types of oven cleaners, bowl cleaners, drain cleaners, paint and wax strippers, ammonia, bleaches and certain detergents.

Other typical consumer products include: enamels, varnishes, BBQ lighter fluid, lamp oils, Varsol, turpentine and camp stove fuel.

Any of the above products, because of their size and intended use, do not require a supplier label or a material safety data sheet when used by workers at a workplace.

A drum of gasoline, even though often available through retail outlets such as gasoline bulk dealers, would not fit the above criteria and would be a controlled product if used at the workplace.

To ensure workplace safety, some suppliers separate their products into two distinctive streams, one for consumer use with consumer labeling and another for industrial use with WHMIS labeling and material safety data sheets.

The employer's responsibility for consumer products at the workplace is to ensure that employees handle and use them correctly and safely. Some basic training on the hazards of such products should be included in the WHMIS training program.

This page has intentionally been left blank.

CHAPTER 26 - QUESTIONS

1. WHMIS controlled products are divided into

    a) 12 classes identified by letters.
    b) 6 classes identified by letters.
    c) 12 classes identified by numbers.
    d) 6 classes identified by numbers.

2. The classification criterion for flammable gas is

    a) critical temperature.
    b) the "lower flammable limit", LFL.
    c) specific ranges of flammability.
    d) the flash point.

3. The Material Safety Data Sheet is supplied by the

    a) federal government.
    b) trucking company.
    c) supervisor.
    d) supplier of the controlled product.

4. The criterion for a combustible liquid is a flash point between

    a) 23°C and 37.8°C.
    b) 61°C and 93.3°C.
    c) 37.8°C and 93.3°C.
    d) 44.6°C and 102.3°C.

5. The term LD_{50} relates to the

    a) concentration of a poison in air.
    b) lethal dose that kills half of the test population.
    c) lowest concentration known to kill rats.
    d) time required for the lethal dose to kill the test population.

CHAPTER 26 - ANSWERS

1. (b)

2. (c)

3. (d)

4. (c)

5. (b)

WHMIS Part II -
Labeling of Controlled Products

LEARNING OUTCOME

When you complete this chapter you should be able to:

Describe the methods required by the Workplace Hazardous Material Information System (WHMIS) for the labeling of controlled products in the workplace.

LEARNING OBJECTIVES

Here is what you should be able to do when you complete each objective:

1. Describe the supplier and workplace labeling system.

2. Describe vessel and pipeline marking requirements.

3. Describe general label information with respect to bulk shipments and colour rules.

INTRODUCTION

This chapter is designed to help develop an understanding of the Workplace Hazardous Materials Information System's labeling requirements. It will provide an outline of the three basic labeling methods:

1. Supplier label

2. Workplace label

3. Vessel and pipeline marking

Supplier labels are a requirement of sale or importation and are normally prepared by the manufacturer of the product. Occasionally, the distributor of controlled products may replace the original supplier labels with his own. This practice is quite acceptable since all the law requires is that the supplier to the workplace is identified.

Workplace labeling and marking is a responsibility equally shared between employers and employees. Workplace identification of decanted or in-process controlled products takes the form of labels or signs, or specific colour coding. Colour coding is more practical than labels for piping systems and large process equipment. In most workplaces, both methods will be found.

OBJECTIVE 1

Describe the supplier and workplace labeling system.

SUPPLIER LABEL

Controlled products imported into Canada for the purpose of being used at a workplace and those sold to a workplace require that a supplier label be affixed to their package or container. The basic parts of a supplier label are shown in Figure 1.

Figure 1	Basic Supplier Label

1. A special hatched border matching the one depicted in Schedule III (Subparagraph 20(a)(ii) of the federal legislation.

2. Product identifier, the actual identification of the product by name, code, or brand name as chosen by the supplier.

3. Supplier identifier, the name and address of the supplier of the controlled product.

4. Statement that a Material Safety Data Sheet is available.

5. One or more of the eight WHMIS hazard symbols.

6. Applicable risk phrases.

7. Precautionary statements.

8. First aid measures.

IMPORTANT:

For containers of less than 100 mL capacity, only the first five items above need to appear on the supplier label.

The size of the label, unlike the graphic layout, is not important, as long as the information on it is legible.

Figure 2	Basic Supplier Label – Vertical (Letter) Format

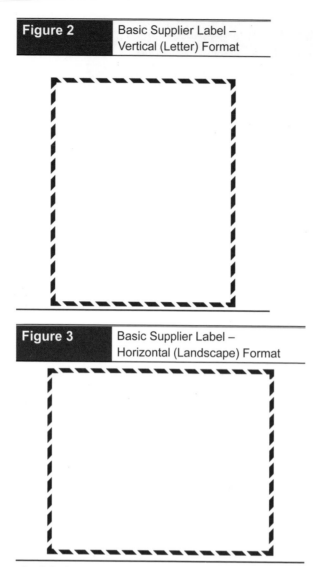

Figure 3	Basic Supplier Label – Horizontal (Landscape) Format

The label must be rectangular (Fig. 4) and in proportion to the graphics provided in Schedule III (Subparagraph 20(a)(ii) of the federal legislation.

Figure 4	Basic Supplier Label – Rectangular

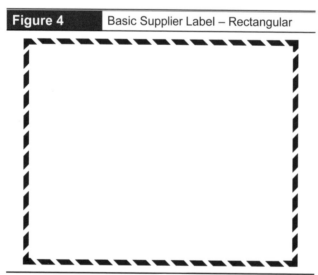

Figure 5, a standard supplier label, contains a specific statement/symbol in all seven areas required. Depending on the controlled product and its specific hazards, additional information may appear on the label. The supplier label is the first indicator of a product's hazard; whereas, the MSDS will provide additional, more detailed information.

Figure 5	Typical Supplier Label

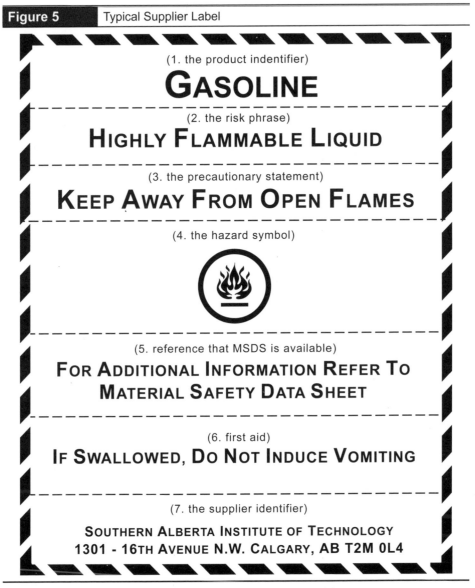

(1. the product indentifier)
GASOLINE

(2. the risk phrase)
HIGHLY FLAMMABLE LIQUID

(3. the precautionary statement)
KEEP AWAY FROM OPEN FLAMES

(4. the hazard symbol)

(5. reference that MSDS is available)
FOR ADDITIONAL INFORMATION REFER TO MATERIAL SAFETY DATA SHEET

(6. first aid)
IF SWALLOWED, DO NOT INDUCE VOMITING

(7. the supplier identifier)
SOUTHERN ALBERTA INSTITUTE OF TECHNOLOGY
1301 - 16TH AVENUE N.W. CALGARY, AB T2M 0L4

Inside the WHMIS border, only WHMIS information should appear.

Supplier labels must be bilingual or both a French and English version of the label must be affixed to each package or container. They must be sufficiently durable and legible and prominently displayed.

Figure 6 is a sample of an acceptable bilingual supplier label. It contains all the necessary information as specified in the regulations.

It is only one approach. As long as the label serves the intended purpose of supplying the right information to the workplace, it is acceptable. The basic principle of a supplier label is to supply an initial warning to the worker about the hazards inherent in the product. The material safety data sheet will add to that basic information.

There are three immediate warning signs on the supplier label in Figure 6:

1. The distinct WHMIS border

2. The hazard symbol for acute toxicity

3. The hazard symbol for corrosive materials

Often, a controlled product will have more than one hazard. In such cases, the number of hazard symbols must reflect all the hazards of the product.

| Figure 6 | Bilingual Supplier Label |

SULPHURIC ACID, FUMING
ACIDE SULFURIQUE

Risk phrases:
HIGHLY IRRITATING TO SKIN, EYES AND NOSE.
Health Hazard Data:
STRONG ACID, VAPOURS HIGHLY TOXIC. BURNS SKIN ON CONTACT.
Precautionary Statements:
EYES: FACESHIELD AND GOGGLES
GLOVES: RUBBER
Personal Protective Equipment:
RUBBER APRON, RUBBER BOOTS.
First Aid Measures:
EYES: FLUSH WITH LARGE QUANTITIES OF WATER. CONSULT PHYSICIAN AT ONCE.
SKIN: FLUSH WITH WATER. CONSULT PHYSICIAN.
Ingestion:
TREAT WITH BAKING SODA, MILK OF MAGNESIA OR LARGE QUANTITIES OF MILK. DO NOT INDUCE VOMITING!

Risque(s) possible(s):
EXTREMEMENT IRRITANT POUR LA PEAU, LES YEUX ET LE NEZ.
Reinseignement sur les dangers pour la sante:
ACIDE FORTE. TRAITER COMME POUR L'ACIDE FORTE.
Surexposition aigue: PEAU ET YEUX.
Measures de precaution:
EQUIPEMENT DE PROTECTION SPECIFIQUE:
YEUX: ECRAN FACIAL ET LUNETTES
GANTS: EN CAOUTCHOUC
Autre vetements et equipment:
TABLIER EN CAOUTCHOUC, BOTTES EN CAOUTCHOUC.
Premiers Soins:
YEUX: BIEN RINCER A GRANDE EAU PENDANT 15 MINUTES, CONSULTER UN MEDECIN.
Peau: RINSER A L'EAU CONSULTER UN MEDECIN
Ingestion: TRATIER COMME POUR L'ACIDE FORTE. CONSULTER UN MEDECIN.

REFER TO MATERIAL SAFETY DATA SHEET FOR FURTHER INFORMATION.
POUR PLUS D'INFORMATION, CONSULTER A FICHE SIGNALETIQUE.

SOUTHERN ALBERTA INSTITUTE OF TECHNOLOGY, 1301 - 16 AVENUE N.W. CALGARY, AB T2M 0L4

An example would be ethylene oxide, a gas (Class A) that is highly flammable (Class B, Division 1), very poisonous (Class D, Division 1, Subdivision A) and a strong oxidizer (Class C). An example of a supplier label for ethylene oxide is shown in Figure 7.

| Figure 7 | Multiple Hazard Product Supplier Label |

Ethylene oxide

Extremely flammable gas.
Extremely poisonous gas.
Very strong oxidizer

Keep away from all ignition sources
Use only in closed systems
Do not inhale

FOR ADDITIONAL INFORMATION REFER TO
MATERIAL SAFETY DATA SHEET

If inhaled, remove worker from contaminated area to fresh air. If unconscious, start resuscitation immediatly. Get medical aid at once.

SOUTHERN ALBERTA INSTITUTE OF TECHNOLOGY
1301 - 16TH AVENUE N.W. CALGARY, AB T2M 0L4

Four hazard symbols are displayed on the label, one each for the different classes of the product. In cases of acute and chronic toxicity, only the skull and crossbones symbol is displayed, not both!

Figure 8	Acute and Chronic Toxicity Labels

Never displayed
together!

The supplier label is required to be on packages and containers of controlled products as a condition of sale or importation. Since some forms of shipments would not lend themselves to labeling (bulk shipments of gasoline and diesel fuel), actual supplier labels are not required period.

Often, signs are used instead. A large storage tank may simply be identified by a sign giving nothing more than the product's name.

Figure 9	Bulk Container Labeling

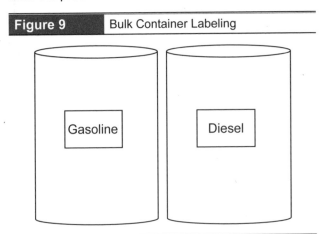

Drums filled from the tanks shown in Figure 9 and prepared for sale would have to be labeled with a supplier label, whereas drums used in-house on a day to day basis would only require a workplace label.

If controlled products reach the workplace with a supplier label, but those labels become lost or unreadable, they can be replaced by a workplace label. All controlled products used, handled or stored at a workplace must be labeled, including wastes to be discarded.

WORKPLACE LABEL

The next step in WHMIS labeling is the workplace label, shown in Figure 10. It is normally applied to controlled products decanted at the workplace.

Figure 10	Workplace Label

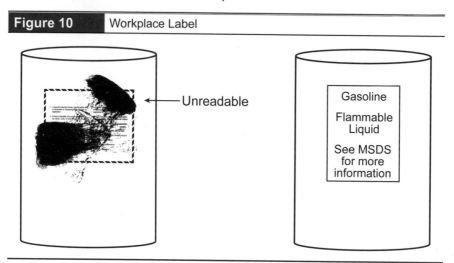

Almost every time a controlled product is decanted, a workplace label is required. Some simple rules for compliance, shown in Figure 11, are:

- the controlled product arrives at the workplace with a supplier label
- for normal day-to-day use, a three part workplace label is required
- for use by one worker, only the product identifier is required
- for immediate use, labeling rules do not apply

Figure 11	Workplace Label Requirements

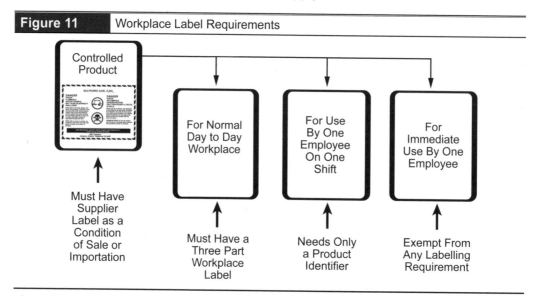

The workplace label requires compliance with three specific areas of the WHMIS system:

1. The product identifier
2. Basic risk phrases
3. A statement that a material safety data sheet is available

A basic workplace label is shown in Figure 12. As long as those three areas are adequately covered, all requirements of WHMIS are met.

| Figure 12 | Basic Workplace Label |

(1. product identifier)

GASOLINE

(2. precautionary/risk statment)

HIGHLY FLAMMABLE

KEEP AWAY FROM OPEN FLAME

(3. reference to MSDS)

REFER TO MATERIAL SAFETY DATA SHEET FOR ADDITIONAL INFORMATION

Enhanced workplace labels (Fig. 13) may also be used. The use of the WHMIS border and hazard symbols will provide additional information to those workers whose first language is not English or French.

| Figure 13 | Enhanced Workplace Label |

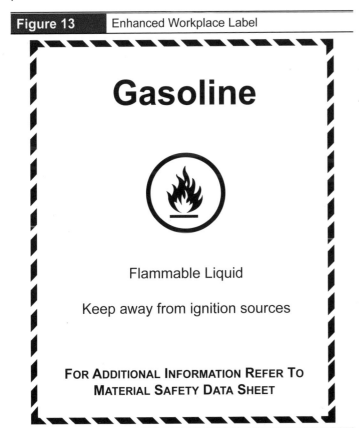

Gasoline

Flammable Liquid

Keep away from ignition sources

FOR ADDITIONAL INFORMATION REFER TO MATERIAL SAFETY DATA SHEET

The use of the workplace label is primarily the responsibility of the worker. The employer normally provides the necessary labels, either completed or blank; the worker then makes sure that the correct ones are put on the container into which the controlled product is decanted.

OBJECTIVE 2

Describe vessel and pipeline marking requirements.

VESSEL & PIPELINE MARKING

Instead of a workplace label, specific colour coding or marking may also be used at the workplace. An example would be a process system containing piping, vessels, pumps, reactors and tanks. It would be very difficult to put labels on such equipment. An alternative could be to identify the hazardous materials with different colours or bands of colours. An example of pipeline marking is shown in Figure 14. Pipelines could be marked by painting them a solid colour or by putting different coloured tape on them at specific intervals.

Figure 14	Pipeline Marking

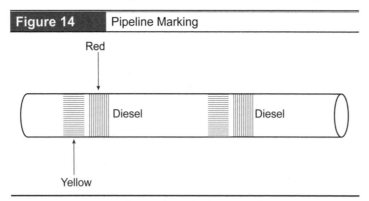

Process equipment (Fig.15) could be identified with appropriate signs to warn workers that they contain controlled products.

Figure 15	Process Equipment Marking

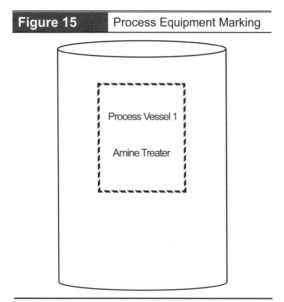

Any marking system that tells the workers that controlled products are present is acceptable for workplace identification. As long as the workers understand the code or signs, all requirements of WHMIS for worksite labels have been met.

Figure 16 is an example of identifying parts of a process system containing controlled products. The raw materials on the left come with applied supplier labels on them if they are controlled products.

Identification of the process piping is normally achieved using colour coding. The finished product containers are labeled depending on their final destination.

These containers

- must have a supplier label as a condition of sale.
- only require a workplace label if destined for export.
- require a workplace label for in-house use.
- require a temporary workplace label until it is labeled with supplier label at a later time.

Figure 16	Process System Marking

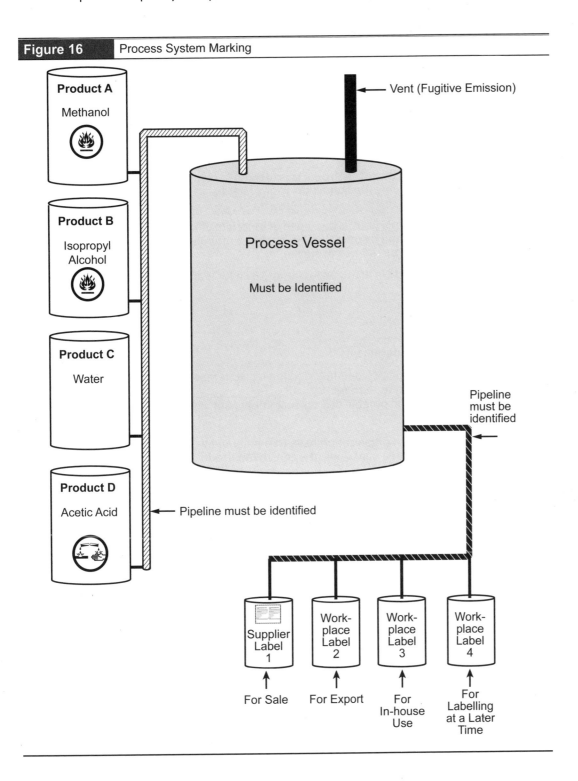

OBJECTIVE 3

Describe general label information with respect to bulk shipments and colour rules.

GENERAL LABEL INFORMATION

Bulk shipments of controlled products do not have to be labeled, but all applicable hazard information must have been sent to the purchaser in one of three ways:

1. WHMIS supplier label
2. MSDS
3. In writing

As long as the outer package containing controlled products is marked in compliance with the Transportation of Dangerous Goods (TDG) Regulations, only the containers inside that package would have to have supplier labels on them.

Controlled products from laboratory supply houses packaged in amounts of less than 10 kg and intended for use in a laboratory, do not have to have the distinct WHMIS border, a "supplier identifier" or WHMIS hazard symbols. If an MSDS is available, it must be marked as such.

Laboratory samples of controlled products in amounts less than 10 kg for which no MSDS has been prepared require the following label information:

- Sample identifier
- Supplier identifier
- Chemical identity for all known ingredients
- An Emergency telephone number included in the following statement: "Hazardous Laboratory Sample. For hazard information or in an emergency, call _____/Enchantillon pour laboratoire de produit dangereux. Pour obtenir des renseignments sur les dangers ou en cas d'urgence, composer_____."

Samples collected and analyzed within an organization have to be marked with a product identifier only. If a supplier label cannot readily be affixed to a container of a controlled product (a very small vial or cylinder), a tag (Fig.17) may be used instead.

Figure 17	Supplier Tag

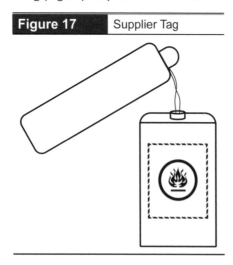

COLOUR RULES

To avoid conflict with colours used by other regulations, certain colours (Fig. 18) cannot be used for WHMIS hazard symbols:

Figure 18	Colour Rules

The green/white combination cannot be used for poisonous, corrosive or flammable gases.

Yellow cannot be used in any combination for this symbol. Unless the product reacts with water to emit a flammable gas, the color blue cannot be used.

Red and/or blue cannot be used in any combination with any other color.

Any other color than Pantone 151 Orange may be used for this symbol. Orange is reserved for Explosives, Class 1 of the TDG Regulations.

Any other color than Pantone 151 Orange may be used for this symbol. Orange is reserved for Explosives, Class 1 of the TDG Regulations.

Any other color than Pantone 151 Orange may be used for this symbol. Orange is reserved for Explosives, Class 1 of the TDG Regulations.

Any other color than Pantone 151 Orange may be used for this symbol. Orange is reserved for Explosives, Class 1 of the TDG Regulations.

Any other color than Pantone 151 Orange may be used for this symbol. Orange is reserved for Explosives, Class 1 of the TDG Regulations.

This page has intentionally been left blank.

CHAPTER 27 - QUESTIONS

1. The person who must label the package containing controlled products is the
   a) trucking company official.
   b) supplier of the products.
   c) industrial hygienist.
   d) consignee (receiver of the goods).

2. The distinct WHMIS border is required on
   a) the workplace label.
   b) the pipeline marking.
   c) the supplier label.
   d) controlled products weighing more than 10 kg.

3. Supplier labels normally must contain information in
   a) 7 specific areas.
   b) 6 specific areas.
   c) 4 specific areas.
   d) 5 specific areas.

4. If you decant a controlled product into a container that you keep around the workplace, you must
   a) identify it with a product identifier only.
   b) place a supplier label on the container.
   c) affix a workplace label on it providing information in three areas.
   d) ignore all labeling.

5. WHMIS supplier labels display at least
   a) two hazard symbols.
   b) one hazard symbol.
   c) information in 14 areas.
   d) 4 risk phrases.

6. Which of the following statements is a risk phrase?
   a) Highly flammable
   b) Wear eye protection
   c) Identify with a correct WHMIS label
   d) Use only with proper ventilation

CHAPTER 27 - ANSWERS

1. (b)

2. (c)

3. (a)

4. (c)

5. (b)

6. (a)

WHMIS Part III - Material Safety Data Sheets

LEARNING OUTCOME

When you complete this chapter you should be able to:

Explain the components of the WHMIS Material Safety Data Sheet, and its application in the worksite, and terminology used on the MSDS.

LEARNING OBJECTIVES

Here is what you should be able to do when you complete each objective:

1. State the purpose and describe the general content of each section of the Material Safety Data Sheet (MSDS).

2. Discuss WHMIS exposure limits.

3. Discuss the training requirements for WHMIS and describe the Hazardous Materials Information Review Act in relation to the MSDS.

4. Define various terms used on the MSDS.

5. Relate Hazard symbols to Classes.

INTRODUCTION

All jurisdictions in Canada have similar legislation in place concerning safety and health. Since it is impossible to refer to them all, the Alberta acts, regulations and codes will be referred to in this chapter. The student is encouraged to refer to the appropriate documents for his or her province or territory.

This chapter is designed to help develop an understanding of how to provide and use the information supplied by the Material Safety Data Sheet (MSDS).

Because WHMIS relates directly to a product's ability to affect the health of a worker, much of the information found on an MSDS is chemical and physical in nature.

One of the major areas and perhaps the most difficult to understand, deals with toxicology of the product. The information relating to toxicology, or how poisonous the product is, is expressed in three distinct terms:

1. Acute toxicity - Immediately dangerous materials

2. Chronic toxicity - Materials that have chronic effects on the workers' health

3. Infectious toxicity - Toxicity of biological agents, such as bacteria and viruses

It is the responsibility of the employer to train employees to work safely with controlled products in the workplace.

OBJECTIVE 1

State the purpose and describe the general content of each section of the Material Safety Data Sheet (MSDS).

MATERIAL SAFETY DATA SHEET (MSDS)

The heart of the WHMIS system, the Material Safety Data Sheet (MSDS), provides additional information for every specific controlled product at the workplace.

Like the supplier label, it must be provided as a condition of sale or importation for every controlled product supplied to a Canadian worksite. An example of an MSDS is shown in Figures 1(a) and 1(b).

The MSDS must provide information in nine specific sections:

1. Product identification and use

2. Hazardous ingredients

3. Physical data of product

4. Fire and explosion data

5. Reactivity data

6. Toxicological properties (poisoning information)

7. Preventive measures

8. First aid measures

9. MSDS preparation and update information

<u>NOTE:</u> **The order in which the nine sections are presented in an MSDS is optional, provided they are each included. The order shown above and in the remainder of this Objective is one example only.**

Product Identification and Use

This section provides information on who supplied the product to the workplace, including full name and address, emergency telephone numbers, product identifier and intended use.

- Product identifier (the "name" of the product)

- Intended product use (such as "motor fuel" as an intended use for gasoline)

- Manufacturer's or supplier's identification (the name of the actual supplier of the product)

- Full name and address of either above

- Emergency telephone number (a phone number where additional information is available)

- Product identification number, UN or NA, as per Transportation of Dangerous Goods Regulations (the product identification number of gasoline is UN 1203)

Hazardous Ingredients

This is a listing of all hazardous ingredients forming part of the controlled product.

- Any ingredient that is a controlled product or requires disclosure in actual percentages or allowable percentage ranges because of the Ingredient Disclosure List.

- CAS (Chemical Abstract Service) identification number

- LD_{50}, species and route (lethal dose that results in death of 50% of the tested population)

- LC_{50}, species and route (lethal concentration that results in death of 50% of the tested population)

Physical Data of Product

A description of the product's physical state such as liquid or solid, density, vapour pressure, boiling point, and freezing point, is provided in this section.

- State of the product, such as solid, liquid or gas

- Physical appearance and odor

- Odor threshold (how easily can it be detected by nose)

- Absolute vapour pressure of the product (measured on a scale of 0–760mm)

- Density of the product's vapour compared to air as "1"

- Rate of evaporation of the product compared to a standard

- Boiling point (the temperature at which the product changes to a gas or vapour)

- Freezing point (the temperature at which the product turns into a solid)

- pH, a relative measure of acidity or alkalinity (measured on a scale of 0 to 14, with 7 being the neutral point)

- Specific gravity (compared to water as "1" at standard conditions)

- Solubility coefficient in oil/water or water/oil systems (a measure of the product's solubility in water or oil)

| Figure 1(a) | Material Safety Data Sheet (Page 1) |

Material Safety Data Sheet
Fiche D'Information

MSDS

C L A S S	A	B	C	D₁	D₂	D₃	E	F

Section 1: Product Identification and Use

Product Identifier

Product Use

Manufacturer Name		Supplier Name	
Street		Street	
City	Province/State	City	Province/State
Postal Code/ Zip Code	Emergency Telephone No.	Postal Code/ Zip Code	Emergency Telephone No.

Section 2: Hazardous Ingredients

Ingredients (list only controlled products)	%	CAS Number	LD_{50} of Ingredient and Species and Route		LC_{50} of Ingredient and Species and Route	

Section 3: Physical Data - UN Number

Physical State	Odour and Appearance			Odour Threshold
Vapour Pressure mm/Hg	Vapour Density	Evaporation Rate	Boiling Point	Freezing Point
pH	Specific Gravity (Water = 1)	Density (kg/m³)	Coefficient of Water/Oil Distribution	**UN:**

Section 4: Fire and Explosion Data

Flammable? Yes ☐ No ☐   If Yes, under what conditions ▷

Means of Extinguishment   .

Flash Point, °C and Method	Lower Flammable Limit, % in Air	Upper Flammable Limit, % in Air
Autoignition Temperature, °C	Hazardous Combustion Products	
Explosion Data ▷ Sensitivity to Impact	Sensitivity to Static Discharge	

Section 5: Reactivity Data

Chemical Stability Yes ☐ No ☐   If No ▷

Incompatibility with other substances Yes ☐ No ☐   If Yes ▷

Reactivity, and under what conditions?

Hazardous Decomposition Products

Figure 1(b)	Material Safety Data Sheet (Page 2)

Material Safety Data Sheet
Fiche D'Information **Page 2**

Product Identifier

Section 6: Toxicological Properties

Route of entry:

Ingestion ☐   Inhalation ☐   Eye Contact ☐   Skin Absorption ☐   Skin Contact ☐

Effects of Acute Exposure

Route of Chronic Exposure

Exposure Limits	Irritancy of Product	Sensitization to Product	Carcinogenicity
Teratogenicity	Reproductive Toxicity	Mutagenicity	Synergistic Products

Section 7: Preventive Measures

Personal Protective Equipment

Respirator (specify type)	Gloves (type and material)	Eye Protection Required (type)
Clothing (specify type)	Footwear (type)	Other

Specific Engineering Controls

Handling Procedures and Equipment

Leak and Spill Containment and Disposal

Waste Disposal

Special Storage and/or Temperature Requirements

Special Shipping Instructions

Section 8: First Aid

Specific First Aid Measures

Section 9: Preparation Information and Update

Prepared by (group, department or person)	Telephone Number ( )	Date (yy/mm/dd)
Updated by: Date (yy/mm/dd):	Updated by: Date (yy/mm/dd):	Updated by: Date (yy/mm/dd):

Fire and Explosion Data

This part supplies information about ignition and flammability characteristics of the product, including: flash point, flammability range and auto ignition temperature.

- Condition under which the product is flammable

- Means of extinction (how to fight and control fires)

- Flash point and method of determining it (expressed in degrees Celsius)

- Lower Flammable Limit (the lowest mixture in air that will ignite and continue to burn)

- Upper Flammable Limit (the highest mixture in air that will burn)

- Auto ignition temperature (the temperature at which the product ignites in the absence of flame or spark)

- Products of combustion that are hazardous (such as toxic gases created during the burning of certain plastics)

- Explosion data due to mechanical shock

- Explosion data due to static spark

Reactivity Data

Data on the chemical instability of the product and its incompatibility with other chemicals is listed in this section.

- Conditions under which the product is chemically unstable (such as carbide reacting with water to form acetylene)

- Classes and individual chemicals with which the product is incompatible (such as incompatibility of strong oxidizers and hydrocarbons)

- Conditions under which the product becomes reactive (such as: heat, pressure or exposure to light)

- Hazardous decomposition products (for example, ether can decompose to form dangerous peroxides)

Toxicological Properties (Poisoning Information)

This section, is one of the most important, provides the information about the toxicology of the product. In other words, it tells how poisonous it is and more importantly, how it can enter the worker's system. The three basic routes of entry into the human body are by

- ingestion (orally).
- contact with the skin (dermal).
- inhalation (breathing).

A listing on how the product can be absorbed, its immediate or long term effects and its final result are contained here. Both acute and chronic exposure effects are listed. Acute poisoning relates to immediate and serious effects while chronic poisoning deals with effects after long term exposure to the product.

- The route by which the poison can enter the body, including: oral, dermal and inhalation (eye contact is another possible route; some poisons severely affect eyesight)
- Symptoms of acute exposure to the product (immediate effects such as dizziness, unconsciousness or coma)
- Symptoms of chronic exposure to the product (long term effects, such as cancer or respiratory diseases)
- Respiratory tract sensitization (permanent sensitization to breathing the product's vapours)
- Degree of skin and eye irritation of the product
- Is the product a carcinogen (cancer causing)?
- Is the product a teratogen (causes injury to the unborn fetus)?
- Is the product an embryo toxin (causes injury to the embryo)?
- Does exposure to the product cause mutations (mutation is expressed as heritable or non-heritable)?
- Names of toxicologically synergistic products (combinations with other products that would multiply the poisonous effect)

Preventive Measures

Once the hazards of a specific controlled product are known, adequate protection can be provided. This section provides information on personal protective equipment, engineering controls and emission and spill control.

- Type and specification of personal protective equipment to be used (such as: respirator, breathing apparatus, gloves, or boots)
- Engineering controls (such as: fume hood, spray booth, exhaust or ventilation)
- Spill or leak control procedures (how to contain, neutralize, or clean up spills)
- Storage and shipping procedures (any applicable special instructions for the safe storage and transportation of the product)
- Handling and safety procedures

First Aid Measures

First aid is the immediate response to an acute exposure to a hazardous product. Once such an exposure has occurred, specific reaction can greatly reduce the severity of the incident. Listed here are those immediate steps.

- Specific first response to an acute exposure or injury

MSDS Preparation and Update Information

Every MSDS must include information on who prepared it - a person, a department or a group. Included must be a telephone number so the person, a department or a group can be reached in case additional information is required.

An MSDS cannot be older than 3 years. New ones must either be obtained after that time or the existing ones must be updated. Updates may be done by the employer for those products purchased more than 3 years ago and are still present at the workplace.

- The name and telephone number of the person, group or department which prepared the MSDS
- The date the MSDS was prepared

Conflicting or misleading information must not appear on the MSDS. As an example, it would be incorrect to state that the product is an acute toxin but has an LD_{50} of 1400 mg/kg. The highest cutoff for acute poisons is 1000 mg/kg (dermal); therefore, a product with the above LD_{50} of 1400 mg/kg would not be included in WHMIS for reasons of being toxic.

ADDITIONAL RULES FOR MSDS

Information must be consistent with the classification criteria.

Completion of all areas on the MSDS is required if information is available. If information is not available, the applicable area must be completed by either entering "not available" or an abbreviation. An applicable abbreviation in English would be "na", in French, "p.d." or "s.o.".

na = not available

p.d. = pas disponible

s.o. = sans objet

If applicable, the product identification number for pure chemicals or generic groups of chemicals must be included. These numbers are four digit numbers prefixed by either UN or NA, meaning "United Nations" or "North American".

The Transportation of Dangerous Goods Regulations (TDGR) identify dangerous goods by these numbers. As an example, gasoline is assigned UN 1203. It is classified as a flammable liquid both in TDGR and WHMIS.

To accommodate variances in percentages for manufactured products, the following specific ranges may be used on the MSDS. These ranges are as follows:

0.1–1.0%	10–30%
0.5–1.5%	15–40%
1.0–5.0%*	30–60%**
3.0–7.0%	40–70%
5.0–10.0%	60–100%
7.0–13.0%	

A range of 1% to 5%* would be acceptable, as would a range of 30% to 60%**.

A range of 1% to 6% or 20% to 50% would not be acceptable. These two ranges do not fit any of the above.

Products listed in the Ingredient Disclosure List (IDL), as either 0.1% or 1%, must be listed on the MSDS if they are a component of a controlled product.

OBJECTIVE 2

Discuss WHMIS exposure limits.

EXPOSURE LIMITS

The following are several different exposure limits which are based on time and/or amount of exposure:

- Occupational Exposure Limits (OEL)
- Time Weighted Average (TWA)
- Short Term Exposure Limit (STEL)
- Ceiling Exposure Limit (CEL)
- LD_{50} and LC_{50}

Occupational Exposure Limits (OEL)

These are the maximum limits of exposure to an airborne substance that are believed to be safe for nearly all workers exposed day after day without adverse effects.

Time Weighted Average (TWA)

Time weighted average (TWA) is the average exposure to a contaminant or condition (such as a chemical) to which workers may be exposed without adverse effect over a period such as in an 8-hour day or 40-hour week.

Short Term Exposure Limit (STEL)

Short term exposure limit (STEL) is the maximum level of exposure to which workers may be subjected for no more than 15 minutes at a time.

Ceiling Exposure Limit (CEL)

This is the limit that must not be exceeded at any time. It usually applies to such products as: respiratory tract irritants or fast acting airborne poisons.

LD_{50} and LC_{50}

LD_{50} is the amount of a single dose of a product that will result in the death of 50% of a defined animal population.

LC_{50} is the amount of the concentration in air of a substance that will result in the death of 50% of a defined animal population.

The smaller the numbers are, the more toxic the product. A poison with an LD_{50} of 10 milligrams per kilogram of body weight is much more toxic than a poison with an LD_{50} of 100 milligrams per kilogram of body weight.

The expression "milligram per kilogram of body weight" (mg/kg) relates to the actual weight of the species ingesting the product.

An LD_{50} of 10 mg/kg means that for a rat population weighing about 200 grams (1/5 of a kg) each, a dose of 2 mg given to each rat would result in at least 50% of the rats dying. Or, for a human weighing 100 kg, the dose would be 10 mg/kg × 100 kg = 1000 mg or 1 gram.

Figure 2 is an example of how OEL's apply to the workplace. Hydrogen sulphide, a flammable and poisonous gas, would be a WHMIS controlled product because it meets the classification criteria of Class A and Class D.

Figure 2 | OEL for H₂S

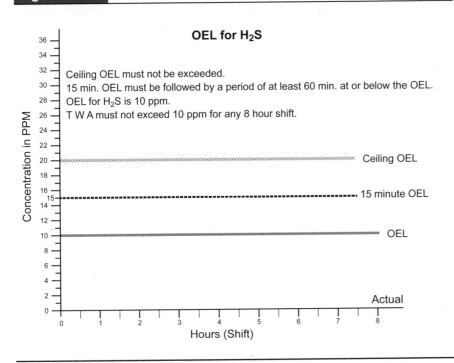

Its occupational exposure level is set at 10 ppm (TWA). At that level or below, the workplace would be considered safe for all workers. Because levels can vary, depending on the process and equipment, the OEL is normally expressed as a time weighted average.

For most controlled products, OEL's have been established.

Other handy references are such publications as: the NIOSH/OSHA "Pocket Guide to Chemical Hazards" and the TLV publication of the American Conference of Governmental Industrial Hygienists, "Threshold Limit Values and Biological Exposure Indices".

OBJECTIVE 3

Discuss the training requirements for WHMIS and describe the Hazardous Materials Information Review Act in relation to the MSDS.

TRAINING REQUIREMENTS

It is the responsibility of the employer to provide training to employees in the handling of controlled products within close proximity or with which they are actually working.

The employee training program must include the following:

- Understanding of the contents required on supplier labels, workplace labels and MSDS's
- The significance and purpose of the information found on supplier labels, workplace labels and MSDS
- Training in procedures for safe handling and storage of controlled products
- Training in safe disposal (waste) procedures
- Emergency response in case of a leak or spill
- Where in use, the meaning of color coding or any other visible identification system used instead of workplace labeling
- Site specific training dealing with the specific products found in the workplace.

The program must lead to the employee being reasonably able to apply the provided hazard information. Training programs must be evaluated at least once per year, or more often if needed, to ensure they are effective.

Information on new controlled products or changes in process involving controlled products must be made available to the employee and if indicated, immediate retraining given.

The responsibilities of the workers are as follows:

- The employee must learn information provided for controlled products and use such information correctly
- Correctly label containers into which controlled products are decanted with the correct workplace label
- Protect his/her health and safety while working with controlled products
- The proof of a successful program is the demonstrated ability of the workers to work safely with controlled products and to understand why the specific safety procedures are required.

HAZARDOUS MATERIALS INFORMATION REVIEW ACT

The manufacturer or supplier of a controlled product has invested a considerable amount of money and time into its development. To ensure that a formula can be protected, WHMIS uses the Hazardous Materials Information Review Act (HMIRA).

Under this act, a supplier may be allowed to keep the hazardous ingredients, their percentages, the Chemical Abstract System (CAS) number and the UN/NA number or anything else that would identify the product's formula off the MSDS.

Hazardous information cannot be deleted. Areas dealing with toxicology, physical data, risk and preventive measures and first aid must be completed in all cases.

Generally, an exemption granted under the HMIRA is valid for a period of three years. When such an exemption has been applied for, the claimant must put the date of the application and the number assigned to that claim on the MSDS/label.

When the exemption is granted, a statement to that effect must be added to the MSDS/label, including the date it was granted. Unless the supplier has followed the above procedure and has been granted an exemption, statements such as "proprietary information" or "confidential" must not be used on an MSDS if hazardous information is applicable.

OBJECTIVE 4

Define various terms used on the MSDS.

DEFINITIONS

The following are some additional explanations for terms used on the MSDS:

- Ingredient Disclosure List (IDL)
- Vapour Density
- Rate of Evaporation
- Specific Gravity
- Lower and Upper Flammability Limits, LFL & UFL

Ingredient Disclosure List, IDL

This list contains approximately 1736 chemicals in alphabetical order. If a chemical found on that list is a component of a controlled product in excess of its stated percentage, either 0.1% or 1.0%, it must be listed as a hazardous ingredient on the MSDS for that product.

Example:

Benzene is a common ingredient of gasoline, listed in the IDL as 0.1%. If gasoline contains more than 0.1% of benzene, the actual percentage (or percentage range) has to be included in the hazardous ingredient section.

Vapour Density

This number compares the weight of a product's vapour with the weight of air which is assigned the number "1". A product showing a number less than 1 as its vapour density would be lighter than air; that is, its vapours would tend to rise. A good example is the gas, helium. It has a vapour density of about 0.4; therefore a balloon filled with helium will rise.

A product showing a number greater than 1 as its vapour density would be heavier than air; that is, its vapours would tend to collect near the ground. A good example would be the gas, propane. It has a vapour density of about 1.6, meaning its vapours are heavier than air. If you filled a balloon with propane, it would not get off the ground.

Rate of Evaporation

To establish some sort of standard of how fast a product will evaporate from an open container, it is often compared to the evaporation rate of normal Butyl acetate. n-Butyl acetate evaporates relatively quickly, much faster than water for example. Therefore, it is assigned the number 1.

Materials having a number of less than 0.8 are considered to have slow evaporation rates; those having a number of between 0.8 and 3.0 are considered to have moderate evaporation rates, while materials having a number of more than 3.0 are considered to have fast evaporation rates.

Specific Gravity

Specific gravity is the ratio of the weight of a volume of a controlled product to the weight of an equal volume of water at a specified temperature. Water is assigned the number 1 at standard temperature and atmospheric pressure. Any solid or insoluble product with a specific gravity of less than 1 will float in water; whereas, any solid or insoluble product with a specific gravity of more than 1 will sink.

A piece of iron with a specific gravity of about 7.5 will sink in water; whereas, a piece of wood with a specific gravity of about 0.8 will float.

Therefore, gasoline having a specific gravity of about 0.8 and being insoluble in water, will float on water.

Lower and Upper Flammability Limits, LFL & UFL

Lower flammability limit is the lowest percentage (by volume) of a fuel in a fuel/air mixture that will ignite and continue to burn. Upper flammability limit is the highest percentage (by volume) of a fuel in a fuel/air mixture that will ignite and continue to burn.

For products to be considered flammable, they must first be in the gas or vapour state. Only the vapours of gasoline will ignite; whereas, liquid gasoline cannot.

Flammable liquids and gases have very specific ranges over which they will burn if mixed with air. Below its lower flammability limit, a product's vapour cannot be ignited. The mix is said to be too "lean". If the mixture contains more than its upper flammability limit, it also cannot be ignited, as the mixture is deemed too "rich".

For example, natural gas (methane, CH_4) has a flammability range of about 5% to 15%. If a mixture of air and methane contains less than 5% methane (by volume), it will not burn. Nor will a mixture of methane and air containing more than 15% methane. However, if the air/methane mixture contains between 5 and 15% methane, it will burn.

OBJECTIVE 5

Relate Hazard symbols to Classes.

| Figure 3 | Classes and Hazard Symbols |

Classes and Hazard Symbols

Class A   Compressed Gas

Class B   Flammable and Combustible Materials

Class C   Oxidizing Material

Class D   Poisonous and Infectious Material

                 Division 1, Acute

                 Division 2, Chronic

                 Division 3, Infectious

Class E   Corrosive Material

Class F   Dangerously Reactive Material

This page has intentionally been left blank.

CHAPTER 28 - QUESTIONS

1. The Material Safety Data Sheet contains information in
   a) 7 sections.
   b) 9 sections.
   c) 6 sections.
   d) 6 Classes.

2. Which of the following terms best describes the "Fire and Explosion Data" section of the MSDS?
   a) Hazardous ingredients, toxicity, emergency
   b) Product identifier related
   c) Flammability, flammable limits
   d) Preventive measures

3. Which of the following represents the highest toxicity?
   a) LD_{50} of 600 mg per kilogram of body weight
   b) LD_{50} of 1800 mg per kilogram of body weight
   c) LD_{50} of 218 mg per kilogram of body weight
   d) LD_{50} of 18 mg per kilogram of body weight

4. Which of these must be vaporized in order to burn?
   a) a flammable gas.
   b) natural gas
   c) a combustible liquid.
   d) a non-combustible solid.

5. The term "respiratory tract sensitizer" relates to
   a) preventive measures.
   b) toxicological properties.
   c) physical data.
   d) reactivity data.

6. Material Safety Data Sheets must be
   a) available for every controlled product.
   b) updated every four years.
   c) assigned by the supplier of the products.
   d) known only to the manufacturer of the controlled product.

7. Which of the following is correct?
   a) All areas of the MSDS must be completed
   b) MSDS must be at least 3 pages long
   c) MSDS must be on a very specific form
   d) MSDS must be color coordinated with the material

CHAPTER 28 - ANSWERS

1. (b)

2. (c)

3. (d)

4. (c)

5. (b)

6. (a)

7. (a)

SAFETY

The Cost & Effects of Workplace Injuries

LEARNING OUTCOME

When you complete this chapter you should be able to:

Describe the cost and effects of workplace injuries on the individual worker and the business.

LEARNING OBJECTIVES

Here is what you should be able to do when you complete each objective:

1. Describe the financial cost of injuries and the impact an injury has on the injured person.

2. Discuss the social and legal implications of injuries.

3. List the steps that can be taken by management to minimize the effects of workplace injuries.

INTRODUCTION

This chapter provides the student with an understanding of why it is essential that businesses pay attention to the reduction of risk of injury to workers. The personal impact on the worker, supervisor and management is reviewed, as well as the financial costs to the company and the effects on society as a whole.

Some of the costs related to workplace accidents and injuries can be offset by the business through Workers' Compensation coverage and other insurance policies. However, the larger costs associated with lost production, investigation of the incident, training of replacement staff, damage to equipment and tools and potential loss of business due to late or incomplete shipments to customers are difficult to measure and usually not insurable.

The human costs related to injuries range from pain and discomfort and the difficulties related to retraining for a new career (if the injury results in the worker not being able to continue in his/her original occupation), to loss of self-esteem and difficulties in personal relationships. The human cost extends beyond the injured worker to his or her family and friends as well.

OBJECTIVE 1

Describe the financial cost of injuries and the impact an injury has on the injured person.

FINANCIAL IMPLICATIONS

Information is available from each province's and territory's Workers' Compensation Board on the number of compensable injury claims filed each year, the types of injuries and their costs. If you wish to obtain the complete report, contact your local office of the Workers' Compensation Board.

The costs related to investigation, retraining, and loss of production are difficult to quantify, but estimates indicate indirect costs range from six to fifty times the WCB insured costs. The WCB costs are commonly portrayed to be "the tip of the iceberg" with the myriad of related costs portrayed as being the "hidden" part of the problem below the water. Check your local WCB website for current statistics.

As an example, Table 1 provides an overview of the statistics reported by the WCB in Alberta for 2005.

Table 1	Alberta WCB Annual Report 2005 Latest Statistics - Year at a Glance	
	2005	**2004**
Number of workers covered	1 539 732	1 428 595
Number of new claims reported	168 685	154 377
Number of time-lost claims	37 100	36 000
Number of recurrent claims	15 471	16 040
Permanent Disability awards	3 053	3 181
Fatality Claims accepted	143	124
Claim Costs (thousands$)	680 972	825 840
Registered employees	117 337	109 195

http://www.wcb.ab.ca/pdfs/2005_ar.pdf Page 63

PERSONAL IMPACT

Although the financial costs associated with workplace injuries are very high, they cannot compare to the personal costs to an injured worker. The worker often feels that the accident was his or her fault, resulting in loss of confidence and self-esteem and problems with personal relationships. Although the worker usually does not cause his or her own injury, it is important to recognize that in many cases the worker's and supervisor's actions have a direct impact on the situation.

The worker's attitude before and after the incident has a large impact on the outcome of the situation. In some cases, a worker's attitude can deteriorate and difficulties in personal relationships resulting from the injury may lead to a break up of the family.

The effects of an injury on a worker are not restricted to the pain and suffering of the initial incident. Often, the worker is unable to return to his/her original job, even after a lengthy recuperation. The Workers' Compensation Board provides rehabilitation and retraining service to assist workers in returning to the workforce as soon as possible. However, the challenge of learning new skills and dealing with a disability is often very stressful for the worker. Again, self-esteem is affected and sometimes a successful return to work is not possible.

OBJECTIVE 2

Discuss the social and legal implications of injuries.

SOCIAL & LEGAL IMPLICATIONS

Because of the strain on personal and family relationships resulting from the personal impact of workplace injuries, social programs that provide support for the injured worker are necessary. The WCB provides support programs designed to help rehabilitate the worker, but in some cases, more help is required when the worker is unable to resume his or her career.

The long term social implications of losing many workers from the industrial work force, usually at the most productive time of their careers (the highest proportion of injuries are reported among young workers in the 16–25 yr old age group), cannot be easily measured.

Each province and territory has an Occupational Health and Safety Act or equivalent legislation that requires an employer to ensure the health and safety of workers as far as it is reasonable and practical to do so.

In the case of a serious injury or death resulting from a workplace incident, the employer is required to notify the Occupational Health and Safety office which can be done through a telephone call to the closest office or 24 hour call centre in locations across the province.

The employer is also required to carry out an investigation into the circumstances surrounding the serious injury or incident and prepare a report to be kept on file, available for inspection by an officer, typically for a period of two years following the incident.

In most cases where a serious or fatal injury occurs, an Occupational Health and Safety officer will require that the work being carried out be stopped until he or she conducts an investigation and no further risk of injury exists. This investigation varies in length, depending upon the type of work being carried out and the type of injury that occurred.

The law usually requires that the scene of a serious accident not be disturbed until an officer has had an opportunity to investigate or has given permission to resume activity. The only exceptions are those duties necessary to attend to injured workers or prevent further injury.

When the officer arrives at the scene, he/she will want to conduct a thorough investigation which will usually include taking photographs, interviewing witnesses and talking to workers, supervisors and management who may have information regarding the circumstances leading to the incident.

The officer has the authority under the OH&S Act to look at records, diagrams, and other documents pertaining to the health and safety of workers at the site. Often, this authority will involve examining training records to determine whether or not workers involved received adequate training to allow them to carry out their jobs safely. Documents pertaining to the safe use and maintenance of equipment and machinery, engineered drawings, plans, procedures and other related items may be inspected, copied and/or temporarily removed from the site for copying.

During the investigation, the officer may stop the work being carried out at the site to facilitate the investigation and may require that work not commence until any serious safety hazards are corrected.

The officer will want to determine who was responsible for conditions at the site, whether there were contractors involved, who the "Principal Contractor" (with the most control) was and what the arrangements were for health and safety concerns to be dealt with at all levels of responsibility.

First aid requirements would also be checked for compliance with the First Aid Regulation or equivalent, particularly if such arrangements as transportation of injured workers to a medical facility would have a direct impact on the severity of the worker's injuries.

Compliance with the occupational health and safety regulations will be evaluated and any contraventions documented. The employer will be required to correct any health and safety hazards and, if found to have been negligent, may be liable to prosecution under the OH&S Act.

It should be noted that all persons at the site carry individual responsibilities for health and safety that workers, supervisors, managers, owners and directors or other officers of the company could be held responsible for contraventions. Individual workers and supervisors, as well as managers and owners have been found guilty and assessed penalties under the OH&S Act, as shown in Table 2.

When a contravention of the law has occurred, the legal responsibilities assigned by the Act can be brought before the Courts and penalties determined.

These sentences can be given to owners, directors, managers, supervisors, workers, and others as determined by a judge.

The cases in Table 2 were taken from Work Safe Alberta, "Completed Prosecutions Under the Occupational Health and Safety Act. Regulation and Code, January 1996 to July 12, 2006". This title reflects the philosophy of Alberta Occupational Health and Safety that prosecution is used as a last resort when other types of intervention to ensure worker health and safety have not had the desired effect. (Note: The names of actual companies and individuals have been modified and any similarities to existing companies or individuals is totally coincidental)

Key: **OHS Act - Occupational Health and Safety Act**

GSR - General Safety Regulation

Table 2	Completed Prosecutions			
Date of Incident	**Employer**	**Incident (Brief Description)**	**Violation (Sections of OHS Act and Regulations)**	**Decision**
April 24/03	ABC Contractors Ltd. DEF Construction Ltd.	Two workers fell through a cover placed over an opening in a floor and fell 5.2 m into a basement. One worker suffered serious fracture injuries to a foot.	Count 1 Sec 2(1)(a)(ii) OHS Act Count 2 Sec 3(3)(a) OHS Act Count 3 Sec 18(6) OHS Act Count 4 Sec 2(1) OHS Act Count 5 Sec 60(a) GSR	**April 12/06** Sentenced to $5000 fine plus 15% ($6000) victim surcharge and $17 500 to XXX and $17 500 to YYY
Feb 11/03	XYZ Drilling Services Inc.	A worker was seriously injured when he was contacted and pinned by the top drive portion of a dual rotary drilling rig.	**XYZ Drilling Services Inc.** Count 1 Sec 2(1)(a)(i) OHS Act Count 2 Sec 16(1)(a) GSR Count 3 Sec 14(4) GSR Count 4 Sec 21(1) GSR Count 5 Sec 185(2) GSR **Fred X** Count 6 Sec 37(3) GSR Count 7 Sec 2(2)(a) OHS Act **GHI Oil Operations Ltd.** Count 8 Sec 3(1) OHS Act Count 9 Sec 3(3) OHS Act	**Nov. 24/05** XYZ Drilling pleaded guilty to one count under the GSR – fined in the amount of $5000 plus $750 victim surcharge and $35 000 to YYY Co.. **Nov. 24/05** Fred X pleaded guilty to one count under the GSR – fined in the amount of $1000 plus $150 victim surcharge and $3000 to YYY Co. **April 25/06** Charges dropped against GHI Oil Operations
Jan. 27/03	JKL Industries Ltd.	A worker was assisting other workers to dismantle a roof and salvage the roofing material to be reused when the worker fell 8 m through an unprotected opening.	1 Count Sec 2(1)(a)(i) OHS Act 1 Count Sec 60(a) GSR 1 Count Sec 21(1) GSR	**May 26/06** **JKL Industries** Ltd. pleaded guilty to one count under the Sec 21 (1 - $50 000 fine plus a victim surcharge of $7500

The Occupational Health and Safety Act requires that Alberta Occupational Health and Safety be notified, "if a serious injury or an accident that has the potential of causing serious injury to a person occurs at a work site". This information is available through your provincial or territorial OHS or workplace safety & Health office or web site. Visit your local web site for local information and the phone numbers of who to call in case of an accident/incident.

OBJECTIVE 3

List the steps that can be taken by management to minimize the effects of workplace injuries.

MINIMIZE THE EFFECTS OF WORKPLACE INJURIES

There are several steps an employer can take to reduce the negative effects of workplace injuries including:

- Effective health and safety program
- Emergency plan
- Supervisor's impact on injured worker

Effective Health and Safety Program

The first step is to ensure that an effective health and safety program is in place to reduce the risk of injuries to all workers.

Emergency Plan

Secondly, the employer should ensure that an emergency plan is in place to deal with any incidents where injuries may occur. This plan includes having adequate first aid kits in place throughout the work site and having an appropriate number of first aid trained personnel available to provide assistance at all times. Workers must be aware of whom to contact if they require first aid attention and where to go for first aid supplies.

Supervisors must know how to contact emergency assistance in the case of fire, medical emergency or other situation. Telephone contact with emergency services is essential, especially in remote areas where help may be some distance away.

Supervisor's Impact on Injured Worker

Finally, when a worker is injured, his/her supervisor must understand the impact that his/her relationship with the worker can have on recovery and eventual return to work time. In all cases, close communication should be maintained between the supervisor and the worker, letting the latter know that blame is not being placed and the company does care about his/her injury and wants to do everything possible to assist the worker in returning to work as soon as possible. The supervisor should involve the worker in the progress of the investigation and ask for assistance in determining what could be done to prevent a similar occurrence in the future.

Where the worker requires assistance in rehabilitation and retraining, the supervisor should assist in obtaining the services and support that are available to both the worker and his or her family.

CHAPTER 29 - QUESTIONS

1. A factor that has a large impact on the outcome of a worker's post accident recovery is his

    a) pre-accident safety record.

    b) attitude before and after the accident.

    c) life style off the job.

    d) support received from the immediate family.

2. During worker rehabilitation the supervisor should

    a) have as little contact as possible with the injured worker.

    b) not inform the worker of investigation progress.

    c) assist the worker in seeking and obtaining support services.

    d) let the worker know the investigators are finding fault.

3. Individual responsibilities for health and safety must be borne by

    a) management only.

    b) employees only.

    c) owners only.

    d) all persons in the workplace.

4. The first step an employer should take to reduce the negative effects of workplace injuries is to

    a) employ an on-site nurse.

    b) ensure supervisors know how to contact emergency assistance.

    c) have an effective health and safety program in place.

    d) establish an appropriate number of trained first aid personnel.

5. The highest proportion of injuries are reported by employees in the age group of:

    a) 26 to 35 years

    b) 16 to 25 years

    c) 36 to 45 years

    d) 46 to 55 years

6. When contractors are involved at the site of an incident the contractor with the most control is called the

    a) principal contractor.

    b) general contractor.

    c) sub-contractor.

    d) building contractor.

CHAPTER 29 - ANSWERS

1. (b)

2. (c)

3. (d)

4. (c)

5. (b)

6. (a)

Personal Protective Equipment

LEARNING OUTCOME

When you complete this chapter you should be able to:

Describe the use, selection and care of personal protective equipment.

LEARNING OBJECTIVES

Here is what you should be able to do when you complete each objective:

1. Describe the basic types of personal protective equipment available.

2. Describe the various types and the training, care and maintenance of respiratory protection.

INTRODUCTION

All jurisdictions in Canada have similar legislation in place concerning safety and health. Since it is impossible to refer to them all, the Alberta acts, regulations and codes are referred to in this chapter. The student is encouraged to refer to the appropriate documents for his or her province or territory.

Personal protective equipment is created to give the user maximum protection for the specific part of the body for which it was designed while the use of personal protective equipment is considered by many workers to be uncomfortable and a nuisance, everyone must remember that this equipment is used for personal protection and not for comfort and good looks. Although manufacturers do their best to make this equipment as comfortable as possible for the user, it is impossible to satisfy everyone. Employees who works under conditions in which personal protective equipment must be worn must come to grips with these facts. It should become a worker's second nature to use the required safety equipment.

When dealing with personal protective equipment in an industrial setting, both employer and employee have certain responsibilities. The employer shall ensure that a worker is provided with, and uses the appropriate personal protective equipment specified for each particular job and work location while it is the employee's responsibility to wear, as well as to care for and maintain the equipment.

Both employer and employee should become fully versed in all areas of the Occupational Health and Safety Act which pertain to personal protective equipment, as well as make sure that all protective equipment used is approved by the Canadian Standards Association (CSA).

OBJECTIVE 1

Describe the basic types of personal protective equipment available.

PERSONAL PROTECTIVE EQUIPMENT

Personal protective equipment consists of the following types:

- Head protection
- Eye protection
- Hearing protection
- Foot protection
- Limb and body protection
- Flame resistant clothing
- Safety belts and harnesses

Head Protection

Where danger of injury to a worker's head exists, a worker must wear proper protection such as a hard hat, welding hat, etc. In most industries, hard hats must be worn at all times while the worker is within plant boundaries. A hard hat consists of a hard shell and the suspension. The shell resists blows, penetration, heat and electricity while the suspension acts as a shock absorber and allows air circulation around the head. To be effective, the suspension must have a clearance of 2.5 - 3 cm from the shell. Figure 1 shows the recommended head clearance for the hard hat suspension. Workers wearing hard hats should check this clearance from time to time to ensure it is always maintained or the hard hat may not be effective. Workers should also be aware that they should never paint their hard hats, as paint will weaken the plastic in the hat. Similarly, only approved stickers or labels should be placed on hard hats, as the glues used can also weaken the plastic. If at any time a hat cracks, or receives any other damage, the user should replace it, as it has become unacceptable for use.

Figure 1	Hard Hat

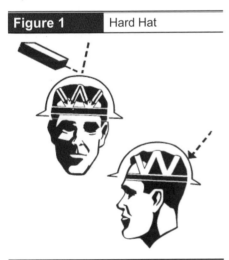

Eye Protection

Where there is danger of injury to, or irritation of, an employee's eyes, the employer shall ensure that appropriate and properly fitting eye protection is worn. There are four different types of eye protection used. The choice depends on the type of job being performed. These types include:

- Safety glasses
- Monogoggles
- Safety goggles
- Face shields

Safety Glasses

Safety glasses give general protection from flying objects and particles and may be used to provide slight visible light reduction. The lenses are made of shatter resistant glass or plastic. Safety glasses can be fitted with side shields (Fig. 2), and although these shields may reduce peripheral vision, their use is highly recommended. When cleaning safety glass lenses, only approved cleaners and wipes should be used to prevent scratching the lenses.

Figure 2	Glasses and Side Shields

MonoGoggles

Goggles are contoured to provide full facial contact around the eyes and eye sockets, thus providing much better protection from:

- Flying objects
- Dust
- Mists
- Liquid splashes

There are many different types of goggles available; they should be selected according to the protection required. Figure 3 illustrates monogoggles which are recommended for hazards caused by dust, fumes, chemical and acid splashes. They are fitted with clear plastic lenses.

Figure 3	Monogoggles

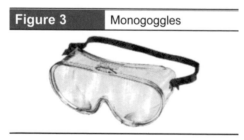

Safety Goggles

When protection against severe impact hazards is required, goggles fitted with mechanically strong glass are used to prevent chips from piercing the eye. A pair of this type of goggles is illustrated in Figure 4.

Goggles for welders and workers in foundries will be the same as those shown in Figure 4, except that lenses to filter the glare will also be present.

Figure 4	Safety Goggles

Face Shields

The fourth type of eye protection (which may also be classified as facial protection) is a face shield. It should be used when working in areas where chemical and acid splashes frequently occur and when performing operations like grinding. **(Note: The best protection from acids and other chemicals is to wear both a face shield and monogoggles).**

Figure 5	Face Shield

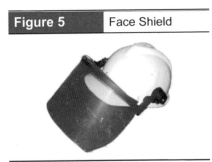

Hearing Protection

Continuous exposure to excessive industrial noise can often result in serious hearing impairment. A worker exposed to noise must, during the time of his or her exposure to noise in excess of the Occupational Exposure Limit as set out in the Occupational Health and Safety Act, wear hearing protection adequate for the work location.

There are two main types of ear protection devices found in the workplace. One is the earmuff type sound protector which is illustrated in Figure 6. It is scientifically designed to reduce harmful high frequency noise even when accompanied by extreme vibration. The second type of ear protection used is the ear plug. There are numerous types of ear plug, from the personally molded type to the disposable type. Ear plugs can be very uncomfortable if they do not fit correctly. Other discomforts can also occur; for example, ear infections can result if ear plugs are not clean and used correctly.

Any type of ear protection used should allow the wearer to be able to detect low level sounds such as a speaker's voice, even while being protected from harmful noise.

Figure 6	Sound Protector

Foot and Limb Protection

Where a danger of injury to a worker's foot may exist, the employer shall ensure that the worker wears safety footwear appropriate to the nature of the hazard associated with the particular work process. Day to day footwear should provide protection to the toes from crushing and the sole from puncturing. There are many types of specialized footwear available; the worker should ensure that the protective footwear being used is in good condition and appropriate for the job.

When there is a danger of injury to a worker's hands, arms, legs or torso, the employer shall ensure that the worker wears properly fitting hand, arm, leg or body protective equipment. The protection worn must be appropriate to the work being done and the nature of the hazard involved.

Included in this type of protective equipment would be hand gloves designed to protect the worker from such hazards as: cuts, burns or electric shock. Gloves may be made of leather, Kevlar, rubber or many other types of material. They also may have wrist or elbow length shields. If gloves are worn thin, or have holes or cuts in them, they should not be used.

Other examples of protective equipment in this category (shown in Fig.7) include:

- Rubber or leather aprons
- Shin protectors
- Foot top protectors

Figure 7	Safety Clothing

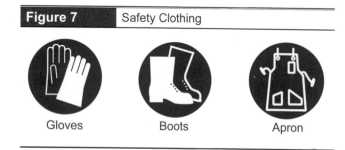

Gloves   Boots   Apron

Safety Belts and Harnesses

In situations involving heights and potential falls, workers must often employ safety belts or harnesses. Before using this type of equipment, it should be checked for any kind of weakness. The life lines used in conjunction with these should be made of a material that is capable of withstanding the shock load which may be applied. The rope should have a diameter sufficient to ensure that a rope grab in use will operate properly. The rope should also be checked for frays or other types of damage. An example of a safety harness is shown in Figure 8.

Figure 8	Safety Harness

OBJECTIVE 2

Describe the various types and the training, care and maintenance of respiratory protection.

RESPIRATORY PROTECTION

Respiratory protective equipment shall be worn

- where there is, or may be, exposure of a worker to an airborne contaminant; or a combination of airborne contaminants; in a concentration exceeding the occupational exposure limits
- when the atmosphere contains, or may contain, oxygen at less than 18 kilopascals partial pressure

Considerations

When making a decision as to what type of respiratory protective equipment to use, the following considerations have to be reviewed:

- The nature of any contaminants
- The need for emergency escape
- The partial pressure of oxygen
- The toxicity of the contaminants
- The warning properties of the contaminants
- The duration, or likely duration, of the workers' exposure
- The concentration, or likely concentration, of any airborne contaminants

Filter Type Respirators

Many industrial operations involve air contaminants. For example, dust generated by handling materials like coal, ashes, flour, cement and sawdust are referred to as "nuisance dusts". They are neither poisonous nor capable of producing fibrous tissue in the lungs, yet are obviously discomforting nuisances to be avoided. Figure 9 shows a respirator which will accept filter cartridges of various types and designs to match the expected hazard.

Mineral dusts and mists containing free silica, including those from sandstone, flint and quartz, can degenerate healthy lung tissue into fibrous or scar tissue which causes the disease known as "silicosis". A related disease arising from asbestos dust is "asbestosis".

Toxic dusts are body poisoning dusts originating from the handling of poisonous materials such as: lead, arsenic and chromium, or their compounds. Whether inhaled or ingested, these dusts dissolve and enter the blood stream causing injury to body organs.

Mists are wet fogs (for example, air containing oil or water droplets) which may contain toxic or lung damaging particles suspended in them. Mists may result from spray coating with paints, enamels or glazes.

The danger of most dusts and mists can be eliminated by using the proper filters. The user of such a respirator should make sure that the correct filters are being used for the job being performed. The filters also have to be changed on a regular basis to ensure that maximum protection is provided. The straps of the respirator should be checked to make sure they are operating correctly and are in good condition. The sealing surfaces should also be checked for cracks and nicks which could prevent a proper seal between the respirator and the face.

Figure 9	Respirator

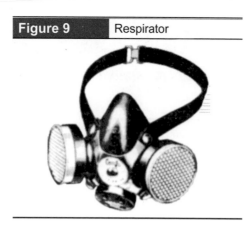

Gas Masks

When work must be done in an area where gases, vapours or chemical fumes are present, the filter type of respirator is inadequate; thus, cartridges or canisters containing activated chemicals must be used. Figure 10 shows an industrial gas mask used for protection against gases, vapours or chemical fumes. This mask has a canister supported by the harness on the operator's back for greater freedom of movement.

This type of gas mask should be checked on a regular basis. The same checks that were described for the respirators should also be followed for the gas mask.

Figure 10	Gas Mask

Supplied Air Breathing Apparatus

The Alberta Occupational Health and Safety Code 2009 has very high standards governing the selection, use and maintenance of Respiratory Protective Equipment. The following excerpts are included from "Requirements Applicable to All Industries", Part 18:

Section 244(1): "An employer must determine the degree of danger to a worker at a work site and whether the worker needs to wear respiratory protective equipment if:

a) a worker is or may be exposed to an airborne contaminant or a mixture of airborner contaminants in a concentration exceeding their occupational exposure limits.

b) the atmosphere has or may have an oxygen concentration of less than 19.5 percent by volume, or

c) a worker is or may be exposed to an airborne biohazardous material"

Section 244(3): "Based on the determination under subsection (1) the employer must:

a) subject to subsection 3(b), provide and ensure the availability of the appropriate respiratory protective equipment to the worker at the work site."

Section 244(4): "A worker must use the appropriate respiratory equipment provided by the employer ..."

Section 245(1): "If respiratory protective equipment is used at a work site, an employer must prepare a code of practice governing the selection, maintenance and use of respiratory protective equipment"

Section 247: "An employer must ensure that respiratory protective equipment used at a work site is selected according to CDA Standard Z94.4-02, Selection, Use and Care of Respirators."

Section 248(1): "An employer must ensure that respiratory protective equipment kept ready to protect a worker is:

a) stored in a readily accessible location.

b) stored in a manner that prevents its contamination

c) maintained in a clean and sanitary condition

c) inspected before and after each use to ensure it is in satisfactory working condition, and

d) serviced and used in accordance with the manufacturer's specifications."

Section 250(1): "An employer must ensure that respiratory protective equipment that depends on an effective facial seal for its safe use is correctly fit tested and tested in accordance with:

a) CSA Standar Z94.4-02, Selection, Use and Care of Respirators, or.

b) a method approved by a Director of Occupational Hygiene"

Self-Contained Breathing Apparatus

Figure 11 is an example of a self-contained breathing apparatus designed to provide extensive mobility. It can be used with either a 30 or 60 minute cylinder which is charged to 31.03 MPa. The unit equipped with a 60 minute cylinder is about 5kg heavier than that equipped with a 30 minute cylinder. The cylinder is locked into the backpack and can be easily changed without tools. This type of equipment is designed for total portability for emergency use, such as isolating equipment and rescue operations. It can also be used for maintenance jobs that can be accomplished in a short time.

The apparatus is equipped with a positive pressure regulator connected to the facepiece. The regulator, which maintains a slight positive pressure to ensure that toxic air cannot enter the facepiece, is supplied with air from the pressure reducer through a small diameter hose. The regulator also contains a warning device to alert the user to a diminishing air supply, usually by both sound and feel, which is especially important when working in a high noise environment.

Figure 11 | Self-Contained Breathing Apparatus

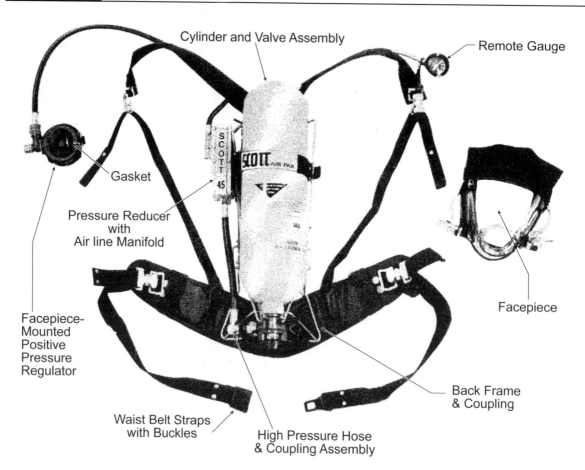

Cylinder and Valve Assembly

Remote Gauge

Gasket

Pressure Reducer
with
Air line Manifold

Facepiece-
Mounted
Positive
Pressure
Regulator

Facepiece

Back Frame
& Coupling

Waist Belt Straps
with Buckles

High Pressure Hose
& Coupling Assembly

(Courtesy of Scott/Safety Supply Canada)

The regulator has an automatic shut-off that reduces air flow while putting on or taking off or when the facepiece is dislodged, thus preventing unnecessary loss of air.

Some units also offer the option of an air line connection to a fixed air supply through a hose up to 100 m long. While using the air line setup, the cylinder valve must be turned off to preserve the cylinder air supply. The user can activate the cylinder air supply for entrance into or exit from the work area when disconnected from the air line supply.

Remote Air Supply Breathing Apparatus

The device shown in Figure 12 has a connection for an external air line for extended use in contaminated areas in combination with an air bottle which can provide a limited supply of air for escape purposes, in accordance with safety regulations. The user attaches the apparatus to the external supplied air system before entering the contaminated atmosphere. If it is necessary to escape from the contaminated atmosphere, the air line may be detached and the supply from the 5 minute cylinder opened, allowing the user to escape the contaminated area unimpeded by an air hose. The supplied air, self-contained combination allows the user to work in the contaminated atmosphere for an extended time with a lightweight apparatus having a mass of around 4.5 kg compared to the 30 or 60 minute portable systems having a mass of 10 or 16 kg.

This type of respiratory device must also be equipped with a regulator to assure a positive pressure inside the face mask. An example is shown in Figure 12.

Figure 12	Remote Air Supply Apparatus

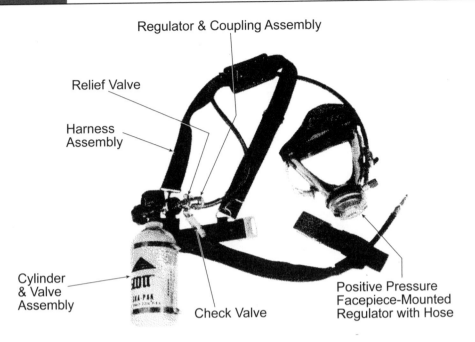

(Courtesy of Scott/Safety Supply Canada)

Training

IMPROPER USE OF ANY BREATHING APPARATUS IN A HAZARDOUS ATMOSPHERE MAY RESULT IN INJURY OR DEATH. PERSONNEL MUST RECEIVE ADEQUATE TRAINING PRIOR TO USE.

The training of personnel who are required to use breathing apparatus cannot be overstressed. The manufacturers of the equipment provide excellent guidelines.

Care and Maintenance

The maintenance and sanitizing of breathing apparatus is outlined by the manufacturer and the CSA regulation makes it mandatory. The student is advised to become familiar with CSA regulation Z94.4, Selection, Care, and Use of Respirators.

Summary

In this chapter, equipment from only one manufacturer has been used for illustration purposes. There are several other types on the market, some having varied features giving advantages over others. All must be approved by CSA and OH&S regulations. Their selection must be according to the guidelines of CSA Z94.4.

ADEQUATE SKIN PROTECTION MUST BE WORN IN ATMOSPHERES CONTAINING GASES OR VAPOURS THAT POISON BY SKIN ABSORPTION.

It must also be remembered that some harmful atmospheres may require total body protection. Special types of breathing apparatus that protect the whole body from harmful atmospheres are available. The devices used for illustration, with their full face masks, protect only the respiratory system and the face. Some devices do not provide eye protection and can only be used in atmospheres which are non-irritating to the eyes.

This page has intentionally been left blank.

CHAPTER 30 - QUESTIONS

1. Shatter resistant glass or plastic applies to

   a) face shields.
   b) safety glasses.
   c) welding goggles.
   d) welding helmet lenses.

2. Employers must ensure employees wear self-contained breathing apparatus when

   a) entering any confined spaces.
   b) handling toxic chemical dusts.
   c) entering an area where there is a threat to life or health due to reduced oxygen content.
   d) fighting fires in the plant.

3. One of the most important requirements of any breathing apparatus is

   a) proper training prior to use.
   b) the user be clean shaven daily.
   c) that it be self sanitizing.
   d) the face mask pressure be maintained slightly negative.

4. The filter type respirators with the proper colour code will effectively protect against

   a) low oxygen concentrations.
   b) chemical fumes.
   c) mineral dusts.
   d) harmful gases.

5. Hard hat suspension minimum clearance is

   a) 2.5 to 3 cm
   b) 1.88 cm
   c) 1.25 cm
   d) 3.25 cm

6. The pressure in a fully charged Self-Contained Breathing Apparatus is

   a) 31.03 kPa.
   b) 101.3 kPa.
   c) 31 030 kPa.
   d) 15 515 kPa.

7. The best eye protection when working with acids and other chemicals would be:

   a) face shield PLUS monogoggles
   b) monogoggles alone
   c) safety goggles PLUS safety glasses.
   d) face shield alone

CHAPTER 30 - ANSWERS

1. (b)

2. (c)

3. (a)

4. (c)

5. (a)

6. (c)

7. (a)

CHAPTER 31

Isolation of Mechanical & Electrical Equipment

LEARNING OUTCOME

When you complete this chapter you should be able to:

Describe the general procedures involved in the isolation of plant equipment.

LEARNING OBJECTIVES

Here is what you should be able to do when you complete each objective:

1. Discuss the general considerations required for the mechanical and electrical isolation of equipment.

2. Describe the typical safe isolation of various pieces of plant equipment.

OBJECTIVE 1

Discuss the general considerations required for the mechanical and electrical isolation of equipment.

GENERAL

To prepare for maintenance, inspection or overhaul of any equipment requires proper isolation of the equipment involved. Some important aspects of equipment isolation, and the associated work permits, include the following:

1. The employer must be prepared to bear the cost of necessary procedures to ensure that the safeguarding of life and property is a priority at all times. Shortcuts to minimize production losses should not be allowed.

2. Anyone involved in the isolation of equipment must be properly trained in the operation of that equipment. The person must know functions and isolating points of all connections to suction, discharge, supply, exhaust, vent, drain and flare headers from a pump, compressor or any other piece of mechanical equipment, as well as any electrical connections that may be present. Also, the person performing the isolation must be very familiar with valve and breaker locations, plant equipment identification systems and any other information that will guarantee isolations are correct.

3. Authorized procedures must be in place for the safest possible method of isolating the equipment in question; these procedures must be adhered to.

4. It must be understood that both Operating and Maintenance Departments are responsible for the isolation of any equipment before work commences. For example, if the operating department isolates a piece of equipment, the maintenance people who will work on the equipment should verify that the isolation is complete and correct. In other words, everyone must take responsibility for his/her own safety. If a person is not sure a piece of equipment is safe to work on, a qualified individual should be asked to point out the isolating points and explain the isolation.

5. Various types of permits (safety, hot, entry and electrical) might be necessary before work can be started and may require updating from time to time as work progresses. These permits must bear the signatures of the parties involved. Also, "Do Not Operate" tags must be in place, as specified by a permit; the person signing a permit should verify the tag. In all cases, a person working under a permit must take responsibility for his/her own safety and for the safety of anyone working under his/her supervision.

6. Sometimes, particular safety precautions may be specified on a safe work permit. For example, instructions to, "check vessel oxygen content before entering" may be written on the permit. Any person accepting a permit by signing it must ensure these instructions are carried out.

7. Monthly safety meetings must be conducted to ensure all personnel are properly trained in the use of personal protective equipment. Equipment isolation is a topic that should be included in those meetings, so that everyone understands the permit systems in use. The importance of maintaining safety equipment in good condition should also be stressed.

Only generalities have been discussed here, but each industrial workplace will have safety procedures implemented that must be followed.

OBJECTIVE 2

Describe the typical safe isolation of various pieces of plant equipment.

TYPICAL EQUIPMENT ISOLATION

The standard devices used to isolate piping and vessels are valves and blank flanges. Valves must be secured in either closed or open positions using locked chains and/or wire seals. In most cases, particularly those associated with potentially explosive work (fires, toxic fluid contact or vessel entry) a single closed valve is insufficient for isolation purposes. In such instances, a blind flange is installed in the piping. Alternatively, some situations can be addressed by the use of a double block and bleed assembly. In this arrangement, the piping consists of two block valves separated by a section of piping with a "T"; the "T" line contains a third vent, or drain valve, known as a bleed. Proper isolation, in this case, consists of chain locking both block valves in the closed position and chain locking the bleed valve in the open position.

The following are examples of equipment isolation:

- Pump and driver
- Steam boiler
- Sodium zeolite softener

Isolation of a Pump and Driver

Refer to Figure 1, in which a pump is driven by a steam turbine. Header valves for both the pump and the turbine are shown connected to their respective headers and are usually located on pipe racks above . The turbine drain valve drains the casing directly to atmosphere. The pump casing drain has two isolation valves, which is a requirement when the pumped fluid is explosive, corrosive or poisonous. In this case, the pump casing drains into a "closed drain", which is a completely sealed collection system that has no outlet to atmosphere. Thus the pump liquid can be drained without endangering life, property or the environment. If the pump liquid is not hazardous, the pump casing drain may have a single isolation valve and does not require a closed drain system. A collection system may still be required to preserve and handle the pumped liquid.

All possible hazards must be considered before the isolation proceeds.

Figure 1	Turbine Driven Pump

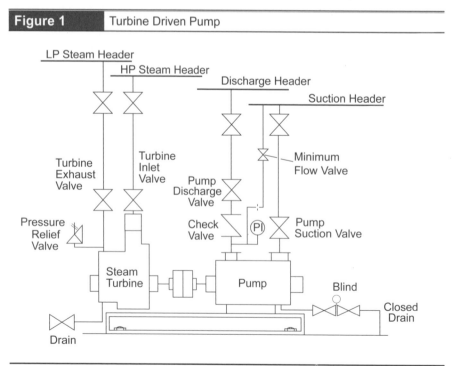

The procedure to isolate the equipment shown in Figure 1 is as follows:

- Close the high pressure steam supply valve.
- Close the turbine low pressure steam exhaust valve.
- Open the turbine casing drain.
- Close the pump discharge valve.
- Close the pump suction valve.
- Close the minimum flow line isolating valve.
- Open the pump casing drain.

After the pump has been depressurized and drained, if the pump drain line is a "closed drain", the line should be broken between the two drain valves (with the downstream valve closed), and a suitable blind flange installed.

Note: This is a minimum isolation only. Often, further isolation could be necessary. In many cases, a double block and bleed arrangement may be present. In this situation, both block valves should be closed and the bleed (vent) valve should be opened prior to opening the system.

Prepare **DO NOT OPERATE** tags and place them in full view on all isolation valves of the arrangement. Depending on the application or plant safety procedures, it may be necessary to "chain lock" the valves.

When an electric motor is used to drive the pump, one or a combination of the following procedures must be used, depending on the installation:

1. Open the breaker.
   - Install a "Lockout" clamp and lock on the breaker lever.
   - Have maintenance personnel also place a lock on the clamp.

2. Remove fuses
   - to be done by a qualified electrician.

3. Isolate motor control.
   - Lock and tag all local and remote switches.
   - Ensure that only properly qualified personnel do the isolation procedures.

4. Try the control switch before locking and tagging to ensure it is isolated.

Enter the completed equipment isolation procedures in the logbook.

Recommended procedure, when performing isolation, is to isolate the driver first. This practice ensures that a piece of equipment, particularly if it is started remotely, cannot be started while the isolation is being carried out. For example, a person could be operating valves at a pump when it is suddenly started. At the very least, the person would be startled and a reflex action could lead to injury. Worse, the person's hands or clothing could get caught on the shaft.

If the driver is isolated first, the driven equipment itself is also protected from possible damage. Suppose a person had just opened the breaker on a lubricating oil pump that supplies oil to the bearings of a large boiler feed pump. If the feed pump breaker were to be closed at that time, it could be started with no lubricating oil, damaging the pump. Therefore, as a general rule, always isolate a driver first.

Note: The procedures discussed in this chapter serve only as examples of the type of isolation procedures that must be followed to ensure the safe isolation of any piece of equipment. It is the responsibility of all personnel involved to personally review the isolation procedures of their workplace to ensure there is no possible way for anything to enter the isolated process equipment. As well, contents must be drained and equipment depressurized. For electrical equipment, personnel must ensure that it is de-energized and that there is no way of accidentally reconnecting power. Rotating equipment must be secured against inadvertent movement.

Isolation of a Steam Boiler

Assume that the water tube boiler represented in Figure 2 is to be inspected both externally and internally. The preliminary work that must be completed might include:

- Isolation and draining of the boiler by closing or opening the necessary valves.
- Cooldown of the boiler
- Ventilation of enclosed spaces
- Preparation for hydrostatic test
- Notification of the Boiler Inspector

The best possible method of ensuring the boiler is isolated would be to install blind flanges in the headers leading to and from the boiler.

- Blind flange lists must be prepared ahead of time and will contain such information as:
- Date installed and by whom
- Blind flange and tag number
- Location
- Size of blind (use the diameter of the inside of the bolt circle for ease of identification)
- Spacing to be installed (upstream or downstream)
- Date removed and by whom
- Operator
- Other useful information, as required

A "Tag" board may be in place for easy verification of tags.

Refer to Figure 2. After the preliminary work has been completed, the procedure to isolate the boiler is:

- disconnect electrical power from the motor driving the forced draft fan using the procedures described earlier for motor isolation
- install a blind flange downstream of the fuel gas valve
- install a blind flange downstream of the feedwater isolation valve
- install a blind flange upstream of the quick-opening blowdown valve with a spacer on the boiler side
- install a blind flange on the upstream side of the boiler steam stop valve. Leave the header drain valve open

The boiler in Figure 2 is now ready for cleaning and inspection. Enter the above procedures in the logbook.

Figure 2	Simple Steam Boiler

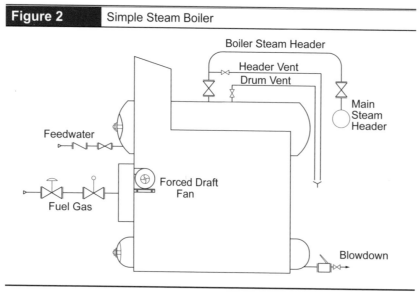

Isolation of a Sodium Zeolite Softener

In Figure 3, the softener is shown in operation delivering water to the deaerator. Isolation is required to replace the sodium zeolite.

Figure 3	Sodium Zeolite Softener

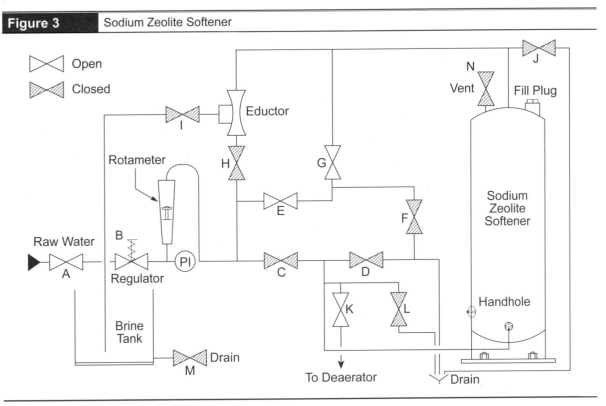

To isolate the softener proceed as follows:

- Close the effluent valve (K)
- Close the supply valve (A)
- Open the drain valve (L)
- Open the vent valve (N)

The valves (K, A, L and N) are tagged in their respective positions.

Depending on the piping arrangements, other valves might have to be operated to ensure all lines are drained and no water can enter the vessel. Ventilation might also be required and other safety precautions would have to be specified.

Enter the procedure in the logbook.

This page has intentionally been left blank.

CHAPTER 31 - QUESTIONS

1. If a person is not sure a piece of equipment is safe to work on, he/she should
   a) ask the foreman if it is safe.
   b) ask a qualified worker to indicate and explain the points of isolation.
   c) check with a co-worker before proceeding.
   d) rely fully on the permit information.

2. Ensuring the complete isolation of a piece of equipment prior to maintenance is the responsibility of the
   a) Plant Safety Committee.
   b) Operations Department.
   c) Operating and Maintenance Departments.
   d) Maintenance Department.

3. After completing the isolation of equipment, you must
   a) open the equipment drain valve.
   b) close the equipment outlet valve.
   c) notify the foreman.
   d) enter the completed isolations in the log book.

4. In order to protect driven equipment from damage, the first step should be to
   a) close the discharge valve.
   b) place a lock on the drain valve.
   c) isolate the driver.
   d) remove the belts.

5. When isolating a motor for maintenance, you should
   a) remove the fuses.
   b) install a lockout clamp on the breaker handle.
   c) place a DO NOT OPERATE tag on the breaker.
   d) do all of the above.

6. The first step to be followed to prepare a boiler for internal and external inspection is
   a) isolate, drain and lock out boiler.
   b) ventilate enclosed spaces.
   c) notify boiler inspector.
   d) cool down boiler for entry.

CHAPTER 31 - ANSWERS

1. (b)

2. (c)

3. (d)

4. (c)

5. (d)

6. (a)

Confined Space Entry

LEARNING OUTCOME

When you complete this chapter you should be able to:

Describe procedures needed to enter and work safely within confined spaces.

LEARNING OBJECTIVES

Here is what you should be able to do when you complete each objective:

1. Define and give examples of a confined space and describe the hazards of being inside a confined space.

2. Describe procedures to be used when performing a confined space entry, including completion of an entry checklist.

OBJECTIVE 1

Define and give examples of a confined space and describe the hazards of being inside a confined space.

Confined Space

"Confined Space" may be defined as any enclosed or partially enclosed space having restricted access and egress and which, due to its nature, may become a life threatening environment.

Confined spaces include, but are not limited to, such things as:

- Bins
- Tanks
- Trenches
- Tunnels
- Silos
- Sewers
- Vaults
- Pipelines
- Vessels

During the course of our everyday lives, we are called upon to enter into confined spaces and, in most cases, don't give any thought to them. These could include areas in our homes, at work, or in our recreational activities.

Most often, a confined space is thought of only in terms of an enclosed tank or vessel, but the term can apply to many common areas of our worksites.

POTENTIAL HAZARDS OF CONFINED SPACES

There are several potential hazards associated with confined spaces and, in particular, entry into them:

1. Escape and/or rescue in an emergency may be difficult, since entry, exit, and/or movement within the confined space is restricted.

2. Lack of proper or sufficient air ventilation may be, or may become, a life threatening problem because of design or construction.

3. The atmosphere within the space may be deficient in oxygen and thus unable to sustain life. The minimum acceptable oxygen level is 20%, by volume.

4. The atmosphere within the space may contain elements that cause it to be toxic, explosive and/or flammable.

5. Harmful substances and/or creatures may be present.

6. The environment, or work in progress, may cause equipment being used to become a hazard.

7. The use of improper equipment (for example, 110 volt electrical equipment being used in a vessel) creates potentially dangerous conditions.

8. Improper or insufficient lighting makes it difficult to see or identify hazards.

OBJECTIVE 2

Describe procedures to be used when performing a confined space entry, including completion of an entry checklist.

All jurisdictions in Canada have similar legislation in place concerning safety and health. Since it is impossible to refer to them all, the Alberta acts, regulations and codes are referred to in this chapter. The student is encouraged to refer to their local jurisdiction for the appropriate documents.

ALBERTA REGULATIONS FOR CONFINED SPACES

Alberta Occupational Health and Safety (OH&S) Regulations governing the requirements for confined space entry are summarized in this section.

1. No worker shall be required or permitted to enter a confined space:
    - Unless an approved ventilation system is being used to ensure the removal of any harmful gases, vapours, smoke, fumes, mists or dusts from within the confined space, or;
    - Until appropriate tests have been made immediately prior to entry to confirm the absence of any harmful gases, vapours, smoke, fumes, mists, dusts, or a deficiency of oxygen has not developed.

2. When tests indicate the presence of any harmful gases, vapours, smoke, fumes, mist, or dusts, or a deficiency of oxygen, the entry may only be made after:
    - The confined space has been, and is kept, adequately ventilated, or;
    - The worker has been provided with and is wearing approved respiratory protective equipment, and;
    - All sources or potential sources of ignition have been controlled or eliminated when flammable or explosive gases are present.

3. A worker required or permitted to enter a confined space where a harmful atmosphere exists or may develop, shall in addition to the requirements in 1. and 2.:
    - Wear a safety belt to which is attached a lifeline tended at all times by another worker stationed outside the entrance, and so equipped as to be capable of affecting rescue, and;
    - When the worker has entered from the top, wear a safety belt or harness of a type which will keep the worker in a vertical position in case of rescue.

4. A worker required, or permitted to enter a confined space being ventilated and in which a harmful atmosphere cannot develop shall:
    - Be attended by and in communication with another worker stationed at or near the entrance, or;
    - Be provided with a means of continuous communication with a worker outside, or;
    - Be visually checked by a designated worker at intervals as often as may be required by the nature of the work to be performed.

5. The person assigned to attend a worker who has entered a confined space must:

    •   Never leave the station while the worker remains within the confined space, unless properly relieved by a qualified person.

    •   Be in possession of a means of summoning assistance without leaving the station should any emergency arise and be able to sound alarm.

    •   Remain alert at all times to conditions that may affect the safety of the worker in the confined space.

    •   Frequently monitor the environment within the confined space to ensure the safety of the worker inside. Many unfortunate accidents have resulted because of failure to recognize a deterioration of the environment due to the work being carried out.

PLANNING & PROCEDURES

It is vitally important to carefully plan a confined space entry. This may be done relatively quickly, such as in the case of an open trench, or it may be very extensive, such as in a complex industrial application. The important things to remember are to plan thoroughly and to not make quick, unqualified assumptions.

Some important questions to consider are during the planning are:

Is the confined space structurally safe to enter; that is, in the case of a trench, for example, has sufficient provision been made to prevent cave-in? If not, what more is required?

Has the space been made secure from outside contamination; that is, are vessel nozzles and all connections disconnected, and blinds installed or ventilation equipment situated so that contaminants are not introduced into the confined space?

Is the required oxygen level measured and assured (minimum level 20% oxygen)?

Has the area been tested for the presence of hydrocarbon or other explosive or toxic gases? If present, have procedures been followed to clear them from the confined space or to provide equipment to work safely with them present?

Is the temperature in the space tolerable for workers?

In preparation for a confined space entry, it is useful to write or review a confined space entry procedure. Following is an example of a checklist that might be used. The final step in preparation would be to issue a safe work agreement or permit to indicate what further steps are required so that the entry can be completed safely.

CONFINED SPACE ENTRY CHECKLIST

ITEMS TO CHECK	YES	NO	IF NO, EXPLAIN
A. • Has the purpose of the procedure been well established?	☐	☐	_____
• Are all the potential hazards 'unique' to this entry listed?	☐	☐	_____
• Are all the potential operating problems 'unique' to this entry listed?	☐	☐	_____
B. MATERIALS HAZARDS: Has the procedure listed the material hazards 'unique' to this entry:			
• Pyrophoric materials?	☐	☐	_____
• Toxic chemicals?	☐	☐	_____
• Toxic gases, i. e. H_2S and chlorine?	☐	☐	_____
• Flammable gases?	☐	☐	_____
• Corrosives?	☐	☐	_____
C. MECHANICAL HAZARDS: Are all the potential mechanical hazards 'unique' to this entry listed?	☐	☐	_____
D. WATER POLLUTION:			
• Can steam condensate from steaming operations go to the pit or disposal?	☐	☐	_____
• Can drainings from vessels go to the pit or disposal?	☐	☐	_____
• Can tank hydrocarbons be flooded to the pit or disposal?	☐	☐	_____
• Can chemicals go to the pit or disposal?	☐	☐	_____
E. NOISE POLLUTION:			
• Can excessive noise be prevented when venting or steaming high pressure vessels?	☐	☐	_____
• Is there a provision for ear protection in noisy areas?	☐	☐	_____
F. AIR POLLUTION:			
• Can hydrocarbon and/or toxic gases be vented to the atmosphere?	☐	☐	_____
• Will flaring be excessive?	☐	☐	_____
G. STATIC ELECTRICITY HAZARD:			
• Is grounding of trucks, hose lines, air movers, etc. required?	☐	☐	_____
• Has steam purging of tanks been avoided?	☐	☐	_____
H. ENTRY PREPARATION: Has the procedure provided for:			
• complete and adequate purging?	☐	☐	_____
• gas testing for H_2S?	☐	☐	_____
• gas testing for LEL, oxygen, and toxic materials?	☐	☐	_____
• calibration of gas tester?	☐	☐	_____
• complete and adequate blanking?	☐	☐	_____
• blanking as close as possible to the confined space?	☐	☐	_____

CONFINED SPACE ENTRY CHECKLIST

ITEMS TO CHECK	YES	NO	IF NO, EXPLAIN
H. ENTRY PREPARATION: Has the procedure provided for: (cont'd)			
• lock out and tagging of mechanical equipment?	☐	☐	_____
• possibility of a dust explosion?	☐	☐	_____
• adequate ventilation and nitrogen displacement?	☐	☐	_____
• temporary equipment such as patches, diversion lines, tie-ins, etc?	☐	☐	_____
• checking of roof strength by mechanical inspectors?	☐	☐	_____
• safety net installed in furnace?	☐	☐	_____
• decking or flooring support for workers?	☐	☐	_____
• protection from falling, splashing or dripping material?	☐	☐	_____
I. EMERGENCY PREPARATION: Has the procedure provided for:			
• adequate fresh air breathing equipment?	☐	☐	_____
• adequate arrangements for removing a worker?	☐	☐	_____
• worker trained in artificial respiration?	☐	☐	_____
• aerosol emergency horn? (good in warm weather only)	☐	☐	_____
• unit evacuation and assembly point?	☐	☐	_____
• barricading of roads and adjacent areas?	☐	☐	_____
J. Has the procedure provided for changing conditions, such as:			
• stirring up sludge during cleaning?	☐	☐	_____
• changing temperatures?	☐	☐	_____
• smoke or toxic releases due to welding or burning?	☐	☐	_____
K. Has the procedure provided for inspection of hydrocarbon trapped in pockets, such as:			
• high suction on tanks?	☐	☐	_____
• total draw off pans on towers?	☐	☐	_____
• baffles in treaters?	☐	☐	_____
L. HOT WORK: Has the procedure specified:			
• no hot work on metal unless the opposite side has been inspected and cleaned?	☐	☐	_____
• no hot work outside of the confined space while there are valid confined space entry permits issued?	☐	☐	_____
• periodic gas testing of confined space atmosphere?	☐	☐	_____
M. Has the procedure provided for:			
• limitations of work?	☐	☐	_____
• adequate confined space cleanliness?	☐	☐	_____

CHAPTER 32 - QUESTIONS

1. A hazard that specifically applies to confined spaces is:

   a) they are too noisy.

   b) it is more difficult to rescue someone in an emergency.

   c) workers refusing to work in confined spaces.

   d) there is room for only one worker.

2. Using the Alberta OH&S Regulations as an example, whenever a worker is inside a confined space:

   a) it is mandatory to always wear respiratory protective equipment.

   b) the confined space MUST have at least 20% oxygen.

   c) another person must be assigned to communicate with and visually check the worker.

   d) ventilation fans MUST be running.

3. When entering any confined space, it is good practice to

   a) ensure that at least two workers enter the space.

   b) remove your safety belt to avoid it getting caught on something.

   c) inform the Plant Manager of your whereabouts.

   d) plan the entry using a confined space entry checklist.

4. An open trench is considered to be a confined space.

   a) True

   b) False

5. Which of the following is not an item that MUST be considered when vessel entry permits are prepared?

   a) Is the required oxygen level measured and assured (minimum level of 20% O_2, by volume)?

   b) Is the temperature in the space within tolerable working limits?

   c) Is the confined space structurally safe to enter?

   d) Has the head of the plant safety department been notified?

CHAPTER 32 - ANSWERS

1. (b)

2. (c)

3. (d)

4. (a)

5. (d)

Handling & Storage of Gases

LEARNING OUTCOME

When you complete this chapter you should be able to:

Describe the procedures for safe storage and handling of cylinders containing compressed gases.

LEARNING OBJECTIVES

Here is what you should be able to do when you complete each objective:

1. Describe gas cylinder markings.

2. Describe the safe procedures for handling gas pressure regulators and changing gas cylinders.

3. Describe the care, maintenance and storage of gas cylinders.

4. Describe gas cylinder safety features and inspection.

INTRODUCTION

In many installations requiring gases for fuel or operating procedures, many or all of the gases are sent or delivered to the locations complete with their own containers called cylinders. Such cylinders are simply metal pressure vessels which can be easily transported. In cylinder storage systems, the individual cylinders are connected to the pressure regulating equipment which is left permanently attached to the user's gas system. When empty, the cylinders are completely removed, replaced by other full cylinders and taken back to the bulk plant for filling.

In the interest of safety, it is important that employees are thoroughly trained in safe practices for handling and storing cylinders containing gases. This chapter is intended to inform the student of the standards and rules for handling and storing gases contained in easily movable and readily portable cylinders. Compliance with these standards will help to reduce the number of accidents in your place of work, but compliance alone will not guarantee a safe installation which can only come through combining the knowledge the student receives from a thorough study of this chapter with the knowledge he/she gains through experience in work processes of your particular industry.

GAS PROPERTIES

Cylinder gases, or "bottled gases", are commonly used by the industry for fuel purposes. Most of these "fuel" gases liquefy under moderate pressure, but, upon relief of the pressure, are readily converted into the gaseous phase. The industry takes advantage of this characteristic and for convenience, the gases are shipped and stored under pressure as liquids. When in the vapour state, these gases present a hazard comparable to any flammable natural or manufactured gas, except that being heavier than air, ventilation requires added attention. The range of combustibility is considerably narrower and lower than that of manufactured gas. Propane, for example, is a liquid at atmospheric pressure and temperature below -40°C and normally does not present a flammable liquid hazard. However, rapid vaporization takes place at temperatures above the boiling point. Likewise, butane at atmospheric pressure and temperature below 0°C is a liquid, but will vaporize quickly at temperatures above 0°C.

It is advisable that employees working with gas cylinders be aware at all times of the type and density of gases contained in the cylinders, whether they are in a liquid or vapour state, the vapour pressure and other related details. The vapour pressure is a number indicating the pressure of the vapour at the top of the container at 38°C and therefore indicates the suitability of a container for a specific product.

For example, if a container is a type 100, it means it is a container designed for a product with a vapour pressure not exceeding 690 kPa at 37.8°C. Because propane has a vapour pressure of approximately 1310 kPa at 37.8°C, it cannot be placed safely in a type 100 tank. On the other hand, butane may be placed in a Type 100 tank because its vapour pressure is about 275 kPa at 37.8°C.

OBJECTIVE 1

Describe gas cylinder markings.

GAS CYLINDER MARKINGS

Employees responsible for handling and using gases contained in cylinders should be aware of the general information marked on the cylinder.

Gas cylinders are commonly marked with the following information:

- Size or capacity
- Service pressure
- Metal specifications under which they were made
- Tare weight (TW)
- Ownership symbol
- Serial number
- Inspector's official marking
- Original test date
- Manufacturer's symbol

Size or Capacity/Service Pressure/Metal Specifications

Most of the above information is requested by authorities, such as the Canadian Transport Commission (CTC) or Department of Transport (DOT,) who are responsible for the safety of these containers. Size or capacity of the cylinder is rated by the number of kilograms, litres or cubic metres it is designed to hold exclusive of the weight of the cylinder itself. For example, a 220 kg propane cylinder can hold 220 kg of propane with enough space left inside to allow for safe expansion of the liquid when the temperature rises. Such cylinders vary in size and capacity, from those small enough to carry conveniently to those weighing several hundred kilograms when filled.

Cylinders must be manufactured to rigid specifications set by the CTC or DOT. The numbers stamped on the cylinder indicate the metal specifications under which the cylinder was made, plus the service pressure of the cylinder. For example, in DOT-4BA-240, the DOT stands for Department of Transport, the 4BA for the construction specifications involved and the "240" for the fact that the cylinder is designed for service pressure of 240 pounds per square inch (1655 kPa in the metric system). The service pressure tells the employee whether or not the container is safe for a specific product.

Tare Weight

The tare weight (TW) is a number indicating how much the cylinder weighs when empty, including all permanently attached fittings except the valve protecting cap. This marking indicates to the employee how much the cylinder should weigh when filled correctly to capacity and follows the letter "TW", or "Tare WT", on the cylinder head.

Ownership Symbol

This marking identifies the purchaser of the cylinder and is registered with the Bureau of Explosives. This symbol is also called the Purchasers' Registered Mark.

Serial Number

The serial number identifies the container and cannot be duplicated. It provides a control record of each cylinder which is registered and maintained by the Bureau of Explosives.

Inspector's Official Marking

This marking indicates who performed or supervised the original test of the cylinder.

Original Test Date

The original test date shows the date of the first test performed on the cylinder, as well as the month and year the cylinder was manufactured. In addition, the cylinder must carry the date of each subsequent inspection, so the employee will know when the next inspection date is due.

Manufacturer's Symbol

This symbol indicates who made the cylinder.

OBJECTIVE 2

Describe the safe procedures for handling gas pressure regulators and changing gas cylinders.

SAFE HANDLING OF GAS CYLINDERS

Gas cylinders are not considered fragile equipment. Nevertheless, they should be handled with care, for, if dropped, they can be damaged and cause serious injury to an employee.

Cylinder valves, which provide a means of filling and discharge as well as a safety relief device, are screwed onto the top of the cylinder. The valve is provided with a piping connection and is kept closed except when in use or during filling. It is the most easily damaged part of a gas container. It is commonly made of brass, which is not as strong as the metal used in the cylinder and is screwed into the cylinder in such a position that it could be broken off. If the cylinder falls over and the valve strikes a projection, it could break off and release the product. The valve could also be damaged if an object were to fall and strike it. As well, it can be affected by exposure to the weather and the valve could be incorrectly used as a handle by a person moving the cylinder. In any case, serious injury could result. Therefore, the valve protection cap, when supplied, should be securely screwed in position whenever the cylinder is not in use or being filled.

When moving cylinders, always use hand trucks to avoid back strain and take special care not to drop them when loading them onto a truck. Personnel must ensure the cylinder protection caps are kept lubricated, so they can be easily and completely screwed on each time.

Not all cylinders have protection caps; those which do not have a guard ring permanently mounted on the cylinder to protect the fittings. A guard ring or cap is necessary on all cylinders. When used in the construction industry or when used inside a structure, cylinders must always be kept in a position which will allow the safety relief valve to connect with the vapour space. This positioning will ensure that any product which is released is in a gaseous form. If the safety relief valve were to connect with the liquid space, it would vent liquid when it opened. A small amount of liquid could vapourize rapidly to become a large amount of flammable gas. For this reason, cylinders must always be stored upright.

GAS PRESSURE REGULATORS

Gas cylinders are connected to a pressure regulator commonly located on the user's property. Such an installation may have a single cylinder, two cylinders (most common) or, in some cases, multiple cylinders. The use of more than one cylinder lets the gas buyer use one cylinder while waiting for an empty cylinder to be replaced.

Gas cylinder installations consist of the cylinders, pigtails, manifold, regulator and piping. The cylinders, as mentioned earlier, are equipped with the cylinder shutoff valve and the safety relief valve. These are only the basic parts of a cylinder valve which may have other parts including a fixed tube liquid level gauge to indicate when the maximum safe filling limit is reached. The cylinder valve has a female thread to receive the pressure hose which provides a connection between the cylinder valve and the manifold. This connection is left permanently attached to the manifold when changing cylinders. The threads may be left-handed or right-handed, depending on the intended contents of the cylinder.

The manifold is usually one of the three following types:

- Tee block
- Manual
- Automatic throw over

They all have the same function, to let the delivery person remove the empty cylinder and replace it with a full one without interrupting the gas supply from the cylinder that remains in service. Manifolds also prevent gas from escaping during the changeover of cylinders. The pressure regulator reduces the cylinder gas pressure from a relatively high pressure to one suitable for the user's equipment.

DELIVERING & CHANGING OF GAS CYLINDERS

Empty portable cylinders are replaced by full cylinders and taken back to the company's refilling plant. Each employee involved in such deliveries should be constantly attentive to safe practices. Cylinders, for example, are provided with foot rings, strengthened metal rings on the bottom of the cylinder. These should always rest on a hard, level surface and never be placed on the bare ground.

A regular routine should be followed when changing cylinders to ensure that safety rules are always applied. The procedure for changing cylinders is as follows:

1. Full and empty cylinders must always be loaded and carried on trucks in an upright position and securely anchored or chained to prevent shifting or falling.

2. When the delivery truck cannot closely approach the cylinder installation, a hand truck should be used to carry cylinders.

3. Cylinders should not be dropped or thrown from the truck, but should be eased to the ground.

4. Before disconnecting the empty cylinder from the installation, the cylinder valve must be closed to prevent air and moisture from entering the cylinder and causing corrosion.

5. The proper hand wrenches to fit the various connecting nuts must be used when changing cylinders. This practice will ensure that no damage occurs on these fittings. Also, the employee must be certain that the connection is turned in the correct direction since many fittings have left hand threads.

6. Cylinder connections such as pigtails, hoses and manifolds should be disconnected slowly, allowing pressure to bleed down before entirely removing the nut. If pressure does not drop, the cause should be found. If necessary, the remaining cylinders should be shut off to prevent escape of gas.

7. The cylinder valve and connections should be examined and those with worn or damaged threads should be replaced. If the cylinder valve is damaged, the entire cylinder should be taken back to the filling plant for repair. Any dirt around the cylinder valve or valve connections should be removed promptly.

   It is advisable to "crack" the valve open briefly to blow out any accumulation of dirt.

8. Each time a new cylinder is installed, the employee should make a quick safety check of related equipment, such as the regulator and manifold valve assembly. If accumulations of rubbish or other hazardous conditions exist near the installation, the user should correct the situation at once.

9. Cylinders must be installed vertically on their foundations. When hoods or cabinets are used, they must be closed before leaving.

10. After the full cylinder has been installed and the connection made, the cylinder valve must be opened and the connection checked for leaks. Leak checking should be done with a soap or other suitable solution, never with a flame. The solution is applied to the connection and leakage is indicated by the presence of bubbles.

11. If it is necessary to shut off the gas supply to the user's line, gas should not again be turned on until all appliance valves and pilots have been turned off. Such stoppage of gas flow to the user might be required in order to change a single cylinder installation, or when all cylinders of a multiple cylinder installation are empty, or if it is necessary to repair or replace the regulator, manifold or other fittings.

12. The valve protection cap from the filled cylinder should be placed on the empty cylinder before moving it to the truck.

OBJECTIVE 3

Describe the care, maintenance and storage of gas cylinders.

CARE & MAINTENANCE

Gas cylinders represent a substantial investment on the part of the company. Therefore, they must be handled and operated with care and maintained in top condition. In order to maintain gas cylinders and their fittings correctly, the employee must follow recommended procedures for:

1. cleaning and painting cylinders.

2. checking cylinders for damage each time they come to the plant.

3. making periodic visual inspections or pressure tests as required by regulations or standards.

4. disposing of fire damaged cylinders and cylinder fittings.

5. inserting or replacing valves and gauges when necessary.

6. purging cylinders of air.

7. deodorizing cylinders.

STORAGE PROCEDURES

Locating and storing containers filled with a gas is as important as handling and moving them for refilling or maintenance work.

According to the Canadian Standards Association, gas cylinders shall not be placed below ground level except by special permission of the regulatory authority. These standards also stipulate that the cylinders should be located outside of the building when connected to gas consuming equipment. However, where portability of cylinders is necessary and outside location is impractical, cylinders may be located for use inside a building but not for storage. In such an installation, the gas is to be used for industrial processing or repair work only and the building has to be of an industrial nature.

When in storage, gas cylinders must be provided with solid bases and be in an upright position while firmly secured to prevent settling or rolling over. They should be protected from the weather by proper housing and guarded from physical damage to the regulating equipment.

The discharge from safety valves on cylinders located outside shall not terminate in any building or beneath any building and should be located not less than one metre horizontally away from any building opening. Always ensure gas cylinders are stored away from any direct heat or open flame and are protected from vehicular traffic and falling debris. They should be kept away from oil and grease at all times and ventilation must be appropriate in storage areas. Empty and full cylinders should not be grouped together in storage.

Never store acetylene and oxygen cylinders together; they should be stored at least 6 metres apart to prevent explosive mixtures forming in the event of leakage.

Finally, before leaving the cylinders in storage, make sure all hoses, piping, pressure regulators, gauges, manifold connections and fittings are free from defects, leaks or the presence of oil and grease.

OBJECTIVE 4

Describe gas cylinder safety features and inspection.

GAS CYLINDER SAFETY FEATURES

The features and fittings with which gas cylinders should be equipped are summarized in the following sections.

Filler Valves

These are fittings used for product transfer into cylinders. They permit product to flow in, but a check valve prevents backflow.

Vapour Valves

These valves allow product flow only when a hose is connected and are equipped with a seat, disc and a spring device to prevent excessive flow of vapour in the event that a hose or pipe ruptures.

When both filler and vapour valves are used, there is a separate service valve to pass vapour out. Occasionally, all of these valves are combined in a combination valve. Standard types of cylinders have a single valve only - the cylinder valve mentioned earlier - which passes liquid and gas through a single opening.

Cylinder Valve Cap

The cylinder valve cap is the metal screw on cap used when it is necessary to protect the gas outlet and pressure relief valves from operational or accidental damage.

Pressure Relief Valve

The pressure relief valve is part of the cylinder output valve; it is used to release product if the pressure in the cylinder gets too high. It is commonly a spring loaded valve designed to vent horizontally away from the cylinder.

Top Guard Ring

The top guard ring is used with some gas cylinders to protect the outlet and relief valves from damage. These cylinders usually do not have valve caps. The guard ring is also used as a handle when moving the cylinder.

Foot Ring

The foot ring is a reinforced metal ring welded to the bottom of the cylinder to keep it upright and protect the lower part of the cylinder from rust and damage. Some cylinders have flat bottoms which rest directly on the ground and do not require foot rings.

GAS CYLINDER INSPECTION

Gas cylinders are usually checked by personnel each time they come in for refilling. However, the law requires that pressure vessels, and of course gas containers, be subjected to more complete and conclusive inspections and tests at regular intervals. The employee must familiarize himself with the required intervals for inspections and tests for the particular type of gas and cylinders he is with which he is working and watch for any cylinders requiring such an inspection.

There are generally two types of inspections:

- Visual inspection
- Pressure test

Visual Inspection

During visual inspections, the employee must follow approved methods established by his company and based on certain standards.

The visual inspection is the most frequent and commonly used method; it is performed by a qualified person to establish whether the cylinder is fit to remain in use. During this inspection the person must:

1. Check all seams for signs of corrosion or damage.

2. Check the areas most subject to corrosion, such as inside the foot ring and on the bottom head. All rust, scale, dirt and caked paint must be removed to reveal the full extent of corrosion. When corroded areas are badly pitted and there is danger of leaks, the cylinder must be discarded.

3. Check for dents and cylinder wall deformations. If such dents are very large or deep, or have sharp angles, the cylinder may not be safe for further service.

4. Check for cuts or gouges caused by sharp objects.

5. Inspect for broken or damaged foot or protective ring. If the ring needs welding or replacing, the work must be done by a qualified welder since it is subject to approval by the local inspection authority.

6. Check for fire damage. Cylinders deformed by fire are usually destroyed. Scorched units may be returned to the manufacturer for repair and testing. Valves and safety devices are always replaced on cylinders which have been exposed to fire.

7. Keep an accurate record of the inspection and work done on each cylinder. Include such details as how the cylinder was disposed of after the inspection and whether it was sent to the manufacturer for repairs, or was finally scrapped.

Pressure Test

The cylinder pressure test may be of the "water jacket" or hydrostatic type. In the water jacket test, the cylinder is filled with a liquid and lowered into another container full of water. It is then subjected to a pressure twice the working pressure stamped on it, causing it to expand. This expansion forces the water out of the tank which, when collected and measured, indicates the amount of expansion to which the cylinder was subjected to. Then the pressure is removed from the cylinder and if an excessive amount of the initial expansion still remains in it, the metal has lost its elasticity and must be either heat treated by the manufacturer or removed from service.

With the hydrostatic test, the cylinder is filled with water and the pressure increased to twice its working pressure. It is then examined visually for leaks.

After a cylinder has undergone the required test or inspection, it is stamped with the date of the test near the previous test date.

This page has intentionally been left blank.

CHAPTER 33 - QUESTIONS

4th Class • Part A1

1. Portable gas cylinder capacity

   a) is expressed by the tare weight stamped on the cylinder.

   b) must take into account liquid expansion due to temperature change.

   c) is a function of the pressure within the unit at ambient temperature.

   d) may be increased on approval from the DOT or CTC.

2. Gas cylinder valves are normally constructed of

   a) steel.

   b) polycarbonate.

   c) brass.

   d) lead.

3. Before disconnecting an empty cylinder from a manifold system

   a) crack the connecting joint in order to purge it of excess gases.

   b) check the area for gases with an analyzer.

   c) unchain the cylinder.

   d) close the cylinder valve to prevent air entering the cylinder.

4. As applied to bottled gases, vapour pressure is defined as the pressure of the vapour above a liquid inside the cylinder when the temperature is at

   a) 100°C

   b) 50°C

   c) 25°C

   d) 38°C

5. The type of information not stamped on the gas cylinder is the

   a) manufacturer's symbol.

   b) date the cylinder was tested for the first time.

   c) ownership symbol.

   d) date the cylinder was changed.

6. A gas cylinder hydrostatic test will

   a) result in a new test date being stamped on the cylinder.

   b) subject the cylinder to a pressure equal to its working pressure.

   c) subject the cylinder to a pressure of one and one half times its working pressure.

   d) remove any dents the cylinder may contain.

CHAPTER 33 - ANSWERS

1. (b)

2. (c)

3. (d)

4. (d)

5. (d)

6. (a)

Handling of Hydrocarbon Fluids

LEARNING OUTCOME

When you complete this chapter you should be able to:

Describe the safe procedures for the loading, storage, unloading and transportation of hydrocarbon fluids.

LEARNING OBJECTIVES

Here is what you should be able to do when you complete each objective:

1. Describe the significant properties of the most common hydrocarbon fluids.

2. Describe the sources of ignition for a hydrocarbon.

3. List the safety requirements for the loading and unloading of hydrocarbon fluids.

4. Describe the general safety issues associated with the storage and gauging of hydrocarbon liquids.

5. Describe the important health and safety guidelines associated with bulk sour oilfield products.

INTRODUCTION

To safely handle hydrocarbons, it is necessary to know their properties. This chapter will deal only with the properties that are important to persons responsible for the loading, unloading, storage and transportation of hydrocarbon fluids.

OBJECTIVE 1

Describe the significant properties of the most common hydrocarbon fluids.

SIGNIFICANT PROPERTIES

The significant properties of the most common hydrocarbons include:

- Flammable or explosive limits
- Flash point
- Ignition temperature

Flammable or Explosive Limits

Gaseous fuels, and vapours released from liquid fuels (see note at bottom of page), will mix with air in order to burn. However, the proportion of fuel in the fuel/air mixture must be within certain limits before the mixture will ignite. These limits are called the flammable (or explosive) limits.

A flammable limit is expressed as a percentage, which is the percentage of the fuel, by volume, in the air/fuel mixture. A flammable range occurs between the lower flammable limit (LFL or LEL) and the upper flammable limit (UFL or UEL) and fuel/air mixtures outside the flammable range will not burn or explode. Stated another way, for combustion to occur the percentage of fuel in the fuel/air mixture must be at or between the upper and lower flammable limits.

Table 1 lists the flammable limits of some hydrocarbon fuels (gas and liquid) plus hydrogen sulphide.

Table 1	Flammable Limits	
Fuel	**Flammable Limits in Air, %**	
	Lower	Upper
Methane	5.0	15.0
Propane	2.2	9.5
Butane	1.9	8.5
Gasoline	1.1	7.5
Kerosene	0.7	5.0
Hydrogen Sulphide	4.3	45.5

When the percentage of fuel is less than the lower flammable limit, the mixture is called "lean"; if the percentage of fuel is greater than the upper flammable limit, the mixture is called "rich".

The flammable limits shown in Table 1 are correct only at atmospheric pressure and normal ambient temperature. The flammable range is wider at higher pressures and/or temperatures.

Also, the flammable range for a hydrocarbon is much wider in oxygen than it is in air. For example, the flammable range for a propane/oxygen mixture is 2.2% to 57%, compared to a range of 2.2% to 9.5% for a propane/air mixture.

When dealing with a mixture that contains more than one hydrocarbon, the mixture should be assumed to have the flammable properties of the most hazardous component. For example, a mixture of gasoline and kerosene will exhibit the flammable properties of gasoline. In actual practice, great care must be taken when using values from Table 1 since a substantial safety factor must be applied to compensate for inevitable errors in gas/vapour sampling.

Note: As stated, a fuel must be in the gaseous or vapour state in order to mix with air. Liquid fuels must be heated to a temperature at which vapours are released; this temperature is called the "flash point".

Flash Point

The flash point of a liquid is the lowest temperature at which enough vapours are given off to form a flammable mixture of vapour and air immediately above the liquid surface. The lighter hydrocarbons are gases at room temperatures and, as such, are above their flash point. Hydrocarbons will not burn until changed from the liquid state to the vapour state (see Fig.1).

Figure 1	Hydrocarbon Burning

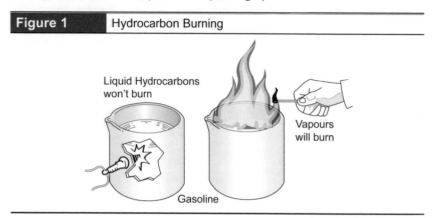

Liquid Hydrocarbons won't burn

Vapours will burn

Gasoline

Table 2 gives the flash points of some liquid hydrocarbons.

Table 2	Flash Points

Hydrocarbon	Flash Point
Butane	-60°C
Gasoline	-45°C
2-D diesel fuel	58°C
Kerosene	49°C
Denatured alcohol	21°C

Ignition Temperature

The ignition temperature is the lowest temperature at which a fuel/air mixture will burn or explode. The ignition temperatures of some hydrocarbons and hydrogen sulphide are listed in Table 3.

Table 3	Ignition Temperatures

Hydrocarbon	Ignition Temp.
Methane	650°C
Propane	490°C
Natural gasoline	480°C
Kerosene	295°C
Fuel oil	340°C
Hydrogen sulphide	260°C

A high ignition temperature does not mean that a liquid hydrocarbon is safe. The temperatures of common ignition sources can be extremely high. For example, the flame of a match can be at a temperature of approximately 870°C; the temperature of an electric arc can be over 5000°C.

It is very important to remember that a fuel/air mixture within the flammable range will ignite if the temperature of the mixture is raised above the ignition temperature. For example, a kerosene/air mixture within the flammable range will ignite without a spark or flame if its temperature is increased beyond 295°C.

OBJECTIVE 2

Describe the sources of ignition for a hydrocarbon.

SOURCES OF IGNITION

When fuel vapours mix with air in the correct proportions, the resulting flammable mixture could be ignited by one of many ignition sources present in the workplace.

The following are some obvious sources of heat in or around a workplace:

- Welding operations
- Cutting with oxygen/acetylene
- Hot piping (steam, etc.)
- Furnaces
- Friction
- Overheated bearings
- Engine ignition systems
- Sparks from electrical equipment
- Cigarettes and matches
- Lightning

The following sources of ignition may not be readily recognized:

- Pyrophoric iron sulphide
- Static electricity
- Autoignition
- Catalytic effect of fresh metallic surfaces

Iron sulphide, the product of a chemical reaction involving iron and hydrogen sulphide, is brown or black in color and may appear grainy, scaly, lumpy or powdered. It can be in a mixture with coke, oil or sand. If it is allowed to dry out, it will burst into flame in the presence of air; thus, it must be kept wet to prevent it from igniting.

Static electricity is present wherever materials are in motion and in contact with other material, such as when hydrocarbons move through piping or filters.

The autoignition temperature of a hydrocarbon fuel is the lowest temperature at which the mixture will spontaneously ignite in a normal atmosphere, without an external source of ignition such as a flame or spark. The autoignition temperatures of some hydrocarbons are listed in Table 4.

Table 4	Autoignition Temperatures
Hydrocarbon	**Autoignition Temp.**
Gasoline	257°C
Diesel	210°C
Jet fuel	210°C
Hydrogen	571°C
Butane	500°C

The fact that the catalytic effect of fresh metallic surfaces can cause ignition has been proven under laboratory conditions which could explain why several explosions of flammable mixtures have occurred at the exact time that valves were being opened.

It is important to ensure that none of the possible ignition sources are present in hazardous areas. Ignition sources are so numerous that extreme care must be taken at all times to prevent fires from occurring.

THE FIRE TRIANGLE

The combustion process is often described using the fire triangle, as shown in Figure 2. The three sides represent fuel, oxygen and a source of ignition, respectively. A fire or explosion can only occur when all three are present. To be absolutely safe, fuel and air should only be mixed under strictly controlled conditions since there are so many sources of ignition.

Consider how a very small amount of oxygen in a propane stream can cause a flammable mixture. When the propane is transferred to storage, some of it vaporizes above the liquid and as with the propane vapour, the oxygen leaves the liquid. The vapour contains a much higher concentration of oxygen than does the liquid. If the tank is further filled, the propane will return to the liquid state, but the oxygen becomes more concentrated because of the compression. Eventually, the vapour space can become small enough that the mixture can be within flammable limits.

Since it is difficult, if not impossible, to eliminate all sources of ignition, and, since the product being considered is hydrocarbon liquid, every effort must be made to prevent oxygen from coming in contact with hydrocarbon vapours.

Figure 2	The Fire Triangle

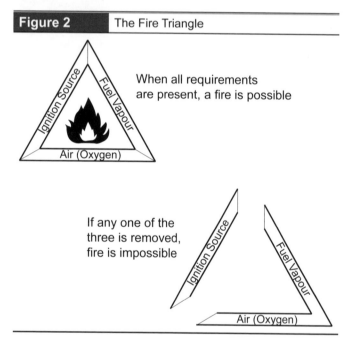

When all requirements are present, a fire is possible

If any one of the three is removed, fire is impossible

OBJECTIVE 3

List the safety requirements for the loading and unloading of hydrocarbon fluids.

LOADING & UNLOADING HYDROCARBON FLUIDS

Transferring Liquids from One Container to Another

Before pouring a flammable liquid from a dispensing container into a receiving container, the containers must be bonded together to ensure a good electrical contact between them. This bonding is done because a potential difference can be produced between the exteriors of the containers when a flammable substance is poured from one container to the other. A static spark "jumping" across the gap between the containers could result in a fire or explosion.

Loading Tank Cars and Tank Trucks with Hydrocarbon Liquids

Such liquids as: kerosene, diesel fuel, fuel oil and lubricating oil, when in tank cars or trucks, may not present a hazard because they have a high flash point. But, suppose a liquid with a low flash point such as gasoline was previously in the tank. The tank would be full of vapours from the gasoline, but they would be too rich to burn. A high flash point product, such as diesel fuel, being loaded will absorb some of the rich vapours from the gasoline and air will enter the tank to replace the gasoline vapour. The vapour space can now contain a flammable mixture because it is no longer too rich to burn. Combine this with the fact that highly refined products, having a high flash point are excellent generators of static electricity, an explosion could easily occur.

The loading of a product having a high flash point after a load of product having a low flash point (sometimes called a high proportion of switch loading) is the principal factor in loading rack fires.

Loading Procedures

Common loading procedures specified for each site must be followed:

1. Before a railway car is loaded, the hand brake must be applied and the wheels chocked. Other site-specific laws required by the Transport Commission, such as installing flags on the track and engaging derails, must also be observed. Transport trucks must have all sources of ignition shut off, the brakes applied and the wheels chocked.

2. The tank car or tank truck must be suitable for the product which will be loaded. If it is necessary to flush the tank, the washing steam should enter the tank slowly to reduce the risk of a spark from static electricity.

3. The loading rack grounding connections must be in good condition. This item should be recorded on a preventive maintenance list. The grounding conductors can be easily checked with an ohmmeter.

4. Trucks must be grounded immediately after being placed in position at the loading-rack and before the loading spout is inserted. Grounding eliminates any potential charge between the truck and the loading-rack, but it does not eliminate the possibility of a spark discharge from the liquid surface in the tank.

5. The compartments must be inspected to ensure they are completely drained, if the product to be loaded is different from the previous load. Any loose foreign objects must be removed as they could become spark promoters during the loading operation.

6. To prevent "switch loading" accidents, the tank compartments should be purged with carbon dioxide (CO_2) or nitrogen (N_2), or eduction equipment should be used to remove low flash point vapours before loading high flash point liquids. Switch loading is responsible for 90% of loading-rack truck fires.

7. The top-entering loading spout is extended to the bottom of the tank being loaded, as shown in Figure 3.

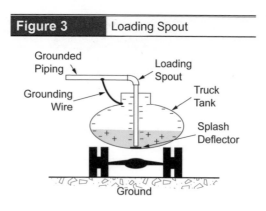

Figure 3   Loading Spout

8. A proper deflector should be installed on the loading spout to prevent it from being thrown out and to prevent splashing and spraying which generate mists and help to produce static electricity. A tee fitting installed on the end of the spout is not satisfactory because it produces splashing and spraying. Refer to Figure 3.

9. After loading a tank, a delay of one minute must be observed before withdrawing the spout. This delay allows the static charge on the surface of the liquid to be reduced. A spark from the liquid surface to the spout could be a source of ignition.

10. During loading, or for at least one minute after loading, samples must not be obtained via the top opening because a spark between the liquid surface and the sample dipper could occur, possibly causing an explosion.

HANDLING LIQUEFIED PETROLEUM GAS (LPG)

LPG must be stored and transported under pressure; therefore, proper procedures and proper equipment must be used. The laws for the transportation of LPG are strictly enforced by Federal and Provincial Transportation Departments.

Loading

Several important fundamentals for safe loading and unloading of LPG products are common to both trucks and rail cars. Before handling LPG, loaders should be aware of the following:

1. Every effort should be made to ensure that no truck or tank car containing air is ever loaded with LPG. To ensure that the tank to be loaded contains no air, a sample of vapour must be checked for acceptable oxygen content, using a portable oxygen analyzer.

2. Containers must be designed for the particular type of LPG product to be transported. For example, propane, which has a higher vapour pressure than butane, should never be transported in a container designed strictly for butane.

3. Before loading, a check should be made to ensure liquids from a previous load are not present. If liquids are present, they must be identified as acceptable or be removed.

4. An LPG container should never be completely filled. If the temperature of the contents of a full container rises during transit, the relief valve will open due to pressure build up caused by liquid expansion; as a result liquid product will be released. Very little liquid has to be released to create a large cloud of vapour. The space left above the surface of the liquid is called an "outage". Check the liquid level frequently while loading to ensure that the tank car or tank truck is not overfilled.

5. Outages left in LPG containers must conform to local regulations. Outages must be carefully calculated from information given by the tank car manufacturer concerning the volume of the tank car. The temperature and relative density of the loaded product must also be considered when calculating the outage. Accurate outage calculations must be made to take full advantage of the maximum carrying capacity of the car, yet still leave a vapour space for liquid expansion. Records of outage calculations must be kept.

6. Loading hoses designed for LPG service must be hydrostatically tested at least once per year. They should be inspected regularly for cuts, cracks, rusted clamps and other signs of damage.

7. The container must not be overpressured. As the liquid LPG flows into a vessel, it compresses and condenses the vapour in the tank to make room for the incoming liquid. This action produces heat which increases the pressure in the receiving container. Overpressure is sometimes controlled by venting the receiving vessel back to the vessel being emptied. If this method is used, the vent line should not be opened until the pressure in the receiving vessel exceeds the pressure in the container being emptied.

8. Before unloading LPG, it must be verified that the tank car or tank truck contains the correct quantity and type of product.

Loading Railway Tank Cars

The purpose of Department of Transport regulations governing rail movement of LPG is to protect the public. Penalties for violation of the regulations can be severe.

It is strongly recommended that persons in charge of loading LPG tank cars work from a check list and use a form for calculating outage of cars. Department of Transport personnel make frequent inspections of loading facilities and procedures.

The following are items to be checked when loading LPG tank cars:

1. A pre-trip inspection of the tank car is required and any defects should be repaired.

2. The tank car and the relief valve test dates must be checked to ensure these dates fall within required test intervals.

3. The suitability of the car for the product to be loaded must be verified.

4. The hand brake must be set and the wheel chocks applied to prevent the car from moving.

5. The "stop" sign must be installed at the entrance to the loading siding to prevent railway crews from entering the loading track when cars are being loaded. Derails, if used, must be set.

6. After the first five steps are completed, the vapour and liquid lines may be connected and the gauge set for 1 m.

7. After the loading operation is started, the sample line should be opened momentarily to remove water from the car.

8. The gauge rod should be fitted with the liquid orifice.

9. The temperature of the liquid entering the car must be checked using the tank car thermowell and an accurate thermometer.

10. The outage required for the particular car must be calculated using the relative density and temperature of the product being loaded. Finally the gauge rod is reset to the calculated height.

11. Odorant should be added if required.

12. When loading is complete, all valves must be closed.

13. After 15 minutes, the gauge rod is raised a few inches and the valve checked for vapour; then the gauge rod is lowered until white mist appears. The gauge is read and the gauging operation is repeated. Then the gauge level, to the nearest 6 mm, is recorded.

14. The gauge rod and thermometer well are secured.

15. The loading hoses are removed and the connections plugged. An explosive meter is used to check for leaks.

16. The "after unloading" instructions are attached in the dome; then the dome cover is closed and a seal installed.

17. The required placards are placed in the four placard holders.

Note: During the loading process, a responsible person must be in continuous attendance.

Unloading Tank Cars

The following are the items to be checked or done when unloading tank cars:

1. Before a tank car is unloaded, it must be protected by flags on the track and have the brakes applied.

2. If the volume of the product in the tank is needed for accounting purposes, the temperature of the contents is checked and the gauge rod is raised to full extension and slowly depressed until white mist is expelled. The temperature, gauge rod reading, relative density of the product and the outage tables of the tank car are used to obtain the volume of the contents.

3. "After unloading", instructions contained in the dome must be followed to disconnect lines and plug connections.

4. The placards must be changed to indicate that the car is now empty.

The company leasing the tank cars provides information on the suggested procedures for their loading and unloading. All persons involved with the the process should become familiar with the information and keep it available for quick reference.

Loading Truck Transports

As with rail transportation of LPG, the federal and provincial governments formulate and enforce strict regulations concerning the safe handling of LPG being transported on highways. All persons charged with the duties of loading or unloading LPG should be familiar with the regulations and realize that stiff penalties may be levied for violating same.

The following is a general procedure to be followed when loading truck transports:

1. No transport should be allowed to approach the loading rack while another transport is loading or unloading.

2. Each transport should be checked by the loading rack personnel for leaks or other obvious defects which should be reported to the supervisor before the transport is loaded. Loaders should also ensure that the tank is properly equipped and in good order.

3. The transport tanks must be level before loading or unloading to ensure that the relief valve connection is not flooded (see Fig. 4). If the tank were subjected to overpressure with the relief valve flooded, liquid would be vented from the valve and a dangerous hazard created. Accurate gauging of tanks also depends on the tank being level.

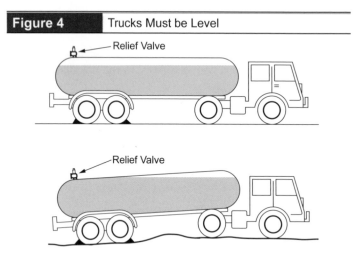

Figure 4	Trucks Must be Level

4. LPG transport trucks are subject to maximum loading regulations. The maximum loading is based on the loading temperature and the relative density of the product. Charts, available for all transport tanks, must be consulted to determine the maximum allowable loading.

5. The quantity loaded into the transport is determined from any of the following methods:

    a) Reading the rotary gauge on the side of the tank

    b) Weighing the unit before and after filling

    c) Using temperature-corrected meters

6. Once the truck is in position, all electrical systems must be shut off.

7. Brakes must be applied and the wheels chocked to prevent the unit from accidentally moving.

8. The vapour and liquid hoses are connected with careful observation for leaks.

9. A qualified person must stand by during the entire loading or unloading operation.

10. Odorant must be applied to the load, if required.

11. Proper documentation for the load must be provided and seals installed, if required. Required placards must be in place.

12. Assurance that loading hoses are disconnected must be obtained before the truck leaves the rack.

OBJECTIVE 4

Describe the general safety issues associated with the storage and gauging of hydrocarbon liquids.

STORAGE OF HYDROCARBON FLUIDS

Water in Storage Tanks

The primary function of storage tanks is to hold hydrocarbon fluids before, during or after various process operations. Most storage tanks have a layer of water below the hydrocarbon fluid which must not be allowed to build up to a level where it can enter the process. Water entering a fractionation tower can cause serious process upsets and possibly damage the internals of the tower. When water contacts hot hydrocarbons, the water immediately "flashes" into steam with a large increase in volume.

Water can enter a tank through open hatches, gauge board cable openings, leaking steam heater coils and leaking roofs.

Drain lines and valves for drawing water from storage tanks must be protected from freezing which could cause them to rupture. When the ice melts, the product will be lost. Also, oil flowing from such a leak could create a fire hazard. Thus, it is important to check for water frequently and to drain it immediately.

Tank Foamover

Foam usually forms when water vaporizes below the surface of oil having a low specific gravity. Under severe foaming conditions, the volume of the foam may be 20–30 times that of the oil. The foam may overflow the tank and perhaps also the dike surrounding the tank. A serious fire hazard can result.

Loading hot heavy oil into a tank or tank truck containing water can result in a foamover. Heavy oil or asphalt that is seasonally stored can collect water. When the oil is eventually heated, foamover could result if the heat is not applied very slowly. Periodic checking and good maintenance of tanks and heaters will do much to eliminate this hazard.

Manual Gauging and Sampling

Many accidents have happened while workers have been gauging or sampling storage tanks. Since most companies have very strict procedures for tank gaugers to follow, accidents have usually occurred because procedures were not followed. The following are some of the hazards involving the gauging of tanks:

- Toxic vapours existing at the gauging hatch
- Using faulty or incorrect equipment
- Not using required personal protective equipment.
- Inadequate training
- Not following correct procedures
- Inadequate fire precautions
- Damaged or unsafe structures
- Gauging or sampling during bad weather

General Precautions for Tank Gaugers

The following precautions should be observed:

1. If hydrogen sulphide might be present, two workers should be assigned to the job. One will do the gauging while wearing self-contained breathing apparatus; the other will observe him from a safe distance so that he can provide rescue aid, if necessary. Both workers must be thoroughly trained in the use of, and be equipped with, approved self-contained breathing apparatus, as well as being trained in gas detection procedures.

2. Tanks should not be gauged when thunderstorms are approaching.

3. Any defects in ladders and stairways should be reported. Tools and materials, which could be a tripping hazard, must not be left on stairways.

4. Smoking is not allowed within a safety zone around storage tanks. "Strike anywhere" matches and single action cigarette lighters should not be carried during the gauging operation.

5. Thief ropes or cords, made of synthetic fibres, may be allowed in some situations. Where there is the possibility of the presence of flammable mixtures, only lines made of a good electrical conductor should be used. (A thief rope is a rope with a measuring scale that can be used to measure the depth to the liquid surface).

6. Where there is the possibility of a combustible vapour/air mixture, the gauging or sampling should not be attempted until the static charge on the liquid surface has had time to be reduced. A metal gauging well, which shields the gauge or thief rope from an electrostatic charge, is supplied in some tanks so that the time interval is not required.

7. Only approved flashlights may be used for gauging operations.

8. A container for carrying gauging equipment should be used so the gauger will have both hands free for climbing vertical ladders. Gauging equipment should be pulled up in a canvas bag or other suitable container using a lightweight cord.

Gauging Procedures

The following is a general summary of typical gauging instructions:

1. After climbing to the top of the tank, rest until breathing has returned to normal. Take up a position upwind of the gauge hatch where there will be the least exposure to tank vapours and no interference while playing out the tape.

2. Allow a sufficient time (up to 30 minutes) for the static charge to be reduced if the tank has just been filled or agitated in any way. A waiting period is not required if the tank is blanketed with an inert gas above the oil, is equipped with a floating roof or a full depth gauging well. A surface charge, resulting from the loading process, could cause the flammable vapour/air mixture at the surface to ignite.

3. Bond the gauge tape to the tank to equalize the electrical potential between the tank and the tape. Open the hatch about 2.5 cm and allow the pressurized vapour to escape. The gauger should avoid inhaling the vapours.

4. Carefully lower the tape into the tank, playing it out against the side of the hatch. The tape must be kept in contact with the tank at all times to permit static discharge and avoid leaving an air gap that could allow sparking.

5. Unroll the tape using the handle on the reel. Avoid dripping liquid when raising a thermometer or tape. Pour the contents of the thermometer cup back into the tank. Wipe up all spills with wipers stored in containers outside the tank area.

Other safety precautions to be followed include:

- Be very careful not to drop any containers into the tank as they can become spark promoters on the surface of the liquid

- Leave gauge hatches in the closed position unless otherwise instructed

- Keep your hands free of oil and your gloves clean, as oil can cause dermatitis

- Clean off the tape with a wiper, not with your gloves

Storage Tanks at Low Temperatures

Some light hydrocarbons must have a gas blanket above the vapour space to maintain a positive pressure in the storage vessel. For example, below 0°C, the vapour pressure of butane is below atmospheric pressure. To prevent air from being drawn into the storage vessel, a positive pressure is produced by admitting fuel gas or an inert gas such as nitrogen. Air must not be allowed to enter because an explosive mixture could result.

Some installations divert a portion of the discharge from the unloading pump through a heat exchanger. Warm vapour is then routed back to the vapour space of the container being unloaded. Propane vapour may also be used to pressurize a tank of butane in cold weather, provided the propane that dissolves into the butane does not impede the subsequent use of the butane. Some installations use fuel gas, controlled through a pressure regulator, to provide the pressure required to unload the butane.

A gas blanket also serves to maintain pressure when the liquid is being removed from the tank, thus preventing the occurrence of a partial vacuum which could damage the tank.

Overfilling Storage Vessels

When cylindrical horizontal tanks and spheres are being filled or emptied, each metre on the level gauge does not represent the equivalent number of cubic metres stored in the vessel. Special charts are used to determine the amount of product in storage and how much can be added. Serious fires have been caused by overfilling storage vessels.

As is the case with mobile storage tanks, a vapour space must be left incase the liquid expands due to a temperature increase. If the safety valve releases liquid, due to the tank being overfilled, a small quantity will result in a large cloud of vapour.

Figure 5 shows how storage tanks are installed with a dike that has the capacity to contain the volume of the storage vessel. Persons entering the area behind the dike must be aware that hydrocarbon vapours and gases, such as hydrogen sulphide, are heavier than air and are invisible; thus, they could be present within the confines of a dike. Self-contained breathing apparatus may be required by site specific procedures before entering these areas.

Figure 5	Storage Tank Dikes

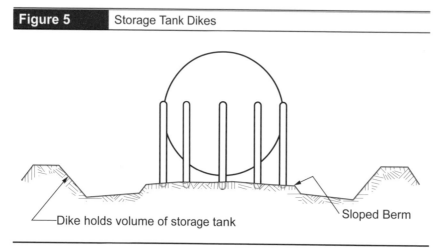

Dike holds volume of storage tank   Sloped Berm

OBJECTIVE 5

Describe the important health and safety guidelines associated with bulk sour oilfield products.

IMPORTANT HEALTH AND SAFETY INFORMATION FOR PRODUCERS AND HAULERS OF "BULK SOUR OIL-FIELD PRODUCTS"

1. Sour Gas (H_2S), from petroleum products and/or by-products being loaded, unloaded or handled during transportation, has claimed the lives of at least four Alberta truckers over the past few years.

2. None were wearing breathing apparatus.

3. Because of these incidents and other "close calls" involving the handling and transportation of bulk products, a committee representing key sectors within the industries was formed to develop guidelines for industry-wide safe operating procedures.

4. It is expected that all companies involved in the handling and transportation of bulk sour product will adopt these guidelines for their operating procedures.

5. The Occupational Health & Safety Division (OHSD) acknowledges the assistance of the following groups:

*   Canadian Association of Petroleum Producers

*   Canadian Association of Oil Drilling Contractors

*   Independent Petroleum Association of Canada

*   Alberta Trucking Association

*   Several concerned individuals

These guidelines were developed by industry members to benefit all groups. Their support is greatly appreciated. For further information and promotional materials (posters, booklets, etc.) on this topic, please contact your local office of Alberta Occupational Health and Safety.

OCCUPATIONAL HEALTH AND SAFETY GUIDELINES
FOR THE
HANDLING AND TRANSPORTATION OF BULK SOUR PRODUCTS

1.0 DEFINITIONS - FOR THE PURPOSES OF THESE GUIDELINES:

    1.1 "SOUR PRODUCT" is defined as "liquid petroleum product or by-product, including produced water, which contains or may contain hydrogen sulphide (H_2S) in sufficient amounts that a worker may be exposed to more than the Occupational Exposure Limit (as prescribed by the Chemical Hazards Regulation) during loading, unloading, gauging or handling the load".

        The Occupational Exposure Limit for hydrogen sulphide (H_2S) currently is:

        10 ppm for 8 hours (time weighted average)

        15 ppm for 15 minutes (time weighted average)

        20 ppm ceiling limit.

    1.2 "BULK" is defined as quantities of 454 litres or greater.

2.0 Where there is the potential for the product being handled or transported to be "sour"

    (i) The producer, or his agent, must notify the carrier

        and

    (ii) The carrier must notify his workers of the potential hazard of the sour product identified by the producer or his agent.

3.0 A person handling or transporting bulk sour product shall hold a valid certificate from the P.I.T.S. H_2S "ALIVE" course or other equivalent course acceptable to a Director of the Occupational Health and Safety Division.

4.0 A person handling or transporting bulk sour product shall ensure that appropriate shipping documentation and placarding is in place as required by law.

5.0 The driver of a vehicle driven to a site for the transportation of bulk sour product, shall ensure that in the cab there is a checklist which identifies the precautions to be followed to ensure protection from hydrogen sulphide gas (H_2S).

    5.1 The owner of the vehicle or the employer of the driver shall provide the checklist referred to in section 5.0.

6.0 Respiratory protective equipment, as required by Occupational Health and Safety Legislation, shall be available at a work site where sour products are handled and must meet the following criteria:

- Is of a type that will maintain positive pressure in the face piece.

- Has a capacity of at least 30 minutes.

- Provides full face protection.

- In the case of remote supplied air apparatus, is fitted with an auxiliary supply of respirable air of sufficient quantity to enable the worker to escape from the area in an emergency, and

- In the case of self-contained breathing apparatus, is fitted with an alarm warning.

    6.1 Where H_2S levels at the work site exceed 20 ppm, workers must wear the above described breathing apparatus.

    6.2 Where the producer or his agent intends that the carrier will provide and maintain necessary respiratory protective equipment, the details should be addressed in a contractual agreement.

Trucking Industry Checklist for Sour Product

The following guidelines have been prepared as a basis upon which a company can develop its own specific or more comprehensive checklist of procedures for drivers to follow when transporting or handling bulk sour product.

Pre-Trip Checklist

- Do you have a valid hydrogen sulphide (H_2S) "ALIVE" Certificate or equivalent?

- Do you have appropriate placards?

Do You Know

- The H_2S concentration of the product to be handled?

- Where the breathing apparatus is located?

- The use, fitting and limitation of the breathing apparatus provided?

- If the breathing apparatus is operational?

- If the air supply is adequate?

Upon Arrival at the Site

- Check for wind direction before entering.

- Check for (and read) all posted signs.

- Check all breathing apparatus for operation.

Loading - Unloading

- While "in attendance" remain up-wind whenever possible.

- Wear breathing apparatus when:

    a) Coupling - Uncoupling;
    b) Checking tank levels;
    c) Opening or closing hatches;
    d) H_2S levels exceed 20 ppm.

Post-Trip Checklist

- Does air supply need replenishing? If so, follow your company's procedures for refilling.

- Return and secure all breathing apparatus.

- Report any unsafe equipment in accordance with your company policy.

Note: If any of the required equipment is not present or not operational, or if you are in doubt over any area of this checklist, always follow your company's sour product awareness guidelines.

This page has intentionally been left blank.

CHAPTER 34 - QUESTIONS

1. If the fuel percentage is below the lower flammable limit, the mixture is said to be

   a) rich.
   b) lean.
   c) invisible.
   d) at the autoignition temperature.

2. The flash point of a liquid is the temperature at which

   a) all molecular vibration will cease.
   b) it will vaporize and burn.
   c) the liquid will burn.
   d) the vapours become inert.

3. Washing steam should enter a tank car or tank truck slowly so as to

   a) prevent injury to the worker.
   b) prevent massive condensation of the steam within the tank.
   c) flush the tank gradually.
   d) reduce the risk of static electricity spark.

4. The explosion of a flammable mixture that occurred at the exact time a valve was opened was likely due to the

   a) pyrophoric effect.
   b) static electric charge buildup.
   c) catalytic effect of the fresh metallic surface.
   d) temperature of the mixture.

5. The ignition temperature of a fuel/air mixture is the

   a) lowest temperature at which a mixture will burn.
   b) temperature at which it is said to have a lean mixture.
   c) temperature at which the fuel may gel.
   d) temperature at which the mixture is above the boiling temperature.

CHAPTER 34 - ANSWERS

1. (b)

2. (b)

3. (d)

4. (c)

5. (a)

CHAPTER 35

Hydrogen Sulphide Safety

LEARNING OUTCOME

When you complete this chapter you should be able to:

Discuss hydrogen sulphide (H_2S) in terms of its properties, its effects on humans, and its presence in the workplace.

LEARNING OBJECTIVES

Here is what you should be able to do when you complete each objective:

1. Describe the physical and chemical characteristics of hydrogen sulphide.

2. Describe the effects on humans of various concentrations of H_2S.

3. Briefly outline how to respond to an H_2S emergency.

INTRODUCTION

All jurisdictions in Canada have similar legislation in place concerning safety and health. Since it is impossible to refer to them all, the Alberta acts, regulations and codes are referred to in this chapter. The student is encouraged to refer to the appropriate documents for his or her province or territory.

Hydrogen sulphide (H_2S) is an extremely poisonous substance, normally encountered as a gas or vapour. Numerous deaths have occurred over the years as a result of exposure to it. Some deaths were caused by falls sustained when workers were overcome by the gas, while others resulted from suffocation when workers were overcome because of brief exposure to the gas.

Hydrogen sulphide is found in varying concentrations in many oil and gas wells. It is also found in septic tanks, sewers, manure pits or anywhere bacteria can break down organic matter in an oxygen deficient environment. H_2S is found in coal mines and is referred to by coal miners as "stink damp". It is produced and liquefied in Western Canada for use in the nuclear power industry for the production of heavy water. It is shipped to Eastern Canada in pressurized tank cars in its liquid state. H_2S is a by-product of many industries. For example, it can be produced when sulphuric acid is accidentally mixed with black liquor in pulp mills.

H_2S must be removed from crude oils and natural gases. After removal, it is converted to elemental sulphur by first burning part of it in a "waste heat" boiler to produce sulphur dioxide (SO_2). This combustion creates heat utilized in the generation of steam for process purposes. The SO_2 is then combined with the remaining H_2S in a catalyst bed, where they chemically react to produce sulphur.

OBJECTIVE 1

Describe the physical and chemical characteristics of hydrogen sulphide.

PROPERTIES OF HYDROGEN SULPHIDE

Workers must thoroughly understand the physical properties of H_2S so they can safely work in an environment that may become contaminated by it. Table 1 lists the properties of H_2S. The following discussion will help the student to understand the importance of the properties of H_2S.

Table 1	Properties of Hydrogen Sulphide
Chemical Symbol	**H₂S**
Relative Density	1.189 (air = 1.0 therefore heavier than air)
Autoignition Temperature	260°C
Flammability	Very flammable, distinctive blue flame
Lower Explosive Limit	4.3% in air by volume
Upper Explosive Limit	46% in air by volume
Colour	Colorless, invisible
Odour	Strong rotten egg
Vapour Pressure	17.7 atm. at 20°C
Boiling Point	-60°C
Melting Point	-83°C
Reactivity	Dangerous with acids and oxidizers
Solubility	Yes in water, hydrocarbons, alcohol
Quoted from National Safety Council Data Sheet 1-284-67	

Chemical Symbol

The chemical symbol for hydrogen sulphide, H_2S, indicates the chemical combination of two atoms of hydrogen with one of sulphur. It is a very simple compound to produce; for example, vinegar mixed with cigarette ashes will produce H_2S.

Relative Density

Hydrogen sulphide is 1.189 times as heavy as air in its pure form. In the petroleum industry, H_2S seldom exists in its pure form, but is usually associated with hydrocarbon gases. Sophisticated processes are required to remove the H_2S gas from hydrocarbon gases because they do not readily separate on their own. All heavier-than-air gases will tend to settle in low lying areas when the air is still and cool. Therefore, workers must be especially cautious in underground installations or tanks and in confined spaces where ventilation is poor.

In the petroleum and other industries, hydrogen sulphide does not naturally separate itself from the gas stream; it will always be present with hydrocarbons. In the event of a leak of sour hydrocarbons, H_2S will not separate and migrate to low areas, but will instead follow the natural air convection currents and be present in both high and low areas. The best location for H_2S sensors is in the path of those normal air currents and close to the most probable source of a leak (for example, above a compressor cylinder).

Autoignition Temperature

Natural gas (methane) requires a very hot ignition source such as an electric spark to produce the required ignition temperature of 650°C. However, H_2S ignites at a relatively low temperature (260°C). Because of its low ignition temperature, workers are advised to use only approved power tools and nonsparking tools to reduce the ignition hazard when it may be present. Also, static electricity from drive belts and other equipment can easily ignite H_2S.

Flammability

H_2S combines with oxygen to produce sulphur dioxide (SO_2) and water vapour. In burning 1 kg of H_2S, approximately 17 000 kJ of heat is produced. it burns with a very light blue flame that is invisible in daylight; the combustion products are visible as a brownish-yellow gas. The SO_2 produced by burning H_2S is also toxic and requires the same respect as H_2S. The only safe way to extinguish an H_2S fire is to interrupt the supply of the gas.

Explosive Limits

All of us have experienced problems when trying to start a gasoline engine either "starved" for fuel or "flooded". This problem occurs because gasoline will not ignite if the fuel/air mixture is too lean or too rich. To ignite, the air/gas mixture must be between 1.3% and 6% gasoline; outside of this range, the fuel will not burn. Therefore, gasoline has a "narrow" explosive range.

Compare this to H_2S, which has a lower explosive limit (L.E.L.) of 4.3% and an upper explosive limit (U.E.L.) of 46%. It is a safe and simple fuel to burn under the controlled conditions of a sulphur recovery boiler. However, its wide explosive range combined with its low autoignition temperature makes it a very dangerous gas, from a fire and explosion standpoint.

Colour

H_2S is an invisible gas. A leak may become visible because of hydrocarbon or water vapour content, but the H_2S component of a leak cannot be seen.

Odour

Rotten eggs have a pungent, repulsive smell because the gas produced in the decay process is H_2S. Therefore, it is often referred to as "rotten egg gas." It is an insidious poison since the gas will dull the sense of smell; a victim will not be able to detect high concentrations. For this reason: **A WORKER CANNOT RELY ON THEIR SENSE OF SMELL TO DETECT H_2S!**

Vapour Pressure

The vapour pressure of H_2S is 1794 kPa at 20°C which means that when it is to be maintained in the liquid state, it must be under a pressure of at least 1800 kPa. Loading liquefied H_2S into tank cars must be done within strict guidelines to ensure the cars are not overloaded and thus become overpressured.

Boiling Point

Because of the low boiling point of H_2S (-60°C), it is normally in the gaseous state at atmospheric pressure.

Melting Point

The melting point of H_2S is -83°C, so it will not be found in the solid state. However, if water containing H_2S gas is frozen, the H_2S becomes part of the solid mass. But, when the ice melts, it will be liberated as a gas.

Reactivity

H_2S reacts violently with acids and oxidizers. It will tarnish silver and reacts with lead acetate to produce lead sulphide. This reaction is indicated by a colour change from a clear lead acetate solution to black lead sulphide and is used to detect H_2S in chemical reaction tubes for use in gas detectors.

Solubility

Gases will dissolve in liquids to a greater or lesser extent depending on the:

- temperature of the liquid.
- pressure on the gas above the liquid.
- solubility of the liquid (some liquids absorb some gases better than others).

Referring to Figure 1, in a closed system, gas will be absorbed by the liquid as the liquid temperature is reduced and the pressure is increased. But, gas is liberated from a liquid if the temperature is increased or the pressure is reduced. Hydrogen sulphide has a solubility (at 20°C and 101 kPa) of 3067 ppm in water and 12 350 ppm in conventional crude oil (C_{6+}).

Figure 1	Solubility of Gas in Liquid

Gas Dissolved in Liquid   **Gas Liberated from Liquid**

Liquid Phase
with dissolved gas

High Pressure
Low Temperature

Gas Phase

Liquid Phase

Low Pressure
High Temperature

The principle of solubility is the basis for one of the processes to remove H_2S from hydrocarbon gases. Liquid amine absorbs the H_2S from high-pressure gas as it comes in contact with that gas. The liquid amine (now containing H_2S) is pumped to another vessel where it is heated and the pressure reduced to liberate H_2S, which is then burned.

Considering the solubility of H_2S in water and crude oil, the concentration of H_2S in the vapour above a slightly sour liquid at low pressure is very high and, in some cases, lethal. Assuming that the pressure above the liquid is 101 kPa and at 20°C, the concentration of hydrogen sulphide in the vapour or gas phase can be calculated by:

$$\text{ppm } H_2S \text{ (gas phase)} = \frac{\text{ppm } H_2S \text{ (water)} \times 10^6}{3067}$$

$$\text{ppm } H_2S \text{ (gas phase)} = \frac{\text{ppm } H_2S \text{ (}C_{6+}\text{)} \times 10^6}{12,350}$$

Table 2 uses these formulae to show the concentration of H_2S in the gas phase above both water and C_{6+} for various concentrations in the liquid phase.

Table 2	Concentration of H_2S Gas in Liquid Phase	
ppm H_2S in liquid	ppm H_2S above H_2O	ppm H_2S above C_{6+}
0.06	20	5
0.25	82	20
1	326	81
2	652	162
5	1630	405
10	3261	810
15	4891	1215
20	6521	1619

Agitation will increase the liberation of gases. A vessel being cleaned which appears to be free of H_2S can suddenly become dangerously contaminated if a worker simply walks through the sludge in the bottom of the tank and liberates the gas. The addition of heat to clean a vessel can liberate H_2S from sand or other solids, such as the H_2S trapped in the metal itself.

Welding on a vessel that contained sour gases or liquids will liberate H_2S from the metal unless it has been heat treated first. Failure to heat treat the metal prior to welding will also result in a brittle weld that will likely fail when placed back into service.

H_2S CORROSION & THE FORMATION OF IRON SULPHIDE

If water is present in an H_2S environment, it will react with the H_2S to produce sulphurous acid (H_2SO_3). This acid will then attack the metal in the steel piping or vessel, removing iron and producing a grey, paste-like material called iron sulphite ($FeSO_3$). In a dry atmosphere, H_2S can be directly corrosive to steel piping and vessels. Its sulphur component reacts with the iron in the metal to produce various forms of iron sulphide (FeS, Fe_2S_3). Iron sulphide is generally recognizable as a grey, grey/black, brown or green powder.

Dry iron sulphide is pyrophoric; it can spontaneously ignite in the presence of air. Since it forms in the presence of H_2S, and H_2S in air has a wide flammable range and a low auto-ignition temperature, the iron sulphide can become a source of ignition if allowed to dry out.

Iron sulphide reacts vigorously in acidic conditions to release H_2S gas which can pose a real problem for unsuspecting workers. Hydrogen sulphide can also cause a type of corrosion known as stress corrosion cracking (SCC) in certain steels. SCC is extremely serious and can create problems such as pipeline fractures.

OBJECTIVE 2

Describe the effects on humans of various concentrations of H₂S

TOXICITY OF HYDROGEN SULPHIDE

Table 3 indicates the toxicity of hydrogen sulphide. Due to the highly toxic effects of the gas, the results are of tests performed on animals. No two individuals are affected in the same way by the gas, so the test results are only approximate. When information is given in ppm, it is often deceptive because the average individual cannot imagine the number 1 000 000. To put the information in Table 3 into perspective, consider the following comparisons:

- The box of a small pickup truck has a volume of approximately 1m³.

- An eyedropper has a volume of 2 ml (2/1000 litre).

- A 1 litre milk carton has a volume of 1/1000 m³.

If just half an eyedropper of H₂S gas were put into the box of the pickup, a concentration of 1 ppm would result, and, at that concentration, the H₂S can just be detected by smell.

IF A VOLUME OF HYDROGEN SULPHIDE EQUAL TO THAT OF A MILK CARTON WERE PUT INTO THE BOX OF THE PICKUP, ONE BREATH COULD BE FATAL.

Table 3		Toxicity of Hydrogen Sulphide
Parts Per Million (ppm)	**Percentage (%)**	**Physiological Effects**
1	0.0001	Rotten egg smell is noticeable
10	0.001	8 hour Occupational Exposure Limit. Maximum allowable concentration for continuous exposure for 8 hours without breathing apparatus.
15	0.0015	15 minute Occupational Exposure Limit. Maximum allowable concentration for exposure for 15 minutes without breathing apparatus
20	0.002	Ceiling Occupational Exposure Limit. This level of exposure cannot be exceeded at anytime without respiratory protection.
100-150	0.01-0.015	Dull sense of smell, causes burning sensation in eyes and throat. Chronic exposure produces headaches, insomnia, irritability, anorexia and nausea.
250-500	0.025-0.05	Attacks respiratory centre of the brain, causes loss of reasoning and balance, persistent cough, sore throat, fogged vision, chest tightening, pulmonary edema.
700	0.07	Causes nausea, vomiting, cyanosis, vertigo, amnesia, convulsions. Casualty quickly loses consciousness; breathing will stop and death will result if not rescued promptly.
1000	0.1	Unconsciousness immediately, permanent brain damage or death occurs if casualty is not rescued and resuscitated immediately.

Note: All provinces (at this time) have the 8-hour TWA at 10 ppm. Most continue the 15 minute TWA at 15 ppm, but may not have a ceiling limit.

Alberta has removed the 15 minute TWA and lowered the Ceiling limit to a maximum allowable concentration for exposure of 15ppm without breathing apparatus.

Saskatchewan uses mg/m measurement units. BC only has a 10 ppm ceiling limit, and NWT has 15 minute TWA at 15ppm and the Ceiling limit at 20 ppm.

* TWA - Timed Weighted Average Exposure over a specified time.

At **1 ppm**, most people can smell the gas. A strong smell does not necessarily mean a high concentration, nor a slight smell, a low concentration.

A person could work in a **10 ppm** concentration of H_2S for 8 hours. If the concentration exceeds 10 ppm for a short period of time, the exposure time must be reduced. At any time if the concentration goes above 10 ppm, Breathing Apparatus must be used.

A concentration of **15 ppm** can be tolerated for a period of time not exceeding 15 minutes in some provinces. There can be no more than 4 exposures of 15 ppm in an 8 hour shift with 1 hour between exposures. Government limits aside, most industries have a standard that if there is any risk at all, respiratory protection must be used.

If the concentration of H_2S exceeds **15 ppm**, a worker must wear approved breathing apparatus. If the concentration is not known, a worker must wear breathing apparatus until the concentration is determined.

If exposed to a concentration of **100 ppm** (1/100 of 1%), one's sense of smell will be lost or become ineffective within in 2 to 15 minutes. The H_2S might cause a burning sensation to the eyes, throat and lungs and could cause headache or nausea. 100 ppm is the concentration considered to be IDLH.

A **200 ppm** concentration will cause immediate loss of smell and a burning sensation in the eyes, throat, nose and lungs. (The hydrogen sulphide combines with alkali in body fluids to form caustic sodium sulphide).

At a concentration of **500 ppm**, the victim will appear to be intoxicated and will lose his sense of balance and reasoning. In this state, the victim may attempt to continue with the job he was doing when he encountered the gas. For this reason, a person MUST know the people with whom he works and be able to detect any unusual behavior of a coworker. A victim must be watched very closely and may require resuscitation; a victim should be taken for medical attention and not allowed to return to work for at least 8 hours.

At **700 ppm**, the victim will be rendered unconscious very quickly and may develop seizures similar to those caused by epilepsy. Loss of bladder and bowel control can be expected. Breathing will stop and death will result, if the victim is not rescued and resuscitated promptly.

At a concentration of **1000 ppm** (1/10 of 1%), the victim will be rendered unconscious immediately. This victim will not begin breathing voluntarily if brought to fresh air.

ARTIFICIAL RESUSCITATION MUST BE COMMENCED WITHIN THREE MINUTES OF BECOMING UNCONSCIOUS DUE TO CONTACT WITH HYDROGEN SULPHIDE!

Effect of H_2S on the Sense of Smell

This effect cannot be emphasized strongly enough. Our sense of smell is usually the first indication of a dangerous airborne substance. A safe concentration of H_2S (10 ppm) can be easily smelled, but once the odor is gone, the victim believes that the danger has passed. It may well be that the gas has dulled his sense of smell and the danger is greater than when it could be detected. Also, it must be remembered that aromatic hydrocarbons can mask the smell of hydrogen sulphide, **BY THE TIME IT HURTS, IT IS TOO LATE**.

H_2S is an Insidious Poison

Another problem with H_2S is that pain, which is a common sign of most gas dangers, does not exist. Gases such as chlorine, ammonia and sulphur dioxide cause a great deal of pain to the eyes, nose and throat, so the victim will try to get away from the hazard. However, the irritation produced by H_2S is relatively slight and the victim does not try to leave the area because he does not feel any pain.

Effect of H_2S on the Nervous System

In small amounts hydrogen sulphide is a depressant, while in larger amounts it is a stimulant. In high concentrations the respiratory centre is paralyzed, causing suffocation.

Note: There is much controversy regarding H_2S entering the respiratory system through a perforated eardrum. Company policies vary widely on the subject, but the Journal of Occupational Medicine (May 1985) makes the following statement:

"We conclude that workers with perforated eardrums should NOT be excluded from working in atmospheres containing concentrations of H_2S."

Effects of Repeated, Chronic Exposure to H₂S

Some of the health problems associated with repeated exposures to hydrogen sulphide are:

- pulmonary edema: an abnormal excess accumulation of fluids in the lungs.

- corneal bullae: blisters on the transparent membrane covering the iris and pupil of the eye.

- conjunctivitis: inflammation of the mucous membrane lining the eyelids.

- photophobia: a high intolerance to light, which can make driving at night hazardous.

- rhinitis: inflammation of the mucous membrane lining the nose.

- bronchitis: chronic inflammation of the bronchial tubes.

- headaches.

- digestive disturbances.

- weight loss.

- general weakness.

"SWEET" VERSUS "SOUR"

One problem in attempting to convince workers of the dangers of H₂S is the result of misleading distinctions made between low and high concentrations. This problem may be due, in part, to the previous definitions that were adopted by producers to distinguish between sweet and sour oil and gas. The new cutoff concentration to distinguish between sweet and sour products is based on the need for processing to make the product saleable. This new distinction is far less confusing to workers since it is more in line with the occupational exposure limit (OEL) for H₂S. A product with a concentration of H₂S not exceeding 0.001% or 10 ppm, is now considered "sweet".

The basis for the Alberta Energy and Utilities Board (AEUB) definition is the production of petroleum products and the guidelines are only concerned with the production steps that must be taken to remove H₂S from the petroleum. The extensive use of the "sweet" and "sour" terminology has perhaps resulted in workers not understanding that the terms relate to production, and not to toxicity.

HYDROGEN SULPHIDE IS A LETHAL GAS. DO NOT ENTER AN AREA WHERE IT MAY BE PRESENT UNLESS YOU HAVE RECEIVED THOROUGH TRAINING ON ITS HAZARDS.

EXPOSURE LIMITS FOR H₂S

The following exposure limit definitions and workplace responsibilities are taken from the "Occupational Health and Safety Act Chemical Hazards Regulation" of Alberta.

Definitions

1. 8 Hour Occupational Exposure Limit (O. E. L.)

   This means the time-weighted average concentration of an airborne substance for an eight hour period. For H₂S, the limit is 10 ppm. It has been determined that a worker could work continuously for eight hours in a 10 ppm concentration.

2. 15 Minute Occupational Exposure Limit in all provinces except AB and BC.

   This means the time-weighted average concentration of an airborne substance for a fifteen minute period. A worker could work for fifteen minutes in a 15 ppm concentration of H₂S.

3. Ceiling Occupational Exposure Limit

   This means the maximum concentration of an airborne substance to which a worker may be exposed by inhalation. For H₂S, the concentration is 15 ppm.

EMPLOYER RESPONSIBILITY

The employer shall ensure that a worker is not exposed by inhalation to concentrations of H_2S in excess of the prescribed O. E. L.

Where a worker is or may be exposed to H_2S, the employer shall ensure that each worker:

- is trained, and utilizes this training to minimize the worker's exposure to H_2S.

- is instructed in the purpose, proper use and limitations of any protective equipment provided.

- is instructed regarding health hazards associated with exposure to H_2S. Where a respiratory device is used to control worker exposure to H_2S, the employer shall:

- provide and ensure that workers wear an appropriate, correctly fitting device.

- ensure that each worker is instructed in the purpose, proper use and limitations of the device.

- ensure that the device provided is stored in a manner that prevents contamination.

- ensure that each device is properly maintained and is regularly cleaned.

EMPLOYEE RESPONSIBILITY

It is the employee's responsibility to:

- wear respiratory protective equipment when it is provided by an employer and ensure that the equipment fits correctly.

- follow the procedures set by the employer.

- participate in any instruction provided by the employer.

Alberta Occupational Health & Safety Act-General Safety Regulations

All workers in Alberta must become familiar with the parts of this Act pertaining to working in an environment that may contain H_2S. Workers should obtain the Workplace Health and Safety Bulletin CH029, entitled 'Hydrogen Sulphide at the Work Site' available through Alberta Employment and Immigration. The following information is condensed from the Act and is directed to persons working with H_2S.

Hazardous work must be performed by competent workers following procedures developed by the employer. The worker must receive adequate training and know the limitations of equipment required to allow the work to be done safely.

TRAINING SESSIONS ARE REQUIRED BY LAW

The laws generally require that all persons working around H_2S receive adequate training including:

- actual practice with breathing apparatus, plus simple maintenance and cleaning of the equipment.

- training in First Aid, including artificial resuscitation.

- training in the use of gas detectors.

OBJECTIVE 3

Briefly outline how to respond to an H₂S Emergency.

RESPONDING TO AN H₂S EMERGENCY

Even when a worker collapses in an area where H_2S is a known hazard, it does not automatically mean that person has been overcome by the H_2S. Various other conditions may have caused this collapse, such as: heart attack, stroke or head trauma. However, from a safety standpoint, always ASSUME H_2S IS PRESENT and wear your breathing apparatus before entering the area.

BEFORE ATTEMPTING TO RESCUE A VICTIM OF H₂S POISONING, A WORKER MUST PUT ON THEIR BREATHING APPARATUS!

PROTECT YOURSELF FIRST!!!

When a co-worker has been "knocked down" in a known H_2S environment, there are certain steps that must be followed to ensure your own safety and survival. Remember that a rescuer who does not take the time to properly assess the situation and get suited up and call for help before attempting the rescue, and who is subsequently overcome, is no good to the victim and creates problems for other rescuers by becoming an unnecessary victim.

1. Get out of the area to properly assess the situation.

2. Sound the alarm.

3. Put on breathing apparatus.

4. Remove casualty immediately.

5. Initiate resuscitation (artificial respiration, CPR).

6. Evacuate to medical attention immediately.

"FATAL HYDROGEN SULPHIDE POISONING MAY OCCUR EVEN MORE RAPIDLY THAN THAT FOLLOWING EXPOSURE TO A SIMILAR CONCENTRATION OF HYDROGEN CYANIDE" . . . (from Dangerous Properties of Industrial Materials).

This page has intentionally been left blank.

CHAPTER 35 - QUESTIONS

1. Hydrogen sulphide is

   a) 1.189 times heavier than air.

   b) always found in its pure form.

   c) found near the top of tanks and rooms.

   d) more difficult to ignite than natural gas.

2. H_2S burns with a _____ flame.

   a) black sooty

   b) red streaked

   c) light blue

   d) orange tipped

3. The degree of hydrogen sulphide concentration which allows a petroleum product to be considered "sweet" must not exceed _____ ppm.

   a) 35

   b) 5

   c) 25

   d) 10

4. A concentration of 15 ppm of H_2S should not be tolerated for a time exceeding

   a) 5 minutes.

   b) 10 minutes.

   c) 15 minutes.

   d) 20 minutes.

5. The safest way to extinguish a hydrogen sulphide fire is to

   a) remove the O_2 source

   b) remove the catalyst

   c) lower the temperature

   d) stop the gas flow

6. At concentrations above _____ppm, hydrogen sulphide causes persons to appear to be intoxicated and impairs judgment.

   a) 500

   b) 125

   c) 1000

   d) 825

CHAPTER 35 - ANSWERS

1. (a)

2. (c)

3. (d)

4. (c)

5. (d)

6. (a)

First Aid & CPR for Adult Casualties

LEARNING OUTCOME

When you complete this chapter you should be able to:

Identify possible or potential medical difficulties in a person, and provide assistance until professional medical aid can be obtained.

LEARNING OBJECTIVES

Here is what you should be able to do when you complete each objective:

1.   Identify and discuss the steps in the assessment process.

2.   Describe the ABC's of first aid.

3.   Describe the first aid procedures associated with heart attack and stroke.

4.   Describe standard emergency assistance procedures.

Note: This chapter is not intended to replace training in first aid or CPR provided by organizations such as the Canadian Red Cross and Saint John's Ambulance. It is strongly recommended that people take proper practical training in first aid or CPR given by those organizations.

INTRODUCTION

Emergencies can occur at any time, in any location and to any person. It is comforting to know that an increasing number of people are learning the first aid skills necessary to assist people in distress. The purpose of this chapter is to provide background information about common emergency situations, as well as a description of their signs and symptoms and of the skills required to assist a casualty before medical personnel arrive at the scene.

GLOSSARY OF TERMS

Airway
Airway, the pathway through which the air moves in order to reach the lungs; it includes the:

- Nose.
- Mouth.
- Throat.
- Trachea (windpipe).

Angina
Angina is a heart condition causing chest pains that occur when the heart is not getting enough oxygen to function properly.

AR (Artificial Respiration)
Artificial respiration is the act of breathing for a non-breathing casualty. It is also known as rescue breathing.

Arteries
Arteries are blood vessels that carry blood away from the heart.

Asphyxia
Asphyxia occurs when there is a decrease in oxygen level in the blood. It leads to damage or death of fundamental tissues and organs.

Atherosclerosis
This is a cardiovascular condition in which there is an excessive buildup of materials such as cholesterol and fatty acids in the vessels, causing a narrowing or "hardening" of the arteries.

Cardiac Arrest
Cardiac arrest is a situation in which the heart has stopped completely or beats too irregularly to pump any blood.

CPR (Cardiopulmonary Resuscitation)
CPR is the procedure, consisting of chest compressions and artificial respiration, performed on a casualty who is not breathing and does not have a pulse. CPR can only be performed by individuals who are specifically trained in its use.

Heart
The heart is a double acting pump located in the centre of the chest, directly under the sternum (breast bone) and in front of the spine. The heart pumps blood to all parts of the body.

Landmarking
Landmarking is the positioning of your hands in order to carry out airway and cardiopulmonary procedures.

Lungs

Lungs are the two organs located in the chest, protected by the rib cage, where the exchange of oxygen and carbon dioxide occurs.

Shock

Shock is a serious condition that arises when all parts of the body cannot obtain an adequate supply of oxygenated blood.

Stroke

Stroke is a condition resulting from an inadequate supply of blood reaching portions of the brain.

Xiphoid Process

Xiphoid process describes the small, cartilage-like bones protruding from the bottom of the sternum (breast bone) where the ribs meet.

OBJECTIVE 1

Identify and discuss the steps in the assessment process.

ASSESSMENT PROCESS

When first reaching a casualty, survey the area to make sure that it is safe. Look for potential dangers that might create continued problems for the casualty or the rescuer. It is not wise to be put into a situation that might result in the rescuer becoming a casualty as well.

If the casualty is conscious, get his/her permission to provide care. A conscious casualty has the right to refuse care, so it is important to obtain consent. Tell the casualty:

- who you are.
- that you are trained in first aid.
- what you are going to do.

The casualty can then give the rescuer permission to give care or refuse care. In the event of a refusal, stay nearby if you can and activate the Emergency Medical Services system.

If the casualty is unconscious, assume consent and proceed with first aid.

In the case of an infant or child casualty, it is important that consent be obtained from the parent or guardian, if that person is available. Otherwise, assume consent and proceed with first aid treatment.

EMERGENCY MEDICAL SERVICES (EMS)

The EMS System consists of all of the people within the medical care system:

- First person on the scene
- Dispatchers
- Paramedics
- Firefighters
- Doctors
- Nurses
- Other hospital staff

Successful emergency care begins with quick recognition of the problem, intervention and activation of advanced emergency care.

One of the most important people in the EMS system is the first person at the scene of an accident because this individual is the one who starts the chain of care for a casualty.

The EMS system is most often activated by a phone call, often by using the "9-1-1" emergency number. When an emergency call is made, the following information should be given to the dispatcher:

1. The service that is required, so that the call can be directed to the appropriate department.

2. The name, address and phone number from which the call is being made. It is a good idea to post the address and phone number by each phone in a household. In the event of an emergency, the information required by the dispatcher will then be available for anyone using the phone; this is important especially for those callers who are unfamiliar with the location.

3. Information about the situation, the number and condition of the casualties and what is being done for them. This information can then be passed on to emergency personnel who have been dispatched to the accident scene.

When you have made contact with the emergency dispatcher, do not hang up the phone until you are told to do so. Newer cell phones now have GPS tracking usually built in, so emergency personnel can be directed to your call location. This feature needs to be activated on your phone, and can be for emergency 911 only or for all calls/all the time. Coverage is not perfect, but can be accurate in most "populated" covered areas.

OBJECTIVE 2

Describe the ABC's of first aid.

THE ABC'S OF FIRST AID

The Canadian and American Medical Associations recognized that using a simple set of procedures is the best method to teach first aid and CPR skills to the general public. It was found that people were better able to retain and remember the necessary information if it were related to something that had been learned in their early years - the alphabet! Therefore, the ABC system (airway, breathing and circulation) was developed as an aid to teaching basic skills.

Airway

Check to see if the airway is open. The most effective method of opening an airway suspected to be closed is by using the head-tilt/chin-lift (or modified jaw thrust) method, illustrated in Figure 1. In this procedure, the casualty will be lying on his or her back. Place one hand on the casualty's forehead; press down on the forehead while your other hand tilts the chin, using two fingers hooked under the jaw. This procedure effectively draws the tongue off the back of the throat.

Figure 1	Open the Airway

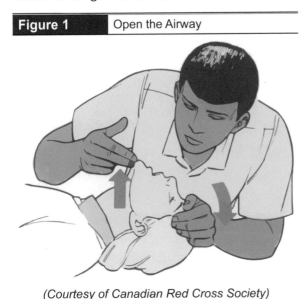

(Courtesy of Canadian Red Cross Society)

Breathing

Look, listen and feel for breathing, as shown in Figure 2. When looking for breathing, look directly at the chest for the rise and fall of the rib cage. To listen and feel for breathing, position your cheek close to the casualty's nose and mouth; listen and feel for any air escaping from his/her lungs onto your cheek.

Figure 2	Check for Breathing

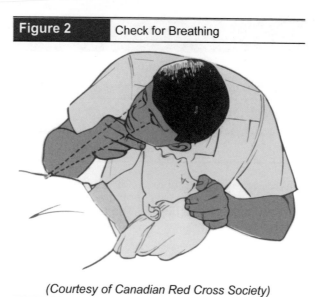

(Courtesy of Canadian Red Cross Society)

Circulation

Check for a pulse. This is done at the carotid artery which is in the neck beside the voice box. This artery is used because of its proximity to the heart and the resultant strength of the pulse. Do not use your thumb to check for a pulse; the pulse you feel with your thumb could be your own since there is a pulse in the thumb.

The pulse should be checked on the side of the neck closest to you, as shown in Figure 3. If you check the pulse on the side of the neck furthest away from you, it might appear to a casual bystander that you are choking the casualty.

Figure 3	Checking for Pulse

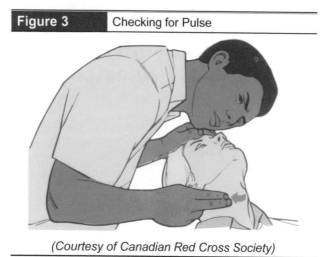

(Courtesy of Canadian Red Cross Society)

OBJECTIVE 3

Describe the first aid procedures associated with heart attack and stroke.

THE HEART & LUNGS

The heart is located in the centre of the chest (Fig. 4) and is approximately as large as a clenched fist. The left side of the heart is slightly larger than the right because it needs to be a stronger, larger pump than the right side. The left side must pump blood to the entire body, whereas the right side of the heart pumps deoxygenated blood only to the lungs to pick up oxygen for transportation to the rest of the body.

| Figure 4 | Location of the Heart in the Chest |

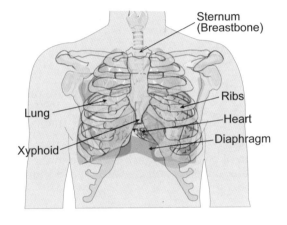

(Courtesy of Canadian Red Cross Society)

When blood travels around the body, oxygen is given up to feed the cells and carbon dioxide is picked up as a waste product. When this deoxygenated blood is pumped to the lungs, the carbon dioxide is exchanged for oxygen from inhaled air. For the heart to transport fresh oxygen to the brain and the rest of the body, the supply must be replenished continually which is accomplished inside the lungs.

HEART DISEASE

Smoking is known to be the major cause of cardiovascular disease (CVD) or atherosclerosis in North America; thousands of people each year die from CVD. Nicotine, tar and carbon monoxide are all contributing factors to heart disease.

Nicotine acts to make the blood sticky inside the blood vessels, making clot formation easier in certain areas. Tar takes up valuable space in the lungs where the oxygen enters the blood stream. The smaller the space available for this exchange, the less oxygen enters the system. Carbon monoxide replaces oxygen in the blood stream. It is, in fact, easier for the hemoglobin in the blood to carry carbon monoxide than oxygen. Carbon monoxide, not useful to the body, reduces the amount of essential oxygen available for organs and tissues.

High blood pressure and high cholesterol are also major factors in the development of cardiovascular disease. These result from narrowing arteries and are contributors to CVD because of the increased strain that they place upon the heart. The heart must work much harder, yet less efficiently, to pump enough oxygenated blood to the brain and other body tissues.

Some factors which affect a person's chances of getting heart disease cannot be changed; these include:

- Heredity
- Age
- Race
- Gender

For instance, it has been found that males are generally more susceptible to heart attacks, as are persons with a family history of heart disease.

Angina

Angina is caused by reduced flow of blood to the heart. The pain of an angina attack is located in the chest and described as a squeezing pain. The casualty may feel nauseous and dizzy and may experience shortness of breath; the skin may also feel cold and clammy.

A person who has been previously diagnosed with angina will have been prescribed medication such as nitroglycerin which opens the blood vessels and relieves the pressure on the heart, reducing the demand for oxygen and reducing the pain. Rest may also relieve the symptoms of angina, as exercise can cause the onset of the symptoms.

Actions for treating angina include:

1. Have the person stop what he/she are doing, sit down and rest.
2. Ask if he/she is taking any medication for this condition, and retrieve it for them.
3. Offer the medication for the sufferer to take.
4. If the medication does not work, activate the EMS system.

Heart Attack

A heart attack occurs when a portion of the heart muscle dies due to lack of oxygen and nutrients. The size of the dead muscular area determines how large the heart attack has been.

The person having a heart attack may have similar symptoms to those of a person having an angina attack. The chest pain will usually be severe and radiate to the arms, back and neck. Shortness of breath, nausea, sweating and vomiting are common symptoms of a heart attack; the skin may also look clammy and blue or ashen grey. If the pulse is checked, it may seem too fast, too slow or very irregular.

One of the most significant signs that an individual is suffering from a heart attack is the fact that the condition will usually be denied very strongly. A combination of the above symptoms and denial are signs to watch for if you suspect that someone is having a heart attack.

Unlike an angina attack, rest and medication such as nitroglycerin will not have any effect on a heart attack.

Actions for treating a heart attack include:

1. Have the individual stop what he/she is doing and rest, to reduce the heart's demand for oxygen.

2. Activate the EMS system.

3. Monitor the individual for breathing and pulse and try to keep him or her comfortable.

4. Be prepared to perform CPR if necessary.

Cardiac Arrest

Cardiac arrest occurs when the heart, for whatever reason, stops beating completely. The casualty will stop breathing, have no pulse and become unconscious very quickly. Rapid intervention is absolutely necessary at this point. Without CPR, the brain will suffer permanent damage unless it receives oxygen within 4 - 6 minutes.

Actions required for treatment of cardiac arrest include:

1. Activate the EMS system immediately.

2. Begin proper CPR.

Stroke

A stroke is a condition that occurs when parts of the brain do not receive the required oxygen and nutrients; these parts of the brain become damaged and may die. When these brain cells die, specific functions related to that part of the brain become affected. Strokes are usually caused by blood clots or a rupturing of a blood vessel inside the brain.

Strokes can cause partial or total paralysis of parts of the body, slurred speech, blurred vision, dizziness and numbness or unconsciousness. These symptoms are serious and must be treated.

Actions required for treatment of stroke include:

1. Have the individual stop the activity he/she is doing and rest.

2. Activate the EMS system immediately.

3. Monitor the individual for breathing, pulse and level of consciousness.

4. In the event that the individual becomes unconscious, be prepared to perform CPR.

OBJECTIVE 4

Describe standard emergency assistance procedures.

EMERGENCY ASSISTANCE PROCEDURES

Artificial Respiration

Artificial respiration is the act of breathing for casualties who, for some reason, are not able to breathe for themselves. In performing this process, the first aider will provide the casualty with sufficient oxygen to maintain important body functions, such as brain and heart activity.

This procedure follows the same ABC's used in other assessments.

1. If you did not see what happened to the individual before you arrived on the scene, ensure there is no danger to yourself. You cannot assist the person if you become harmed in any way.

2. Determine the responsiveness of the individual. Tap his or her feet; if there is no response, pinch the shoulders and shout in both ears. It is recommended that you shout in both ears because the casualty may be hard of hearing in one ear.

3. If the individual has not responded to your actions, shout for help. If another bystander is available, send him/her to call the local EMS system and return to you to let you know whether the call was made.

4. If there are no bystanders available, find a phone and call EMS yourself.

5. Open the airway.

6. If the individual is not breathing, you must breathe for him/her by performing CPR.

It is important to realize that the potential for contracting a communicable disease might be a real deterrent for some people when considering training in first aid. Masks are now available to use in cases where artificial respiration or mouth-to-mouth breathing is indicated

Recovery Position

When the casualty is breathing, has a pulse, but is still unconscious, he or she should be placed in the recovery position in order to maintain an open airway. This position is illustrated in Figure 5.

1. Extend the casualty's arm that is closest to you over his or her head.

2. Bring the other arm across the body towards you.

3. Bend the leg farthest from you at the knee.

4. Support the head and neck, so there is a minimal amount of movement.

5. Roll the casualty toward you by using his/her bent leg as a lever, or by pulling on the hip or some clothing.

6. Position the bent knee as a support so the casualty will not roll over.

7. Place the bent arm and head so that the casualty is resting comfortably. This position maintains the open airway and also allows drainage of any fluids from the mouth.

Figure 5	Recovery Position

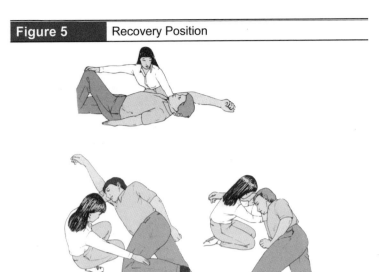

(Courtesy of Canadian Red Cross Society)

Treatment for Choking

In adults, choking usually occurs when too much is being done at once, such as eating, talking and drinking. Food is one of the most common obstructions in adults.

In the unconscious adult, the most common obstruction is the tongue. If the person is lying on his or her back, the tongue has a tendency to fall to the back of the throat and block the airway. This situation can be remedied by turning the individual onto his or her side in the recovery position.

To determine whether a person is choking, look for several warning signs including:

1. Panic

2. A red face

3. The lips, eyelids and finger tips turning blue

Such persons may be grasping at their neck, as shown in Figure 6; this is the universal sign for choking.

Figure 6	Signs of Choking

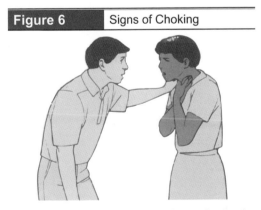

(Courtesy of Canadian Red Cross Society)

Adults, especially in public places, have a tendency to cover up the problem and run to the bathroom to be alone and avoid embarrassment. If you suspect that the person is choking, follow him or her and provide assistance as soon as you can assess the situation properly.

There are two types of choking casualties: those with good and those with bad airways. The difference is that the person with the good airway is getting some air and is able to speak and cough. These people should be encouraged to continue coughing, but continue talking to them for comfort.

People with a bad airway require additional help, as they are unable to help themselves any longer. The following information will help in knowing what to do to help a person who is choking, whether that person may be:

- conscious.
- unconscious.
- pregnant or obese.

Conscious Choking

If you suspect that an individual is choking, take a few steps to ensure that the situation is a real one.

- Ask the person if he or she is choking.
- If the answer is yes, identify yourself as someone who can help. Ask if your help is wanted.

In the case where children or infants are involved, you must have permission from the parent or guardian, if available, before rendering aid.

Follow these steps, illustrated in Figure 7, for treating a conscious choking victim:

1. Place yourself behind the individual.

2. Place your hands so that your fist is above the belly button, but below the xiphoid process. Cover your fist with the other hand for more forceful action.

3. Administer abdominal thrusts, as shown in Figure 7, inward towards the spine and upwards towards the throat (a "J" action) until the article pops out or the individual becomes unconscious. This is referred to as pop or drop.

This method of removing obstructions has been demonstrated as very effective after two to four thrusts.

Figure 7	Abdominal Thrusts

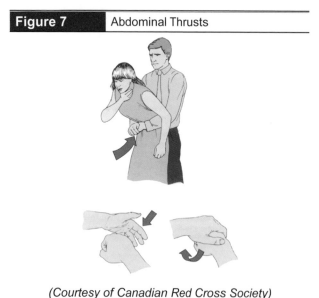

(Courtesy of Canadian Red Cross Society)

Unconscious Choking

If after performing the abdominal thrusts your attempts have been unsuccessful, the casualty will become unconscious in a matter of minutes. In this event, it is essential that help is obtained. Send someone to call EMS, position the person on his or her back and perform the following steps:

1. Check to see if the article causing the obstruction has dislodged itself.

2. If you cannot see the article, complete a finger sweep. Use two fingers and sweep them from one side to the other across the back of the throat.

3. Open the airway with the head-tilt, chin-lift and try to give the victim a breath.

4. If the air does not go in, retilt the head and try another breath.

5. If still unsuccessful, you can assume that the individual is still choking. Straddle the casualty's legs and place the heel of your hand just above the navel, but well below the xiphoid process.

6. Place your other hand on top of the first hand and press into the casualty's abdomen with quick inward and upward thrusts.

7. Repeat Steps 1 through 6 until the article has become dislodged or until emergency help arrives.

8. If the article is dislodged, ensure that the airway is open and give two breaths.

9. Check the pulse. If there is no pulse start CPR procedures.

10. Reassess breathing. If the victim is breathing without help, place him or her in the recovery position and monitor the individual every two or three minutes until medical help arrives.

11. If the person is not breathing without help, perform artificial respiration until medical help arrives.

Pregnant or Obese Choking Victims

For a pregnant or obese adult, abdominal thrusts would be dangerous or ineffective. In these cases, chest thrusts are performed.

In order to complete the chest thrust maneuver, find the xiphoid process at the bottom of the sternum, mark one finger width above it, and place your free hand in a fist above that. Your fist should still be on the lower half of the breastbone. The chest thrusts are carried out straight back toward the spine, as illustrated in Figure 8.

Figure 8	Chest Thrusts For Pregnant or Obese Casualty

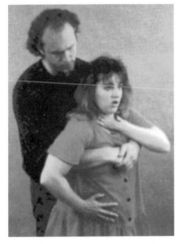

(Courtesy of Canadian Red Cross Society)

FIRST AID FOR OTHER COMMON INJURIES

There are many different types of injuries that require first aid and emergency care. This chapter deals only with the more common ones. It is recommended that you take a full First Aid course if you wish to learn more skills and information.

In responding to many accidents that occur, you must depend on your own resources and the other people around you for assistance.

Shock

Shock can be caused by any trauma, but is usually related to injuries that result in excessive bleeding and decrease the volume of blood in the system.

Typical symptoms of shock include:

- Pale, cold and clammy skin
- Muscle weakness
- Confusion
- Anxiety
- Nausea
- Possible unconsciousness
- Possibly a very weak and rapid pulse

Actions for treatment of shock include:

1. Have the person sit or lie down.
2. Keep the person warm.
3. Reassure the person and try to establish the cause of shock. An obvious cause would be a car accident.
4. If necessary, activate the EMS system.

Bleeding

There are many different types of bleeding injuries. Only simple, external bleeding wounds are covered here.

If the bleeding is extensive, do not worry about cleaning the wound as that will be done at the medical facility.

1. It is essential that a clean cloth be placed over the wound to apply direct pressure to help slow the bleeding. If a cloth is not available, have the person use his/her own hand to apply pressure.
2. Elevate the injured region to slow the flow of blood to that area of the body.
3. Wrap the injured area to keep in place the cloth that is applying direct pressure.
4. If the bleeding soaks through the bandages that have already been applied, continue to add more bandages until the blood no longer soaks through. Do not remove any of the soiled bandages.
5. If necessary, activate the EMS system.

An effective way to remember the above information is to use the acronym RED, which stands for:

R - Rest

E - Elevate the injured area

D - Direct pressure on the injured area

Broken Bones

There are several types of broken bone injuries that can occur. Discussed here are simple fractures of the limbs.

An acronym that works well to help remember the first aid treatment for broken bones and general care of other limb injuries is RICE, which stands for:

R - Rest

I - Immobilize

C - Cold

E - Elevate

Actions for treatment of broken bones include:

1. Have the casualty rest in a position as comfortable as possible.

2. If you have the knowledge and equipment necessary, it is ideal to splint the limb or otherwise immobilize it; however, this is not always possible.

3. Apply an ice pack to the area to minimize the pain and swelling.

4. If possible, elevate the limb, but do not cause discomfort.

5. If necessary, activate the EMS system.

Bites

Bites, whether from insects or animals, can cause serious problems. An animal might carry rabies and pass it on to humans as well, some people are allergic to stings or bites from certain insects.

Insect Bites

Insect bites are painful, but usually do not do much harm unless the person who has been bitten is allergic. People with known allergic reactions to bites or stings should always carry an insect bite kit.

To treat an insect bite:

1. Remove the stinger if it is visible in the skin. Scrape it away with a fingernail or something similar; do not use tweezers as their action may release more poison into the skin.

2. Wash the bite area with soap and water and cover it to keep it clean and reduce the chance of infection.

3. If the swelling or the pain is significant, place a cold compress or ice pack over the bite to reduce the symptoms.

4. Monitor the individual for any signs of allergic reaction.

Animal Bites

Animal bites are serious and can cause a great amount of pain and infection. Rabies is a common and potentially fatal disease that may be transferred through the saliva of an infected animal. Dogs, cats, rodents, bats and other scavenging animals are common carriers of rabies.

To treat an animal bite:

1. Wash the bite with soap and water, unless the bleeding is severe.

2. Treat the bleeding. Watch for a developing infection.

3. Get immediate medical attention. Rabies, if untreated, is fatal.

4. Report the bite to the appropriate authority, so that the animal can be prevented from biting others.

This page has intentionally been left blank.

CHAPTER 36 - QUESTIONS

4th Class • Part A1

1. The result of inadequate blood supply reaching portions of the brain is termed

   a) angina.
   b) stroke.
   c) cardiac arrest.
   d) heart attack.

2. When the pulse is checked at the neck of a victim, it should be done on the side nearest you

   a) so that it will not appear that you are choking the victim.
   b) to prevent obstruction of the airway.
   c) so that you can see the artery pulsing.
   d) so that you can simultaneously check for breathing.

3. To assess an unconscious casualty's condition, the Canadian and American Medical Associations recommend following the _____ system.

   a) RED
   b) ABC
   c) RICE
   d) FOS

4. You notice that one of the men you are working with is lying on the ground. If you find that his breathing has stopped you would:

   a) give him something to drink and then send for help.
   b) send for a doctor.
   c) phone the shift supervisor.
   d) start artificial respiration immediately and summon help.

5. The heart consists of two pumps. One side pumps the blood throughout the body and the other side pumps blood to the

   a) brain.
   b) lower extremities.
   c) kidneys.
   d) lungs.

CHAPTER 35 - ANSWERS

1. (b)

2. (a)

3. (b)

4 (d)

5. (d)

PLANT FIRE PROTECTION

CHAPTER 37

Fires & Extinguishing Media

LEARNING OUTCOME

When you complete this chapter you should be able to:

Describe the fire classifications and the types of extinguishing media suitable for each classification.

LEARNING OBJECTIVES

Here is what you should be able to do when you complete each objective:

1. *Discuss the theory, terminology and the life safety issues associated with fires.*

2. *Explain the four classes of fires and describe the types of fire extinguishing media and how they act on these fires.*

3. *Describe the design and operation of standpipe and sprinkler systems.*

OBJECTIVE 1

Discuss the theory, terminology and the life safety issues associated with fires.

DEFINITIONS

As with any topic, there are certain definitions that must be understood before a student can truly study and understand the subject.

Combustion

Combustion is defined as an exothermic, self-sustaining reaction involving a solid, liquid and/or gas-phase fuel. "Exothermic" means that heat is released in the reaction. The process is usually associated with the oxidation of a fuel with the emission of light. Combustion can occur in inert atmospheres.

Oxidizing Agents

An oxidizing agent is a chemical substance that can supply oxygen to react with hydrogen or with metals. Often, the term is used to refer to any chemical element or compound that could combine with a fuel in the combustion process.

Oxygen is the simplest and most common oxidizing agent; however, the term includes many other chemicals. The following are examples of oxidizing agents:

- Oxygen and ozone.
- Hydrogen peroxide.
- Members of the halogen group such as fluorine, chlorine, bromine and iodine.
- Concentrated nitric and sulphuric acids.
- Oxides of heavy metals such as manganese dioxide and lead oxide.
- Nitrates, chlorates, perchlorates and peroxides.
- Chromates, dichromates, permanganates, hypochlorites and hypobromites.

Most accidental fires involve a reaction with the primary oxidizing agent, air. Atmospheric air is about 21% oxygen by volume. The balance is mainly nitrogen which plays no part in the combustion process.

Reducing Agents (Fuels)

Substances known as reducing agents are involved as fuels in the combustion process where they combine with an oxidizing agent.

The following are the most common materials involved as fuels in fires:

- Carbon.
- Carbon monoxide.
- Compounds rich in carbon and hydrogen.
- Readily oxidizable nonmetals such as sulphur and phosphorous.
- Substances which contain cellulose such as wood and natural textiles.
- Metals such as aluminum, magnesium, titanium, zirconium and the alkali metals such as sodium and potassium.

Materials high in carbon and hydrogen content (hydrocarbons) are common fuels. Such materials are also the most flammable. Methane, butane, propane, fuel oils and gasoline are examples of hydrocarbon fuels.

Temperature

Temperature is a measure of the molecular activity occurring within a substance.

Oxidizing reactions result in heat being generated which in turn increases the molecular activity. This causes fires to endure and renew themselves due to the increase in intensity of the interactions between fuels and oxidizing agents.

Uninhibited Chain Reactions

These reactions are uncontrolled molecular activity. They result from the interaction of the molecules in the fuel and oxidizing agents. The interaction provides the necessary energy to sustain the combustion process.

FIRE THEORY

Although the combustion process is very complex and, in many cases not fully understood, it is known that combustion occurs in two basic modes: **flaming** and **flameless surface (glowing)**. These two modes can occur either singly or in combination.

Examples of fuels that burn in both modes are coal, sugars, starches, wood, straw and other similar vegetable materials, as well as thermosetting plastics which do not melt.

Flaming Combustion

A fire characterized by flame is the most common. It should be noted that there cannot be a flaming fire unless a vapour is burning. This fact is true whether the vapour already exists, or is evaporated, distilled or driven off from a solid or a liquid.

This mode is usually associated with relatively high burning rates.

A requirement for flaming combustion is the occurrence of uninhibited chain reactions. If they are inhibited or interrupted, flame continuity ceases and the flaming combustion reaction is suppressed which will result in the fire being extinguished.

Flammable liquids and gases burn in the flaming mode only.

Although the actual reactions and processes are very complex, it is possible to represent the requirements for flaming combustion in a simple manner.

Referring to Figure 1, the requirements of the flaming mode can be represented as a tetrahedron ("four faces"). Each of the four sides is in direct contact with the other three (pyramid shape). Each side represents one of the four basic requirements for flaming combustion:

- Fuel
- Temperature
- Oxygen
- An uninhibited chain reaction

Figure 1	Fire Tetrahedron

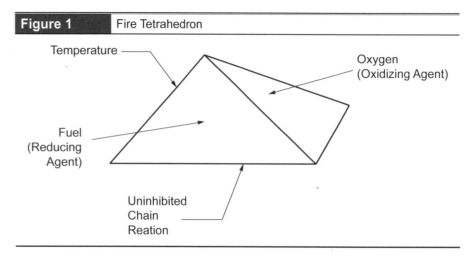

Flameless Surface (Glowing) Combustion

The glowing fire is characterized by the absence of flame and the presence of extremely hot material at the surface where the combustion is taking place. This mode of combustion occurs only with solid fuels.

Figure 2 represents the flameless glowing type of combustion in the form of a triangle. Each side represents one of the three basic requirements for this mode of combustion:

- Fuel
- Temperature
- Oxygen

Carbon, the readily oxidizable metals (such as magnesium, aluminum and uranium) and nonmetals (such as phosphorous) are examples of materials that burn in the flameless glowing surface mode.

Figure 2	Fire Triangle

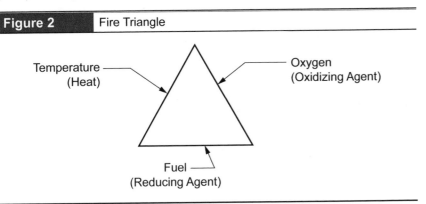

Solid fuels often burn as predominantly flaming fires, but can also be of the flameless glowing type. Frequently, the solid decomposes to give off a vapour, initially burns with a flame and subsequently burns in the flameless mode. An example would be wood which initially burns with flame from the vapours formed as it decomposes. The resultant charcoal, which is formed, will continue the combustion process in the glowing mode.

Conclusion

Both modes of fire involve three essential elements: fuel, oxidizing agents (usually oxygen from the air) and a temperature high enough for the reaction to proceed (heat). In addition, the flaming mode of combustion also involves uninhibited chain reactions (collision of molecules to sustain flame continuity). In each mode, all of the basic requirements must exist for the fire to start and be sustained.

In most cases, flaming combustion will cease if the oxygen concentration is lowered to less than 15% for hydrocarbon gases. Wood will continue to burn in the flameless glow mode with oxygen levels as low as 5%.

Removal of any one of the three (flameless) or four (flaming) basic requirements will provide a means of extinguishing a fire.

LIFE SAFETY

The threat to life from a fire comes not only from the high temperatures, but also from the gaseous products of combustion and the depletion of oxygen in the vicinity of the fire.

It should be noted that at oxygen concentrations of about 17%, a person's motor coordination is impaired. In the range of 10 to 14%, the individual will still be conscious, but will fatigue easily and show impaired judgment. Below a concentration of about 10%, an individual will lose consciousness and will quickly need fresh air or oxygen to revive. These percentages will be higher if the individual has an increased oxygen demand due to exertion.

Some combustion products act basically as asphyxiants; i.e., they reduce the concentration of oxygen in the air. Other combustion products are toxic and/or irritants. In all cases, a person's judgment and/or ability to deal with the situation is likely to be hampered.

OBJECTIVE 2

Explain the four classes of fires and describe the types of fire extinguishing media and how they act on these fires.

CLASSES OF FIRE

Different types of fire need different extinguishing agents. The National Fire Protection Association Extinguisher Standard classifies fires into the following categories:

- Class A
- Class B
- Class C
- Class D

Class A

Fires in ordinary combustible materials (such as wood, cloth, paper, rubber and many plastics) are extinguished by the:

- Heat absorbing (cooling) effect of water or water solutions.
- Coating effect of certain dry chemicals which retard combustion by excluding oxygen.
- Interruption of the combustion chain reaction by halogenated agents.

Class B

Fires in flammable or combustible liquids, flammable gases, greases and similar materials, must be put out by:

- Excluding air (oxygen).
- Inhibiting the release of combustible vapours.
- Interrupting the combustion chain reaction.

Class C

Fires in live electrical equipment, where safety to the operator is a concern, require the use of electrically nonconductive extinguishing agents. (Note: When electrical equipment is de-energized, extinguishers for Class A or Class B fires may be used.)

Class D

Fires in certain combustible metals (such as magnesium, titanium, zirconium, sodium and potassium) require a heat-absorbing extinguishing medium that does not react with the burning metals.

EXTINGUISHING MEDIA

The means of extinguishing a fire can be summarized into four categories; cooling, reduction in oxygen content, removal of fuel and chemical flame inhibition (for flaming fires). Fuel removal refers not only to the physical removal of the fuel, but also to the cutting off of fuel vapours from combustion (flaming mode), or the covering of the glowing surface (flameless mode) to isolate the fuel from the oxidizing agent.

The various broad classes of extinguishing media available use one or more of the following methods to extinguish a fire:

- Water
- Carbon dioxide
- Dry chemicals
- Halogenated agents
- Aqueous film-forming foam (AFFF)
- Dry powder

Water

Water is an efficient and readily available extinguishing agent. It extinguishes by cooling the combustible material, thus lowering its temperature to a point where combustion is no longer sustained. The water may also produce steam which will dilute the ambient oxygen supply.

Carbon Dioxide

Carbon dioxide is noncombustible, and therefore, does not react with most substances. It primarily extinguishes by reducing the oxygen content of the atmosphere to a point where combustion can no longer be supported; CO_2 displaces the O_2 required for combustion. Under some conditions of application, the available cooling effect is helpful, especially where the CO_2 is applied directly to the burning material. The principal advantage of CO_2 is that it does not leave a residue. This consideration is important in laboratories, areas where food is prepared and where there is electronic equipment.

Dry Chemicals

Dry chemical extinguishing agents are either regular or multipurpose. The regular or ordinary, dry chemicals are used for Class B fires (flammable liquids) and for Class C fires (electrical equipment). The multipurpose dry chemicals can also be used on Class A fires (ordinary combustibles) as well as Classes B and C.

"Dry Chemical" should not be confused with the term, "Dry Powder", which relates to compounds used for Class D fires (combustible metals).

When dry chemical agents are introduced directly into the fire area, the extinguishing of the flame is almost instantaneous. Smothering, cooling and radiation shielding contribute to the extinguishing mechanism. The principal mechanism in a flaming mode fire is considered to be a breaking of the chemical chain reaction in the flame. In a flameless surface fire, extinguishing is achieved by removing the fuel from the fire with the coating action of the chemicals.

Dry chemicals should not be used where delicate electrical contacts, relays and switches are present. The chemicals have an insulating property and some are corrosive. Due to their corrosive nature, dry chemicals should be removed from undamaged surfaces as soon as possible after the fire is extinguished.

Halogenated Agents

Halogenated extinguishing agents (Halons) have been developed by substituting fluorine, chlorine, bromine and/or iodine for one or more of the hydrogen atoms in either methane or ethane. This substitution makes the resulting compounds nonflammable and gives them excellent flame extinguishing properties.

The nomenclature used for the Halons is intended to provide a simple unique method of identifying the compound without the complexity of chemical names. This identification is achieved by using a three to five digit number after the name Halon.

The first digit gives the number of carbon atoms in the molecule, the second gives the number of fluorine atoms, the third the number of chlorine atoms, the fourth the number of bromine atoms, and, if present, the fifth gives the number of iodine atoms. For example:

Halon 104 has 1 carbon and 4 chlorine atoms in the molecule. This is carbon tetrachloride, an early "Halon", which is no longer used.

Halon 1211 has 1 carbon, 2 fluorine, 1 chlorine and 1 bromine atom in the molecule.

Halon 1301 has 1 carbon, 3 fluorine and 1 bromine atom in the molecule.

Halon 2402 has 2 carbon, 4 fluorine and 2 bromine atoms in the molecule.

The first three Halons illustrated above are derived from methane, while the fourth is derived from ethane. Halon 2402 is a highly effective extinguishing agent, but its toxicity limits its use.

The presence of bromine in the Halon molecule greatly enhances the fire extinguishing ability; however, it also increases the toxicity of the Halon and its decomposition products.

The effects of the halogens in the "Halon" molecule are as follows:

Fluorine: Increases the thermal stability and reduces the boiling point and toxicity.

Chlorine: Provides a fire extinguishing ability but reduces the thermal stability of the molecule and increases the boiling point and toxicity of the substance.

Bromine: Provides essentially the same effects as chlorine, but to a greater extent.

The extinguishing mechanism of the Halons is not clearly understood; however, it is believed that a chemical reaction takes place which interferes with the uninhibited chain reaction that occurs in the flaming mode of the combustion process.

All halogens are active in "chain breaking" in the combustion process, but, bromine is much more effective than fluorine or chlorine.

Halons are stored as liquids and discharged as gases.

Halons do not leave any residue and are often used to protect electrical and electronic equipment. They are also used in air and ground vehicle engine compartments where speed of extinguishment is essential. The clean up of equipment after Halon use is minimal.

Some situations where Halons are effective:

- Where a clean extinguishing agent is required.
- Where live electrical or electronic equipment is present.
- Where flammable liquids or gases are present.
- Where the speed of extinguishing is essential (e.g. Halon 2402 in aircraft engine compartments).
- Where the area is normally occupied by personnel (Halon 1301).

Halons are ineffective for extinguishing fires involving:

- Fuels that contain their own oxidizing agent.
- Reactive metals.
- Metal hydrides.
- Chemicals capable of auto thermal decomposition.

Note: Due to concerns about the environmental impact of halogenated hydrocarbons, current Canadian Federal regulations prohibit the production of Halons and import and export of recovered Halons, except by permit.

Aqueous Film-Forming Foam (AFFF)

This extinguishing agent is an aqueous film-forming surfactant in water. A surfactant is a substance introduced into a liquid to increase its spreading and wetting qualities. Many detergents are surfactants.

The AFFF agents form air foam and, in addition, can form a water solution film on the surface of flammable liquids. The aqueous layer of solution under the foam maintains a floating film on hydrocarbon fuel surfaces which helps to suppress combustible vapours and cool the underlying layer of hydrocarbon fuel.

The extinguishing action of AFFF is to exclude air, cool and provide a seal for the vapours from the hydrocarbon.

AFFF is suitable for Class A and B fires. On Class A fires, the foam acts as a coolant and penetrant to reduce the temperature below the ignition level. On Class B fires, the foam acts as a barrier to exclude air or oxygen from the fuel surface.

It is not recommended for use on electrical fires (Class C) as it is electrically conductive.

Dry Powder

Dry powder agents are for use on Class D fires (combustible metals).

Metals will burn, particularly if they are in a finely divided form. Some metals burn when exposed to external heat; others burn from contact with moisture or reaction with other materials.

Dry powders, used on combustible metals, are often a combination of chemicals determined by the type of combustible metal or metals for which the powder is to be used. The dry powder is spread over the fire and the extinguishing actions are by smothering to exclude air and cooling.

The agent, extinguisher and method of application should be chosen in accordance with the manufacturer's recommendations.

Be aware that the dry powder used must be suitable for the particular combustible metal. Do not confuse dry powder with dry chemicals.

OBJECTIVE 3

Describe the design and operation of standpipe and sprinkler systems.

STANDPIPE SYSTEMS

Standpipe systems are used in buildings over 3 stories (14 metres) tall, since this is the practical limit for firefighters to couple hoses together from the pumper truck at street level up the stairways to the fire floor. It is also close to the limit from which a fire can be fought externally from ladders and snorkel equipment.

A standpipe system is used to overcome the above difficulties. The standpipe rises up the stairwell or wells. At each floor level, provision is made for the connection of fire hoses. The firefighters need only couple hoses to one of the valved outlets provided to get a water supply.

The connections used are frequently on the floor below the fire which allows the use of the connections on the fire floor as well; the fire is approached from below rather than above. If the fire were approached from above with the stair doors open and the heat of the fire rising, it would be similar to approaching the fire through a chimney.

There are three classes of standpipe systems:

- **Class I**:   These systems use NPS (National Pipe Straight) 63 mm hose and hose connections; they are provided for use by fire departments and those trained in firefighting techniques.

- **Class II**: These systems use NPS 38 mm hose and hose connections; they are provided for use by the building occupants, until the fire department arrives. Subject to approval of the local authority, a minimum NPS 25 mm hose and hose connections can be used in Class II service in light hazard occupancies.

- **Class III**: These systems use both NPS 38 and 63 mm hose connections. The NPS 38 mm is for the building occupants while NPS 63 mm are for the use by those trained in handling heavy hose streams.

The number and location of standpipes and equipment is dependent upon the use, occupancy and construction of the facility.

Provincial and local authorities govern the Fire Acts, Codes and Regulations. In general terms, the number of standpipes and hose stations is the same for each Class.

In each building, and in each section of a building divided by fire walls, there shall be standpipes and hose stations such that all portions of each story of the building are within 9 m of a nozzle, attached to not more than 30 m of hose.

Where in Class II service an NPS 25 mm hose has been approved, then all portions of each story of the building shall be within 6 m of a nozzle, when attached to not more than 30 m of hose.

The standpipe risers are located in non-combustible, fire-rated stairwells. If it is not possible to locate all of them in fire-rated stairwells, additional standpipes may be located in pipe shafts at the building interior column locations.

For Class I and III service systems, at least one NPS 63 mm roof outlet connection shall be provided from each standpipe. Figure 3 illustrates a typical roof manifold system.

Figure 3	Typical Roof Manifold

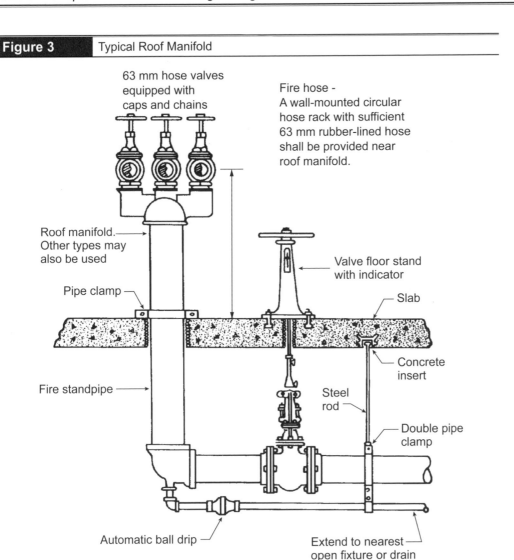

63 mm hose valves equipped with caps and chains

Fire hose - A wall-mounted circular hose rack with sufficient 63 mm rubber-lined hose shall be provided near roof manifold.

Roof manifold. Other types may also be used

Valve floor stand with indicator

Pipe clamp

Slab

Concrete insert

Fire standpipe

Steel rod

Double pipe clamp

Automatic ball drip

Extend to nearest open fixture or drain

The hose connections to the standpipe for Class I service should be located in the stairwell.

For Class II service, the hose connection should be located in the corridor or space adjacent to the stairwell.

For Class III service, the NPS 63 mm hose connection should be located in the stairwell and the NPS 38 mm hose connection in the corridor or space adjacent to the stairwell. Where the building has a large area, the NPS 38 mm connections and NPS 63 mm connections for Class III may also be located at building interior columns.

Standpipes for risers of less than 30 m are usually NPS 102 mm pipe; whereas, over 30 m, the pipe is usually NPS 152 mm. Where a building has a high level fire zone (that is, floors more than 85 m above street level), the riser to these higher floors is usually NPS 203 mm. The water pressure at the topmost outlet of each standpipe should not be less than 450 kPa, with a flow rate in the system of 32 L/s. If the flowing pressure at any hose valve outlet will exceed 690 kPa, then a pressure reducing system shall be installed to reduce the pressure, at the required flow, to not more than 690 kPa.

Figure 4 is a schematic of a typical single zone system; Figure 5 shows a system for buildings having two fire zones.

Figure 4 Single Zone Standpipe

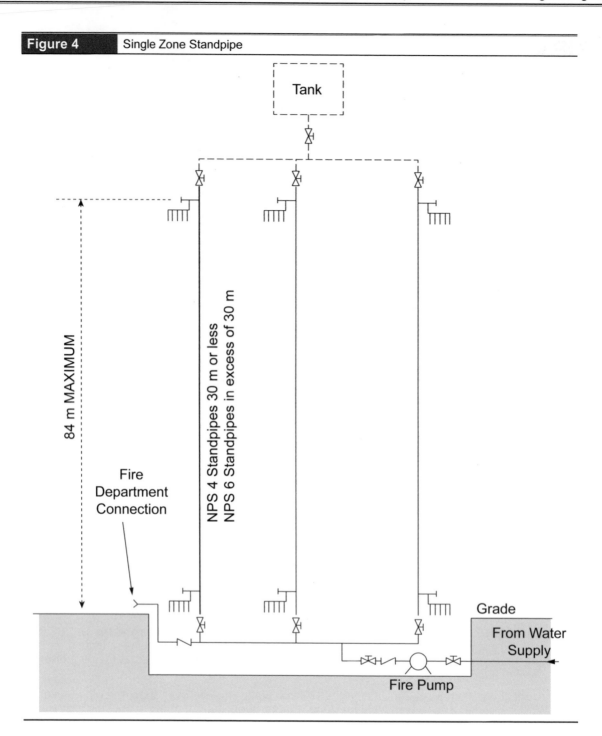

Figure 5   Two Zone Standpipe System

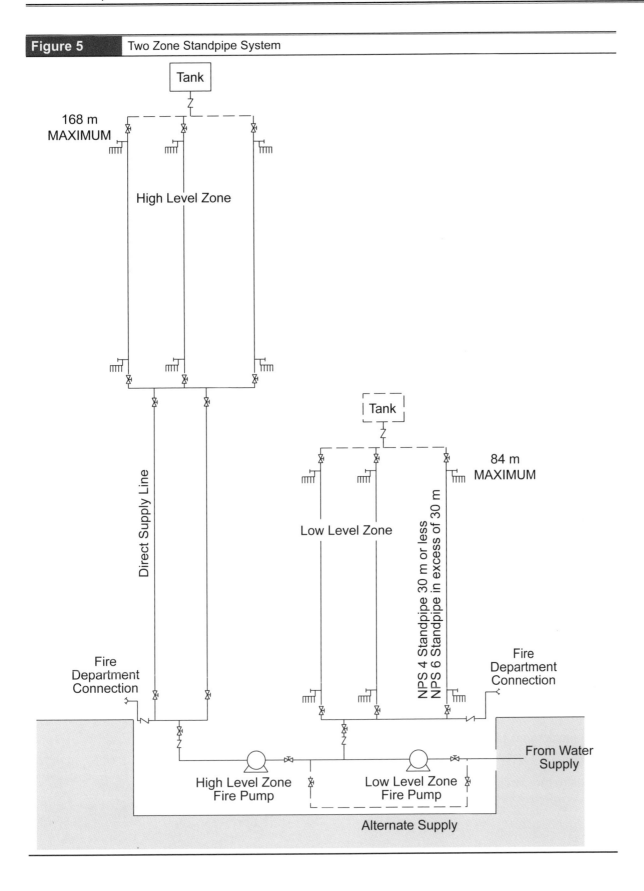

Types of Standpipe Systems

There are two basic standpipe systems:

- Dry
- Wet

Dry Standpipe System

Dry standpipes are normally dry and terminate outside the building with a fire department connection. In the event of a fire that requires fire department participation, a pumper engine will connect to a nearby street hydrant and discharge water into the standpipe system through the fire department connection which features a "Y" piece so that two hoses can feed the standpipe system. This special "Y" piece is called a "Siamese connection".

Wet Standpipe System

Wet standpipes are always filled with water. A Siamese connection is also provided on a wet standpipe system. Class II and Class III systems must be connected to a wet standpipe system as it is essential that the NPS 38 mm hose system has water immediately available.

SPRINKLER SYSTEMS

National Fire Protection Association (NFPA) 13 is the fundamental document that governs the design and installation criteria for these specialized fire protection systems. NFPA 13 is a Standard for the Installation of Sprinkler Systems; thus, it provides the necessary requirements and guidance with respect to the specifics of "how" to design, layout and install a system.

There are five basic types of sprinkler system defined in NFPA 13:

- Wet Pipe
- Dry Pipe
- Preaction
- Combination of Dry Pipe and Preaction
- Deluge

Wet Pipe Systems

This system, shown in Figure 6, is the most common, easiest to design, and simplest to maintain. These systems contain water under pressure at all times and utilize a series of closed sprinklers. Once a fire occurs and produces enough heat to activate one of more sprinklers, the water will discharge immediately from any of the open sprinklers. Wet pipe should only be used when the temperature of the protected area is maintained at or above 4°C.

This system is typically found in:

- office buildings.
- stores.
- manufacturing facilities.
- hotels.
- health care facilities.

Figure 6 | Wet Pipe Sprinkler System

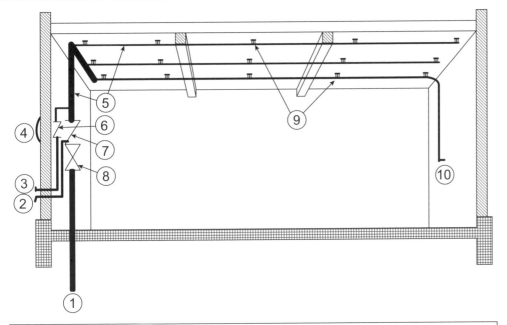

1. Main Water Supply	6. Check Valve
2. Main Drain Connection	7. Alarm Valve
3. Fire Department Connection	8. Water Supply Gate Valve
4. Water Flow Alarm	9. Automatic Sprinklers
5. Water Pressurized Distribution Piping	10. Inspector's Test Connection

Dry Pipe Systems

These systems, shown in Figure 7, are found in environments where the temperature is maintained below 4°C. The system piping contains air under pressure, 275 kPa maximum, under normal circumstances. A dry-pipe valve is used to hold back the water supply and serve as the water/air interface. The valve acts on a pressure differential principle, the surface area of the valve face on the airside being greater than the surface area on the waterside.

When a fire occurs and enough heat is generated, one or more sprinklers will operate. The system air pressure will then escape through the open sprinklers, drop to a predetermined level and allow the dry pipe valve to open. Once the valve opens, the water supply will be admitted into the system piping filling the pipe network. Water will then discharge from any sprinklers that have operated.

These systems are more complex, require a reliable air supply source and involve specific design limitations such as the volume of pipe that can be governed by one dry pipe valve. Special adjustments are necessary for the anticipated area of operation.

Dry pipe systems can be found in buildings that are not maintained at the 4°C limit, such as:

- Outside canopies and structures
- Cold-storage warehouses

Figure 7	Dry Pipe Sprinkler System

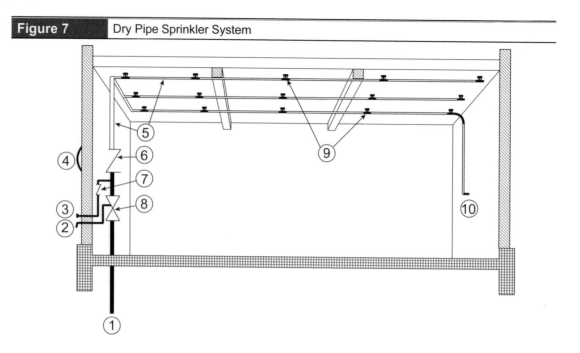

1.	Main Water Supply	6.	Dry Pipe Valve
2.	Main Drain Connection	7.	Check Valve
3.	Fire Department Connection	8.	Water Supply Gate Valve
4.	Water Flow Alarm	9.	Automatic Sprinklers
5.	Air Pressurized Distribution Piping Connection	10.	Inspector's Test Connection

Preaction Systems

The piping for these systems, shown in Figure 8, is typically provided with some minimal quantity of air pressure; thus, the pipe network has no water in it under normal circumstances. The water is held back by means of a preaction valve. The system is equipped with a supplemental detection system. Operation of the detection system allows the preaction valve to automatically open and admit water into the pipe network. Water will not discharge from the system until a fire has generated sufficient heat to cause operation of one or more sprinklers. In essence, the system appears as a wet pipe system once the preaction valve operates.

The small amount of air maintained in the pipe is used to monitor the integrity of it. If the pipe develops a leak, air-pressure will drop and an alarm will sound indicating a low air-pressure condition exists within the pipe. The preaction valve stays in its normal position until the detection system is activated.

Preaction systems are typically found in:

- environments that house computer or communication equipment.
- museums.
- facilities where inadvertent water discharge is of major concern to the end user.

The double-interlock system is most common in deep-freeze facilities where accidental valve operation may result in freezing of the pipe in a matter of minutes.

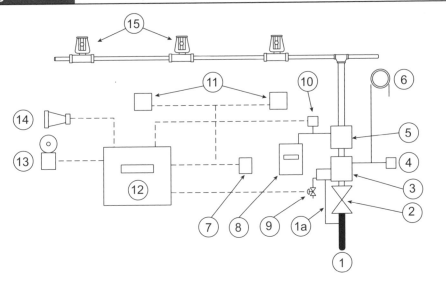

Figure 8   Preaction Sprinkler System

1.	Main Water Supply	8.	Low Pressure Supervisory Panel
1a.	Control Water Supply	9.	Solenoid Valve
2.	Water Supply Gate Valve	10.	Supervisory Low Pressure Alarm
3.	Control Valve	11.	Heat Detectors
4.	Pressure Alarm Switch	12.	Deluge Release Panel
5.	Check Valve	13.	Fire Alarm Bell
6.	Water Motor Alarm	14.	Trouble Horn
7.	Manual Control Station	15.	Automatic Sprinklers

Combination of Dry Pipe and Preaction

Another type of preaction system is the double-interlock variety which has characteristics previously described for both preaction and dry-pipe systems. In order to admit water into this type of system, the detection system must operate and the fire must generate sufficient heat to cause operation of one or more sprinklers, thereby allowing a loss of pressure.

Deluge Systems

Rapidly growing and spreading fires are most effectively protected with this type of system. Deluge systems, shown in Figure 9, are intended to deliver large quantities of water over a large area in a relatively short period of time. Sprinklers used in a deluge system have their operating elements removed. These open sprinklers are attached to branch-line piping in the same manner as other types of sprinklers.

A deluge valve is used to control the system water supply. The sprinkler system pipe is at atmospheric pressure, since the open sprinklers are attached to it. The system water supply is maintained to the system side of the deluge valve. In a similar manner to the preaction system, a supplemental detection system is provided throughout the same area as the sprinklers. Upon activation of this system, the deluge valve is electrically opened, thereby admitting water into the pipe network. As the water reaches each sprinkler in the system, it immediately discharges from the open sprinkler.

The nature of this system makes it appropriate for facilities that contain combustible or flammable liquids and situations in which thermal damage is likely to occur in a relatively short period of time.

Figure 9   Deluge Sprinkler System

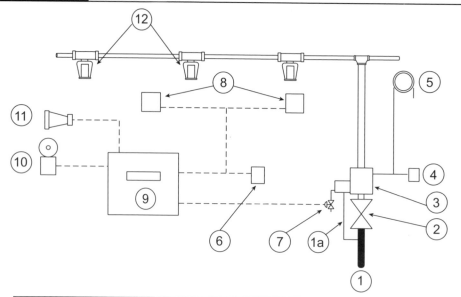

1.	Main Water Supply	7.	Solenoid Valve
1a.	Control Water Supply	8.	Heat Detector
2.	Water Supply Gate Valve	9.	Deluge Release Panel
3.	Control Valve	10.	Fire Alarm Bell
4.	Pressure Alarm Switch	11.	Trouble Horn
5.	Water Motor Alarm	12.	Open Sprinklers
6.	Manual Control Station		

CHAPTER 37 - QUESTIONS

1. A process, which causes fires to endure and renew themselves, is

    a) a reducing agent.
    b) an oxidizing agent.
    c) a flame.
    d) molecular activity due to high temperature.

2. Which of the following constitutes a Class "C" fire?

    a) Fire in a coal bunker
    b) Fire in a fuel tank
    c) Fire in a lumber pile
    d) Fire in an electrical panel

3. Dry chemical fire extinguishers may be used to extinguish electrical fires; however, they are not the best choice because they

    a) fail to cool the fire sufficiently.
    b) conduct electricity.
    c) leave a residue on the equipment.
    d) produce toxic chemicals that may be flammable.

4. Aqueous film-forming foam (AFFF) is suitable for Class _____ and _____ fires.

    a) A, C
    b) A, D
    c) B, C
    d) A, B

5. The maximum air pressure allowed, under normal circumstances, in a dry pipe system is

    a) 275 kPa.
    b) 225 kPa.
    c) 450 kPa.
    d) 150 kPa.

CHAPTER 37 - ANSWERS

1. (d)

2. (d)

3. (c)

4. (d)

5. (a)

Portable Fire Extinguishers

LEARNING OUTCOME

When you complete this chapter you should be able to:

Describe the types of portable fire extinguishers, and their application for each fire classification.

LEARNING OBJECTIVES

Here is what you should be able to do when you complete each objective:

1. *Describe the applicability, types, construction and operation of various types of portable fire extinguishers.*

2. *Discuss the inspection and maintenance of portable fire extinguishers.*

INTRODUCTION

The requirement for fire safety in commercial and industrial buildings and in manufacturing plants is a result of building and fire codes. Various systems such as: communications, fire detection, alarm and annunciation, fire suppression, smoke control and elevator control are required to be installed and maintained.

All buildings and manufacturing plants require portable fire extinguishers. Other protection systems such as; a fire standpipe system, sprinklers or a fire hydrant system are governed by the building's design, size and use.

Fire regulations are for the protection of people and property and the maintenance of fire and life safety systems. Government regulations are directed to the protection of life and safety. Insurance requirements are geared to prevent excessive loss of property based on risk management experience.

OBJECTIVE 1

Describe the applicability, types, construction and operation of various types of portable fire extinguishers.

PORTABLE FIRE EXTINGUISHERS APPLICABILITY

Some portable extinguishers are suitable for only one class of fire, while others are for two or three classes. No extinguisher is suitable for all four classes. Figure 1 shows the most common method of identifying the class of fire for which the extinguisher is suitable. The identification is by:

- the class letter
- a distinguishing shape
- colour code

Figure 1	Fire Extinguisher Markings

ORDINARY   FLAMMABLE   ELECTRICAL   COMBUSTIBLE

COMBUSTIBLES   LIQUIDS   EQUIPMENT   METALS

Extinguisher markings that can be used until conversion to pictographs is complete. Colour coding is part of the indentication system, and the triangle (Class A) is coloured green, the square (Class B) red, the circle (Class C) blue, and the five-pointed star (Class D) yellow.

The most recently recommended marking system is one that combines pictographs of both the uses and non-uses on a single label as shown in Figure 2.

Figure 2	Pictograph Fire Extinguisher Symbols

The pictographs illustrated are designed so that the proper application of the extinguisher can be immediately determined. If the application is prohibited, the background is black and the slash is bright red; otherwise, the background is light blue. The top row identifies an extinguisher suitable for Classes A, B or C. The second row shows an extinguisher suitable for Classes B and C, but not Class A. The third row indicates an extinguisher suitable for Class A and B fires, while the fourth row indicates an extinguisher for Class A fires only.

Rating numerals are also used on the labels of portable fire extinguishers. They give the relative extinguishing effectiveness of the extinguisher. This system is used only for Class A and B fire extinguishers. The numeral precedes the Class letter; for example, an extinguisher may be marked "2A: 40B: C". This marking indicates the effectiveness of this particular make and design as determined by standard reproducible test fires. Class A uses three different standard types of test fire, while Class B uses only one.

An extinguisher with a 4A rating is four times more effective than one with a 1A rating.

Class C indicates the agent is non-conductive and can be used on energized equipment. Class C extinguishers do not have rating numerals. Electrical equipment is made of materials classified as either ordinary combustibles or flammable liquids, or both once they have been de-energized. An extinguisher for Class C fires should be chosen according to the nature of the combustibles in the immediate area and the need for working around energized equipment.

NOTE: A relatively new fire extinguisher class is designated "K". This is a stored pressure extinguisher containing potassium acetate, designed and intended for extinguishing cooking fires involving vegetable oils or fats. They are generally used in commercial kitchens, such as restaurants and cafeterias.

TYPES OF PORTABLE FIRE EXTINGUISHERS

Currently, approved types of fire extinguishers are characterized into six major groups based on the extinguishing agent used as follows:

1. Water

2. Carbon dioxide

3. Halogenated agent

4. Dry chemical

5. Dry powder

6. Foam

Water Extinguishers

Water extinguishers have two basic designs:

- stored pressure
- pump tanks

Stored Pressure

A common type of stored pressure water extinguisher, shown in Figure 3, contains 10 litres and has a mass of about 14 kg. It can be operated intermittently and is easily recharged. The unit consists of a single chamber which contains both the agent and the expellant gas. The cap, or head assembly, consists of a:

- siphon tube.

    » combination carrying handle/operating lever.
- discharge valve.
- air pressure valve.
- pressure gauge.
- discharge hose.
- nozzle.

If the extinguisher is to be used in an area that it may be subject to freezing, it should be charged with a loaded stream (a type of antifreeze agent).

Figure 3 — Stored Pressure Water Extinguisher

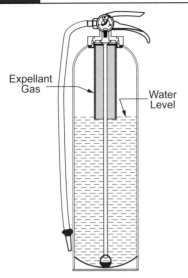

Expellant Gas

Water Level

The extinguisher is pressurized with air or an inert gas in the range of 600 to 900 kPa. The air or gas is charged through a Schrader type tire valve on the head. A 14 kg unit has a horizontal range of 9 to 12 m and will discharge in about 60 seconds. The Underwriters' Laboratory (ULC) classification is 2A.

Most models include a ring pin to lock the operating lever to prevent accidental discharge. To operate the extinguisher, set it on the ground, hold the combination handle loosely in one hand and pull out the ring pin with the other. Move the unit to the best position, hold the hose in one hand and squeeze the discharge lever with the other

Pump Tanks

Two types of pump tanks are available: floor standing and backpack models.

The floor standing model, shown in Figure 4, is cylindrical and has carrying handles either on the container or built into the pump handle. The capacity ranges from about 7 to 25 litres. The pump is a vertical piston type mounted inside the cylinder; a short length of hose with a discharge nozzle is attached to the external part of the pump. The duration of operation ranges from 45 seconds to 180 seconds depending on capacity. The range of the stream is 9 to 12 m.

To operate the pump, the unit is set on the ground and an extension bracket is lowered on which one foot is placed to steady the unit. To force water through the hose, pump the handle up and down with one hand while holding the hose in the other. One disadvantage of this type of unit is that to move the unit, pumping has to stop. Also the force, range and duration of water flow depend to some extent on the operator.

The ULC ratings are given in Table 1.

Table 1 — ULC Ratings

Capacity (litres)	Underwriters Laboratory Canada Rating (ULC)
7	1A
11	2A
18	3A
23	4A

| Figure 4 | Floor Standing Pump Tank Extinguisher |

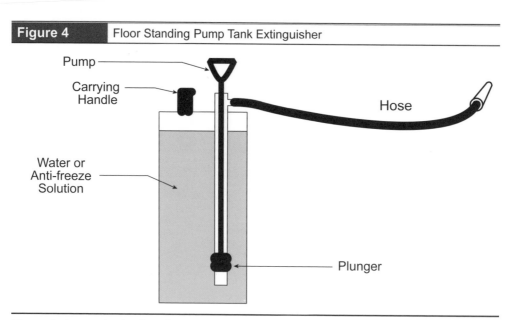

Figure 5 shows the backpack pump type. The principle of operation is similar to the floor model except that the pump is of the "trombone" type and the discharge nozzle is mounted on the pump. The capacity is usually 10 litres; the performance and rating will be the same as the floor mounting type of the same capacity.

| Figure 5 | Pump Tank Extinguisher |

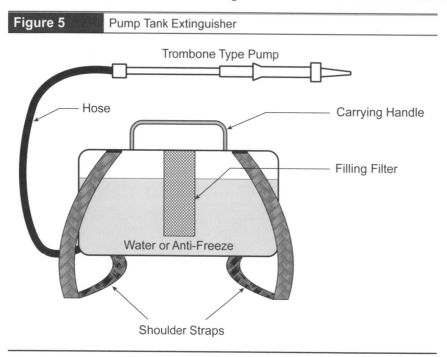

Carbon Dioxide

Carbon dioxide (CO_2) is a compressed gas agent. It is intended for use on Class B and C fires, but can be used on Class A fires until a more suitable agent can be obtained. The carbon dioxide is stored in cylinders as a liquid at 5600 to 6300 kPa at temperatures below 31°C. The maximum storage temperature should not exceed 55°C.

When released from the extinguisher, CO_2 displaces oxygen in the vicinity of discharge until there is not enough oxygen to support combustion. The rapid expansion from a liquid to a gas when the CO_2 is discharged converts about 30% of the liquid into "dry ice" which then sublimes (evaporates directly) into a gas. Carbon dioxide extinguishers have a short range as the agent is expelled in the form of a cloud consisting of a mixture of gaseous and solid CO_2.

If a CO_2 extinguisher is used in a confined or unventilated area, precautions should be taken to ensure people are not overcome due to a lack of oxygen in the atmosphere. The carbon dioxide "snow" may also cause visibility problems and the noise of discharge may frighten anyone who has not used a unit previously. The CO_2 may also drift into adjacent low spaces, if large quantities are released.

Carbon dioxide extinguishers are self-expelling in that they do not require any operating medium to discharge the agent. The extinguisher consists of a pressure cylinder (or shell), a siphon tube and a valve to release the agent. Connected to the valve is a discharge horn or a horn and hose combination. The siphon tube extends from the valve to almost the bottom of the cylinder. Normally, only liquid CO_2 reaches the discharge horn. After about 80% of the cylinder contents have been discharged, the remainder enters the siphon tube as a gas.

Figure 6 shows a typical carbon dioxide extinguisher.

Figure 6	Carbon Dioxide Extinguisher

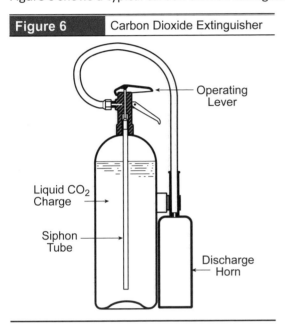

Table 2 shows characteristics and classes of CO_2 extinguishers of various capacities.

Table 2	Characteristics of CO_2 Extinguishers		
Capacity (kilograms)	**Horizontal Range of Stream (metres)**	**Approx. Time of Discharge (seconds)**	**ULC Class**
0.9 – 2.25	0.9 – 2.5	8 – 30	1 – 5B:C
4.5 – 7.0	0.9 – 2.5	8 – 30	2 – 10B:C
9.0	0.9 – 2.5	10 – 30	10B:C
23 – 45	0.9 – 3.0	10 – 30	10 – 20B:C
(Wheeled Units)			

Operation of one type of CO_2 extinguisher is illustrated in Figure 7. The smaller hand held models often have the horn directly connected to the valve assembly by means of a metal tube swing joint connector. Larger models have the discharge horn connected to the valve by a short length of hose. The extinguisher discharge is controlled by squeezing the valve operating lever. Touching the discharge horn during operation should be avoided as it is likely to be very cold. If CO_2 extinguishers are used in subzero temperatures, the valve must remain open until the extinguisher is fully discharged; otherwise, the discharge system may become blocked unless a special low temperature charge has been added.

Carbon dioxide extinguishers have a limited range and are affected by wind and drafts. Thus, the extinguisher discharge should be directed as close to the base of the fire as possible. The agent should be applied even after the flames have been extinguished in order to allow time for cooling to prevent reflash. For flammable liquid fires, the usual method is to begin at the nearest edge, sweeping from side to side towards the back of the fire. Another method, called "overhead application", can be used. In this method, the discharge horn is pointed down at an angle of about 45° towards the centre of the burning area. Usually the horn is not moved.

| Figure 7 | Carbon Dioxide Extinguisher |

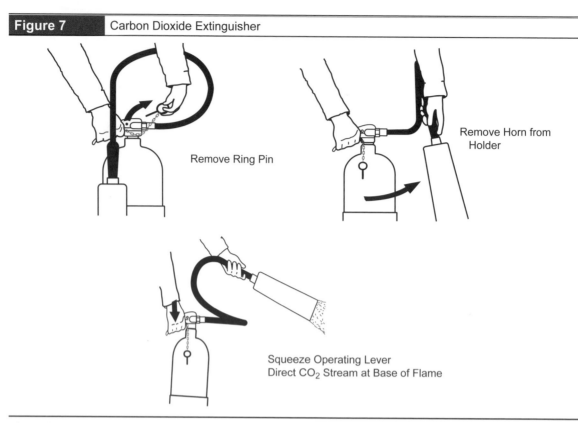

Remove Ring Pin

Remove Horn from Holder

Squeeze Operating Lever
Direct CO_2 Stream at Base of Flame

The side to side sweeping method is likely to give better results on spill fires while the overhead method may be best used on confined fires. For electrical equipment fires, direct the discharge at the source of the flames. The equipment should be de-energized as soon as possible to prevent possible reignition.

Carbon dioxide is nontoxic; however, in the concentrations required to extinguish a fire, it can produce unconsciousness and death due to suffocation rather than toxic effects.

Halogenated Agent

Extinguishers using halogenated agents are mostly intended for use on Class B & C fires. The most common are Halon 1211 (bromochlorodifluoromethane) and Halon 1301 (bromotrifluoromethane). Halon 1211 is effective on Class A fires and extinguisher sizes of 4 kg and greater have Class A ratings. The characteristics of some Halon extinguishers are given in Table 3.

Table 3	Characteristics of Halon Extinguishers			
Type	**Capacity (kilograms)**	**Horizontal Range of Stream (metres)**	**Approx. Time of Discharge (seconds)**	**ULC Class**
Halon	1.0	1.3 to 1.8	8 to 10	2B:C
1301	1.0 to 1.8	2.4 to 3.7	8 to 12	2B:C
Halon	2.5 to 4.1	2.7 to 4.6	8 to 15	1A:10B:C
1211	7.3 to 10.0	4.3 to 4.9	10 to 18	1 to 4A : 20 to 80 B:C

Halon agent extinguishers are operated and applied in the same manner as carbon dioxide extinguishers. Some Halon agents are toxic and the permitted times of exposure are given in Table 4.

Table 4	Permitted Halon Exposure Times	
Type	Concentration % by Volume	Permitted Time of Exposure
Halon 1301	Up to 7	15 minutes
	7 to 10	1 minute
	10 to 15	30 seconds
	Above 15	Prevent Exposure
Halon 1211	Up to 4	5 minutes
	4 to 5	1 minute
	Above 5	Prevent Exposure

Halon 1301 is permitted for normally occupied areas where the concentration will not exceed 10%, or up to 15% in areas not normally occupied. Halon 1211 is not acceptable in areas normally occupied. Both types produce toxic by-products while extinguishing a fire.

To ensure adequate operation of Halon extinguishers over a wide temperature range, the pressure in the Halon cylinder is increased by the addition of nitrogen gas.

Some portable Halon extinguishers may contain a mixture of Halon 1211 and Halon 1301.

Note: Due to concerns about the environmental impact of halogenated hydrocarbons, current Canadian Federal regulations prohibit the production of Halons and import and export of recovered Halons, except by permit.

Dry Chemical

Dry chemical extinguishing agents are known as regular or ordinary dry chemicals as multipurpose dry chemicals. Regular or ordinary dry chemicals are suitable for Class B (flammable liquids) and Class C (electrical equipment); multipurpose chemicals are also suitable for Class A (ordinary combustibles) as well as Classes B and C.

The usual dry chemical agents for use on Class B & C fires include:

- Sodium bicarbonate
- Potassium bicarbonate
- Urea-potassium bicarbonate
- Potassium chloride-base agents

The multipurpose dry chemicals use an ammonium phosphate base agent.

There are two basic designs of dry chemical extinguishers. The first uses a cartridge of carbon dioxide or nitrogen to expel the agent. The cartridge can be either internal or external. The expellant gas is released to the bottom of the shell when the puncture lever is depressed forcing the dry chemical out the nozzle. The rate of flow of dry chemical agent can be controlled by squeezing the operating lever at the nozzle on the end of the hose.

The other design is of the stored pressure type, with either a rechargeable or disposable shell. The disposable shell type has the agent and the expellant gas factory sealed. The shell is then screwed onto a valve and nozzle assembly. Some smaller extinguishers are of a throwaway type where the entire device is disposed of after use. Figure 8 shows both types of dry extinguishers.

| Figure 8 | Dry Chemical Extinguishers |

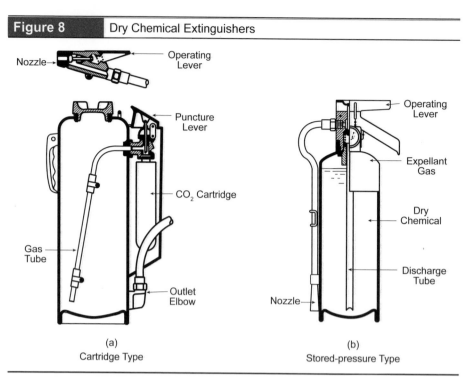

(a)
Cartridge Type

(b)
Stored-pressure Type

Figure 9(a) shows how to operate the cartridge type, while Figure 9(b) shows how to operate the stored-pressure type.

| Figure 9(a) | Using the Cartridge-Type Dry Chemical Extinguisher |

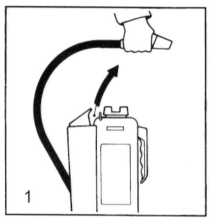

1

If so equipped, remove ring pin.
Remove hose

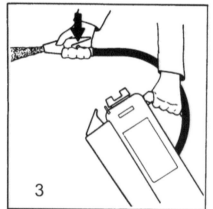

3

Squeeze nozzle operating lever. Direct stream at base of flames using a side to side motion.

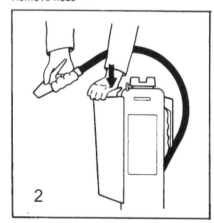

2

Push down on puncture lever.

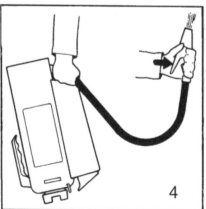

4

After using: Invert extinguisher by grasping elbow, & squeeze nozzle to release all pressure.

Figure 9(b)	Using the Stored-Pressure Dry Chemical Extinguisher

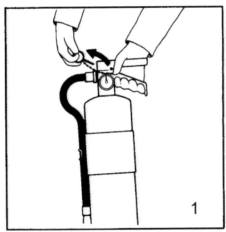

Remove ring pin.

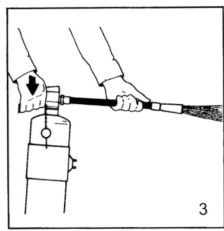

Remove hose from holder.

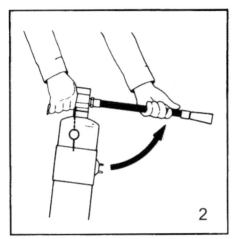

Squeeze operating lever. Direct dry chemical stream at base of flame.

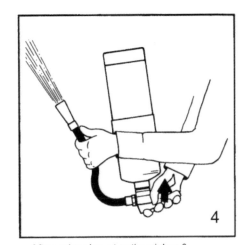

After using: Invert extinguisher & squeeze operating lever until all remaining pressure is relieved.

The characteristics of dry chemicals are given in Table 5. Note that the table does not include all available manufactured sizes.

Table 5	Characteristics of Dry Chemical Extinguishers			
Type	**Capacity (kilograms)**	**Horizontal Range of Stream (metres)**	**Approx. Time of Discharge (seconds)**	**ULC Class**
Sodium	0.5 - 1.0	1.5 - 2.4	3 - 12	2 - 10B:C
Bicarbonate	1.25 - 2.3	1.5 - 6.1	8 - 20	5 - 20B:C
Potassium	1.0 - 2.3	1.5 - 3.7	8 - 10	5 - 20B:C
Bicarbonate	22	6.1	30	120B:C
Potassium	1.0 - 3.9	1.5 - 2.4	8 - 10	5 - 10B:C
Chloride	2.3 - 4.1	2.4 - 3.7	10 - 15	20 - 40B:C
Ammonium	0.5 - 2.3	1.5 - 3.7	8 - 15	1 - 2A &
Phosphate				2 - 10B:C
	0.5 - 4.0	1.5 - 3.7	8 - 15	1 - 4A &
				10 - 40B:C
	21	4.6-13.7	25	20A & 80B:C

Dry Powder

Many agents have been developed to extinguish Class D combustible metal fires. However, there is no one agent that is suitable for all fires. Some agents can be successfully used on several metals while others can be used only for one particular metal.

Agents used for other classes of fire should be avoided in the case of metal fires because of potential violent reactions. For example, water should not be used on sodium fires; vaporizing liquids should not be used on magnesium fires. The agent, extinguisher and method of application should be selected in accordance with the manufacturer's recommendations.

The powder may be applied to the fire by means of an extinguisher using a CO_2 cartridge as the expellant, or from cardboard tubes or metal pails by means of a scoop or shovel. The agent should be applied so that it covers the fire providing a smothering blanket. Additional agent may be required for hot spots. Care should be taken not to scatter the fire. It should be left undisturbed until it has cooled. A dry powder extinguisher is shown in Figure 10.

Extinguishing combustible metal fires involves such hazards as:

- High temperatures
- Steam explosions
- Hydrogen explosions
- Toxic products of combustion

If common extinguishing agents are used, explosive reactions may occur. Dangerous radiation may be generated in the case of certain nuclear materials. General numerical ratings for Class D extinguishers are not used. An extinguisher for combustible metal fires will have a nameplate detailing the type of metal fire for which the agent is suitable.

Figure 10	Dry Powder Extinguishers

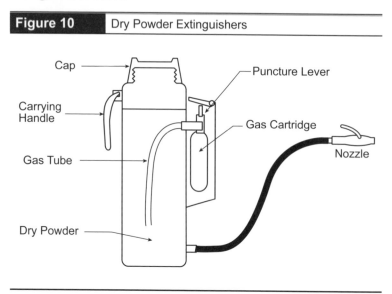

Foam

The AFFF type of extinguisher is suitable for such water soluble flammable liquids as:

- Alcohols
- Acetone
- Esters
- Ketones

AFFF should have nameplate identification for use with various polar solvents. Certain protein foams are not suitable, but AFFF is a surfactant. The characteristics of AFFF extinguishers are given in Table 6.

Table 6	Characteristics of Halon Extinguishers			
Type	Capacity (litres)	Horizontal Range of Stream (metres)	Approx. Time of Discharge (seconds)	ULC Class
Stored Pressure	11	7-8	50	3A:20B
Nitrogen Cylinder	150	9	60	20A:160B

The hand held extinguisher is a stored pressure type. One type has a liquid solution of AFFF in the tank; another has plain water in the tank and a replaceable charge of solid AFFF in a compartment of the nozzle. Both types have an air aspirating nozzle. The two types are shown in Figure 11.

Figure 11	Stored Pressure AFFF Extinguishers

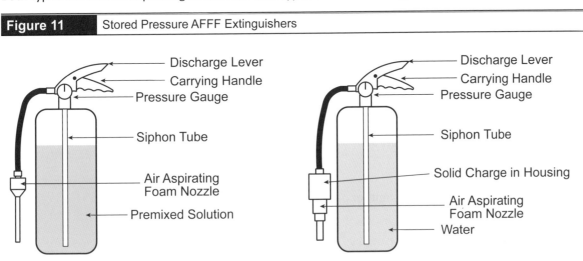

The larger capacity units are of the wheeled type and have a separate cylinder of nitrogen to pressurize the agent container. The discharge is controlled by a special type of aspirating nozzle at the end of the hose assembly. The nozzle induces air into the water/agent solution; the mixing of the air and solution causes the formation of foam. The AFFF type of extinguisher should only be installed or stored in areas where the temperature remains above 5°C.

On a flammable liquid fire of any appreciable depth, the best results are obtained when the discharge is played against the back wall of the tank. The foam should be placed just above the burning surface to permit its natural spread back over the burning liquid. If this method is not possible, stand far enough away from the fire to allow it to fall lightly on the burning surface. Do not allow the foam to splash into the burning liquid. If possible, the operator should move around the fire while directing the foam stream. This pattern will give maximum coverage during the extinguisher discharge period.

For flammable liquid spill fires, the foam can be made to flow over the burning surface by bouncing it off the floor just in front of the burning area. For fires in ordinary combustibles (Class A), the foam can be used to cool and coat the burning surface. Foam is not effective on fires involving flammable liquids and gases escaping under pressure.

OBJECTIVE 2

Discuss the inspection and maintenance of portable fire extinguishers.

INSPECTION & MAINTENANCE OF EXTINGUISHERS

Once an extinguisher has been purchased, it is the responsibility of the purchaser, or an assigned agent, to maintain it. Extinguishers should be periodically inspected, recharged after use and hydrostatically tested as needed or as may be legally required.

Inspection

Inspection is performed by the owner or his agent; it is a quick check that visually determines the fire extinguisher is properly placed and will operate.

The purpose is to give reasonable assurance the extinguisher is fully charged and will function effectively if needed. An inspection should determine that the extinguisher:

1. is in its designated place.
2. is conspicuous.
3. is not blocked in any way.
4. has not been activated and is neither partially nor fully discharged.
5. has not been tampered with.
6. has not been damaged or subjected to a hazardous environment.
7. the gauges are indicating satisfactory operating pressure.

Maintenance

Maintenance is required by Code to be performed annually by a certified agency. It should also be done after each use and when an inspection shows the need is obvious. If an inspection indicates tampering, leakage or physical damage a complete maintenance check should be conducted. Maintenance, as distinguished from inspection, means a complete and thorough examination of each extinguisher as follows:

1. Disassembling the extinguisher
2. Cleaning and replacing any defective parts
3. Reassembling
4. Recharging
5. Repressuring where appropriate

Maintenance checks might reveal the need for special testing of the extinguisher shell or other components. They may, for example, show the need for hydrostatic testing of the shell (cylinder) or even its replacement. Maintenance work is usually contracted out to certified service companies. It is advisable to discharge portable extinguishers prior to sending them for maintenance for two reasons.

1. Personnel have the opportunity to practice using the extinguishers.
2. It ensures that the extinguishers are filled with a new extinguishing agent after servicing.

Obviously, it is not advisable to send all the extinguishers for maintenance at the same time. The maintenance schedule should be staggered and, if possible, replacements taken from storage so that no area is left without an extinguisher. Service companies usually provide loaners. For more detailed instructions, see NFPA 10, Appendix A, Tables A-4-4.2(a) and A-4-4.2(b).

CHAPTER 38 - QUESTIONS

1. Burning metals may be extinguished using

   a) dry chemical extinguishers.

   b) carbon dioxide extinguishers.

   c) AFFF extinguishers.

   d) dry powder extinguishers.

2. What type of extinguisher is suitable for extinguishing all four classes of fires?

   a) Foam extinguisher

   b) Dry chemical extinguisher

   c) Carbon dioxide extinguisher

   d) None of the above

3. Pressure range in a carbon dioxide extinguisher is:

   a) 31 to 55 kPa.

   b) 5.6 to 6.3 MPa.

   c) 5600 to 6300 MPa.

   d) 31 to 55 MPa.

4. Halon extinguishers are mostly intended for use on what classes of fire?

   a) A & D

   b) B & D

   c) B & C

   d) A & B

5. When a stored pressure type fire extinguisher is to be housed in an area where temperatures can be very low, it is protected from freezing by filling it with a

   a) concentrated mixture of water and alcohol.

   b) methanol mixture.

   c) inert gas.

   d) loaded stream.

6. AFFF foam fire extinguishers are used to extinguish

   a) flammable liquids.

   b) electrical fires.

   c) only Class B fires.

   d) burning metal fires.

CHAPTER 38 - ANSWERS

1. (d)

2. (d)

3. (b)

4. (c)

5. (d)

6. (a)

Electrical Fires

LEARNING OUTCOME

When you complete this chapter you should be able to:

Discuss the causes of, and preventive measures for, electrical fires.

LEARNING OBJECTIVES

Here is what you should be able to do when you complete each objective:

1. *List the causes of electrical fires.*

2. *Describe the hazardous location classifications, divisions and groups in relation to electrical equipment.*

3. *Describe suitable fire extinguishing systems for electrical equipment.*

4. *Discuss the ways that fire can be prevented in electrical equipment.*

OBJECTIVE 1

List the causes of electrical fires.

CAUSES OF ELECTRICAL FIRES

The most common cause of fires in buildings in the industrialized world is overheating of electrical equipment.

Electricity is a form of energy that can be converted to other forms of energy. Electric current, passing through a conductor, causes heating and, if confined to the area where heating is required, it can be very useful. Heat produced by a current is calculated by multiplying the resistance of the conductor by the square of the current flow (I^2R). Many of our electrical appliances are designed from this principle.

Another "form" of very useful electricity is the electric arc produced when a current is allowed to jump across an air gap. The arc produces very high temperatures, capable of fusing metals together, as in the arc welding process. The heat produced by the electric arc depends on the current strength and, thus, the voltage of the circuit. Electricity can be very useful, but when heating and arcing are the result of electrical equipment not properly operated, installed or maintained, the results can be disastrous.

When current passes through a loose electrical connection, the resulting arc can cause metal parts to be overheated and melted. As in the arc welding process, molten metal can be spattered, possibly causing combustible material to ignite. Loose connections may not produce an arc, but they will become hot due to the current flow passing through the high resistance of the poor connection. The overheated connection may cause combustible material to be ignited.

Heat is produced in all current carrying conductors, but if the current is kept within the limits specified in electrical codes, the heating is negligible and the heat is easily dissipated to the surrounding atmosphere. But, if more than the specified current is carried, the conductor will be overloaded. Overloaded conductors become a fire hazard not only because of the excess heat generated, but also because the heat causes the insulation to break down. Eventually, dangerous short circuits occur.

Legislation governing the installation and maintenance of electrical equipment includes the requirements which will prevent fires caused by overheating and arcing of electrical equipment. Installation and inspection of electrical equipment must be carried out only by qualified and trained personnel.

OBJECTIVE 2

Describe the hazardous location classifications, divisions and groups in relation to electrical equipment.

Electrical equipment is often required to operate in locations which may contain flammable liquids, gases, dust or fibres. The equipment designed for hazardous locations must meet very exacting standards. Hazardous locations are divided into three classes, depending on the type of hazardous material involved. Each class is then divided into two divisions according to the severity of the hazard.

Equipment approved for use in hazardous locations is marked by the manufacturer to show the class, group and the operating temperature for which it is approved.

Note: The following sections very briefly summarize the main points in the Canadian Electrical Code for hazardous locations. For complete definitions and details, refer to the current edition of The Canadian Electrical Code, Part I.

Class I, Division 1

Class I, Division 1 is the designation of a location where:

1. Hazardous concentrations of flammable gases or vapours may exist continuously or intermittently under normal conditions.

2. Hazardous concentrations of flammable gases or vapours may exist during maintenance or because of leaks.

3. Equipment breakdown or process upsets may release hazardous concentrations of vapours or gases and also cause failure of electrical equipment.

Rotating electrical equipment, lighting equipment, switches and circuit breakers shall be of the explosion-proof type approved for Class I locations.

Class I, Division 2

Class I, Division 2 is the designation of a location where:

1. Flammable liquids or gases are handled, processed or used, but are normally confined in containers or within the process system and can only escape during an accidental rupture or breakdown of equipment.

2. Hazardous concentrations of gases or vapours are normally prevented by a positive ventilation system.

3. The location is adjacent to, but not completely isolated from Class I, Division 1 locations.

Ordinary rotating equipment having no internal switches, contacts, or brushes may be used. However, motors with internal starting switches, brushes, or moving contacts must have a Class I, explosion-proof designation.

Lamps should have explosion-proof enclosures. Switches, circuit breakers, and controllers should be explosion-proof, have their contacts hermetically sealed or be immersed in oil. Portable lights must conform to Class I, Division 1 standards.

Class II, Division 1

Class II, Division 1 is the designation of a location where:

1. Combustible dust is or may be in the air, in concentrations high enough to produce explosive or ignitable mixtures, under normal operating conditions.

2. Equipment failure or abnormal operating conditions could cause such dust-air mixtures to exist and might also provide a source of ignition.

3. Dust of an electrically conductive nature may exist.

Motors must be of the enclosed type, approved for Class II locations. Lighting fixtures, switches, circuit breakers, controllers, and fuses must be equipped with dust-tight enclosures approved for Class II locations.

Class II, Division 2

Class II, Division 2 is the designation of a location where:

1. Combustible dust will not normally be in suspension in the air in quantities sufficient to produce an explosive mixture.

2. Deposits of such dust may be in quantities sufficient to interfere with the safe dissipation of heat from electrical equipment.

3. Dust deposits may be ignited by arcs, sparks or burning material from electrical equipment.

A variety of motors may be used, but all must satisfy the inspector and must have Class II, Division 2 approval.

Lamp holders must be designed to minimize dust accumulation and the escape of sparks, burning material and hot metal. As well, the lighting fixtures must be protected from physical damage by acceptable guards, or location, and shall be clearly marked to indicate the maximum wattage of lamps. Switches, circuit breakers, controllers and fuses are to be designed with tight metal enclosures to minimize the entrance of dust and the escape of sparks.

Class III, Division 1

This is the designation of a location where easily ignited material fibres, capable of producing combustible flyings, are handled, manufactured or used.

Motors should be of the enclosed type. Self-cleaning, squirrel cage, textile motors or open type motors without sliding contacts or switches may be used provided only moderate accumulations of fibres are present and maintenance is satisfactory. Lamp holders, switches, circuit breakers and controllers should be designed with tight enclosures to minimize the entrance of fibres and the escape of burning material and shall be clearly marked to indicate the maximum wattage of lamp which may be used.

Class III, Division 2

Class III, Division 2 is the designation of a location where easily ignited fibres are stored or handled, but are not processed.

Motors should be of the enclosed type. Lamps, switches, circuit breakers and controllers shall meet the same criteria as for a Class III, Division 1 location.

The discussion of the Classes and Divisions of electrical equipment is very basic and should not be used in the design of electrical equipment. Note that using electrical equipment in locations for which it has not been designed could have serious consequences and prosecution for such use is possible.

OBJECTIVE 3

Describe suitable fire extinguishing systems for electrical equipment.

FIRE EXTINGUISHERS

To protect the operator from electrical shock while using fire extinguishers on electrical fires, the extinguisher must be rated Class C. This classification requires that the extinguishant will not conduct electricity. Class C fire extinguishers use carbon dioxide, dry chemical, Halon 1301 or Halon 1211.

The equipment involved in an electrical fire should be de-energized as quickly as possible to eliminate the possibility of shock hazard, in case the extinguisher accidentally contacts the electrical equipment. De-energizing also eliminates fault currents that may have been responsible for the fire originally, from being a source of re-ignition. Fires involving live electrical equipment are usually minor in nature and a short application from a Class C extinguisher will put them out without disturbing the rest of the electrical power system which may be very important where the electrical system is tied into a life support system or a critical process.

It is important to realize that once the power has been cut off from an electrical fire, it becomes a Class A, Class B or a combination Class A and B fire, depending on the material burning in the immediate vicinity.

Carbon Dioxide Extinguishers

Carbon dioxide is primarily intended for Class B and C fires. Hand held models range from 2.2 to 9 kg capacity and wheeled models from 22 to 45 kg capacity. The container is made of steel designed for pressures up to 6000 kPa. A siphon tube, attached to the valve for releasing the agent, extends to almost the bottom of the container, so that only liquid carbon dioxide reaches the discharge horn. The expansion of the liquid to a gas has a refrigerating effect; about 30% of the liquid is converted to a solid, "dry ice", which quickly vapourizes.

Carbon dioxide is an excellent extinguishing agent for electrical fires because it:

- is noncombustible.
- does not react with most materials.
- provides its own pressure for discharge.
- can penetrate to all parts of the fire.
- does not conduct electricity.
- leaves no residue upon application.
- is not poisonous in concentrations of less than 9%.
- is heavier than air, allowing it to displace air above burning surfaces.

When carbon dioxide is applied to burning materials, it envelopes them and dilutes the oxygen content of the surrounding atmosphere, so that combustion is not possible. The solid carbon dioxide has a temperature of approximately -80°C which has a cooling effect on hot material, further helping to put out the fire.

Remember that fires apparently put out with carbon dioxide, as with fires extinguished by other means, may reignite if smoldering embers or hot surfaces remain. An automatic system may be required to maintain an inert atmosphere after a fire is extinguished in rotating electrical equipment. It will allow hot metal surfaces time to cool down, or time for the machine to be safely stopped.

If the enclosure around the machine is reasonably airtight, an initial discharge of carbon dioxide of approximately 1.6 kg/m^3 (1 pound for each 10 cubic feet) of space should put the fire out. After that, an extended discharge will be applied to maintain the atmosphere at a concentration of 30% carbon dioxide until the machine has cooled down.

Halon Extinguishers

The Halon series of extinguishing agents has been derived by substituting fluorine, chlorine, bromine and/or iodine for one or more of the hydrogen atoms in methane or ethane. When one or more halogens are substituted in the hydrocarbon, the resulting compound is not only nonflammable, but it has the ability to extinguish fire also.

The mechanism by which Halons extinguish fires is not completely understood. It is assumed there is a chemical reaction which removes the active elements in the flame chain reaction, since the Halons are more effective as extinguishers than heat removal or smothering can account for.

A simplified nomenclature for the Halons uses a number after the name, Halon, to simply and uniquely identify the compound.

For example:

Halon 1301 is derived from methane, and the four hydrogen atoms have been replaced with one atom of bromine and three atoms of fluorine.

Halon 1211 is also derived from methane; the four hydrogen atoms have been replaced with one atom of bromine, one atom of chlorine, and two atoms of fluorine.

Halons are excellent extinguishing agents for electrical fires because:

- they leave no residue.
- they are noncorrosive.
- they are nonabrasive.
- they do not conduct electricity.
- they are more effective than carbon dioxide on a weight-of-agent basis.
- some have an acrid smell to warn of their presence.

The use of Halons does present a hazard for exposures to concentrations above 10% for Halon 1301 and above 4% for Halon 1211.

Halogen fire extinguishers are built in 1 to 5 kg capacities; they are designated as Class B and C extinguishers. Although similar to the carbon dioxide extinguisher, the space above the liquid in the container is pressurized with nitrogen because of the Halons' low vapour pressure (compared to carbon dioxide). When the valve is opened, the liquid Halon is forced up through the siphon tube to the discharge horn. The drop in pressure allows some of the liquid Halon to change into vapour; thus, the discharge stream consists of a mixture of vapour and liquid droplets. Halon does not have the refrigerating effect of carbon dioxide. On Class C fires, the Halon should be directed at the source of the flame and, if possible, the equipment should be de-energized to prevent re-ignition.

There are many automatic Halon extinguishing systems, each having to be engineered to the system requirements. One system installed in a gas turbine/electric generator plant consists of fire detectors and discharge horns above the combustors. The plant is in a closed building. In the event of fire, the machine is automatically shut down and the whole building is filled with Halon from two 90 kg bottles.

Halon has also been adapted to protect electronic equipment, such as computers, because it leaves no residue and does not corrode the delicate components.

But, Halons are being discontinued in use due to concerns about the environmental impact of halogenated hydrocarbons. Some manufacturers have stopped making them and some automatic systems are not being recharged with them.

Dry Chemical Extinguishers

Dry chemical is an excellent agent for fighting flammable liquid fires and, because it is nonconductive, it can be safely used when live electrical circuits are involved. When dry chemical is used, the fire goes out almost immediately. The extinguishing action of dry chemical is not completely understood. Smothering, shielding and cooling contribute to the efficiency of dry chemical, but a chain breaking action is assumed to make it a superior extinguishing agent.

Portable dry chemical extinguishers may be available in sizes from 1.8 to 13.6 kg. They are usually pressurized by a gas cartridge. The extinguisher consists of a chamber with a large threaded opening. A tube extends almost to the bottom of the container and is connected to a valve and puncture assembly to which is attached a small cylinder of pressurized nitrogen or carbon dioxide. To activate the extinguisher, the nozzle is removed from its holder and held in one hand while the other hand pushes down sharply on the puncture lever. This allows the nitrogen or carbon dioxide to pressurize the main chamber containing the dry chemical. To release the dry chemical, the nozzle valve is opened and the chemical is directed at the base of the flame.

When dry chemical is used on an electrical fire, the first discharge should be to the base of the flame and then rapidly sprayed over the entire burning area. The electrical power should be shut off as soon as possible to prevent re-ignition.

It is important to note that dry chemical can form a conducting path to ground if any moisture is present.

When dry chemical is used on electrical fires, it is essential that the entire agent be removed from electrical equipment before the system is re-energized. Dry chemical can cause corrosion, abrasion, current leakage and reduced conductivity of electrical components. When possible, electrical fires should be extinguished with carbon dioxide or Halon to reduce the clean-up operation after a fire.

OBJECTIVE 4

Discuss the ways fire can be prevented in electrical equipment.

PREVENTION OF ELECTRICAL FIRES

Equipment that has been tested for use in a particular application very seldom causes any problems. But many electrical fires are caused by using equipment in an application for which it is not designed or approved. Installation of electrical equipment must be carried out by qualified people who are well versed in the Electrical Code.

Worn-out electrical equipment, such as deteriorated wiring, can be the cause of electrical fires. Aging of electrical equipment results in the breakdown of insulation and sometimes corrosion of the wires themselves produces a hazard.

Overloading of electrical equipment causes overheating and, while it may not cause an immediate breakdown of the conductors and insulation, it can lead to premature failure.

Motors must be kept clean, because they produce heat which must be dissipated. If dust is allowed to accumulate on a motor, it acts like an insulating blanket and prevents heat dissipation. Insulation failure could result, with serious consequences.

Temporary hook-ups should be designed to the same specifications as those required in the original drawings.

When a process is shut down for scheduled maintenance, the electrical panels should be:

- de-energized.
- locked out.
- checked for corrosion and signs of coming apart.

Hot spots in electrical panels can be detected while the system is in service using infrared photography. When the system is isolated, the conditions causing the hot spots can be repaired.

Fuses and circuit breakers are designed to protect the conductors from overloading. Fuses should be replaced with fuses of the correct current rating.

Motors and conductors must be kept dry unless they are designed for service in wet locations.

A large motor may have a specified minimum time between attempts to start it. This practice allows time for the windings to cool down between starts. The time interval must be closely observed to prevent damage to the motor.

Aluminum wiring was used several years ago in some installations. The connections must be checked periodically to ensure they are tight and not corroded.

This page has intentionally been left blank.

CHAPTER 39 - QUESTIONS

1. Electrical circuit insulation

    a) will never break down or deteriorate.

    b) requires replacement after 10 years.

    c) will deteriorate due to high temperatures.

    d) will not burn.

2. Under the Canadian Electrical Code, if an area contains dust in the air, under normal operating conditions, in concentrations high enough to produce explosive or ignitable mixtures, the electrical equipment must be designed safe for use in an area classification of:

    a) Class I, Division I.

    b) Class I, Division II.

    c) Class II, Division I.

    d) Class II, Division II.

3. Halon from Halon fire extinguishers

    a) may produce a distinct odour which warns of its presence.

    b) is abrasive to electrical equipment.

    c) will act as a conductor if moisture is present.

    d) is derived from bromine, fluorine, or chlorine.

4. A common cause of an electrical fire is:

    a) allowing motors or conductors to stay dry, unless designed for wet locations.

    b) prematurely replacing deteriorated wiring.

    c) following too closely to the Electrical Code when installing electrical equipment.

    d) replacing burned fuses with ones of a higher rating.

5. Halon 1301 presents a hazard for exposures in concentrations above

    a) 4%.

    b) 15%.

    c) 25%.

    d) 10%.

6. Which one of the following with respect to fire prevention in electrical equipment is NOT recommended?

    a) Applying blanket insulation to the outside of a motor in cold climates.

    b) Keeping electrical equipment dry unless designed for wet locations

    c) Using electrical equipment that is designed for the application

    d) Checking aluminum connections frequently for tightness and presence of corrosion

CHAPTER 39 - ANSWERS

1. (c)

2. (c)

3. (a)

4. (d)

5. (d)

6. (a)